80524

D1156926

Journey
to
Tranquility

JOURNEY
TO
TRANQUILITY

~~~~~~

HUGO YOUNG
BRYAN SILCOCK
PETER DUNN

080524

Garden City, New York 1970

DOUBLEDAY & COMPANY, INC.

PHOTO CREDITS

First published in England by Jonathan Cape Limited, London

ACKNOWLEDGMENTS

We owe a number of debts of gratitude. More than one hundred officials past and present of the National Aeronautics and Space Administration, of its prime contractors and of the United States Congress gave us generous portions of their time. It would be meaningless to name them all and invidious, if not a breach of confidence, to name some of them. But they are the main sources of the information in this book, and we are grateful to them.

We wish to thank also: Harold Evans, editor of the *Sunday Times*, for giving us the facilities to write the book; our colleague Timothy Johnson, for much tireless help; Ed Victor of Cape, for some invaluable editorial suggestions; and our secretary Sarah Hill, for her admirable endurance.

Contents

Illustrations

1.

Not Because it's There

A month before Neil Armstrong and Edwin Aldrin landed on the moon, the true purpose of sending them there was put to the ultimate test. The years of preparation were complete. In the rocket and the spacecraft, every one of several million functioning parts had been proved to work. The men, their equipment, their minds, their skills and their tens of thousands of anonymous assistants were poised for the leap. Only a single question remained to be decided, but it was one demanding a cruel inspection of American intentions. How, precisely, should the men from planet earth commemorate the first capture of another celestial body?

One Congressman had no doubt. Richard Roudebush, a ferociously patriotic Republican from Indiana, asked Congress to insist that the species of man which had done the job be correctly identified by requiring the astronauts to plant in the lunar rubble the flag of the United States "and no other." "In all due fairness to the American taxpayer," Roudebush pleaded, "it does not seem too much to ask that our flag, Old Glory, should be left behind as a symbol of U.S. preeminence in space, to which the citizens of this nation can refer with just pride."

Troubled by what seemed a cheap nationalistic gesture, another Congressman, Allard Lowenstein of New York, inquired, "Surely the first man on the moon will not need to be wrapped in an American flag for it to be generally known that he is an American?" Others suggested that the flag of the United Nations would be a better symbol of the fact that America was working for all mankind. If not that, said Lowenstein, why not an image of Buddha, Moses or Jesus Christ? Or what about the President? Could he not be trusted to make the right decision without a congressional edict? "Is his devotion to the flag underdeveloped? Has he been found embracing a Union Jack in secret?"

But Congress had been touched on its most delicate nerve. The solemn instruction went forth from Capitol Hill. Old Glory was "implanted" alone on the moon, reinforced with metallic stiffening to ensure that it remained permanently erect for the contemplation of the American taxpayer.

Any other decision might have pleased idealists but it would have falsified history. The UN flag would have well suited the rhetoric of Project Apollo, with its rotund appeals to human destiny and its tidings of joy to all mankind. But without Old Glory standing there alone, the objective set by President Kennedy when he sent America to the moon in 1961 would have been betrayed in the last stride.

Kennedy's decision has been grossly misunderstood. It was not, as is widely thought, a decision to put man on the moon. It was a decision to put an *American* on the moon before anyone else. "We came in peace for all mankind," says the plaque attached to Armstrong's space-ship, the remains of which will lie forever in the Sea of Tranquility. It is a deceptive epitaph. Americans did not go to the moon for man-kind. They went for America.

On that vital distinction have rested all the critical developments in the history of the assault. It is a distinction which the technical tri-umphs of the space age tended to expunge rather than illuminate. These have been extraordinary, as the book will show. But in their very brilliance they have obscured the facts of earthly life which pro-voked them.

The landing of man on the moon was nothing if not a human enterprise, with all the mortal qualities which men commonly mani-fest. It was done for human reasons, and was marked by human fail-ures as well as triumphs. And only in the context of the problems they overcame can the size of these triumphs begin to be measured.

It is often said that Apollo was an exercise in science, questing on the frontiers of experience for knowledge of inestimable value to man. Even if that were true, which it is decidedly not, it would not explain why Apollo was undertaken. There were many more pressing and profitable questions for science to investigate than the very few to which an answer could conceivably have been expected from putting men on the moon. Some of these lay in space itself. All would have cost but a fraction of the $24,000 million which Apollo has consumed.

But science was not the purpose of Apollo. Nor was its inseparable twin in the rhetoric of space: adventure. Indeed, if adventure was involved at all, it was of a curious brand. The great adventurers of the past were solitary figures, disappearing for years into jungles, in touch with no one, often given up for lost. The astronaut, by contrast, has an army of thousands behind him; he is not only in constant touch with base, his movements are actually controlled from the ground. If risk is the yardstick, moreover, it is questionable whether he is in greater danger in space than he would be in the paddy fields of Vietnam.

Again, it was not for economic profit that men went to the moon. This too is something which distinguishes Armstrong and Aldrin from an explorer like Christopher Columbus. No figure in history is more frequently cited to justify the assault on the moon than the discoverer of America. Yet the comparison is wholly uninstructive. Columbus sailed West in search of marketable riches. Armstrong flew to the moon in the full knowledge that he would find nothing of material value when he got there.

Deeper than the much-trumpeted motives of science and adventure, however, were forces which have always been as potent as the expectation of financial profit. The concepts of politics and war may seem to defile the beautiful picture of brilliant thinkers acting out a private dream. But it is these that were at the root of the decision to launch Apollo. And it is these that gave the journey to Tranquility a troubled, uncertain and sometimes sordid passage.

The true history of Apollo is all but indiscernible in the exultant discourses of the men who made it. Never perhaps has so vast an undertaking, producing so many millions of descriptive words, been so little comprehended. To listen to the propagandists of the American space program is to enter a world devoid of greed or error, tragedy, accident or subterfuge, nationalistic ambition or personal disaster: and to emerge unconvinced.

For Apollo was marked by all of these. On closer inspection it proves, after all, to have had a strong connection with life as it is commonly known on earth. Some politicians built careers on it, others lined their pockets from it. Whole corporations survived on the strength of it, as tiny groups of men decided where its billions of dollars would be distributed.

Before the assault began, devious and powerful pressures were exerted on the question of whether it should be made at all; almost wholly obscured from the public, titanic clashes occurred in the secret councils of the White House and the Pentagon. Before the journey ended, men died of culpable negligence, victims of the consuming speed at which the program was driven toward its objective. After it was completed, its outcome proved to be far more puzzling than the statesman who launched it ever anticipated.

Nothing about Apollo can be fully understood unless the impulse behind it is acknowledged. The birth of Saturn V, the rocket which propelled Armstrong to the moon, resembled the birth of the V-2 rocket which bombed London. Both had the same progenitor, Wernher von Braun; but more important, both were converted from an engineering fantasy into an expensive reality by political leaders acting in what they saw as the overriding national interest. The builders of Apollo were not technicians at work in a laboratory insulated from the world. They were soldiers in an age when technology has become warfare by other means.

Much has happened to blur and cloud this fact. Many years were spent by many people concealing the consequences of the pragmatic nature of the enterprise, and transmuting the Machiavellis of the world into Galileos. Yet fundamentally that was the impulse. And this book will show, in many respects for the first time, how and why it ended with the planting of Old Glory on the moon.

2.

The Destructive Visionaries

Dr. Wernher von Braun, German aristocrat and American citizen, was due to speak at a luncheon held in his honor by the Huntsville, Alabama, Press Club early in 1969, the year of the moon. He was late, detained in a conference on the top floor of the von Braun Hilton—his black-glass office building at the National Aeronautics and Space Administration's Marshall Space Flight Center a mile away.

The doctor appeared quite suddenly in the crowded dining room as though through a hole in the floor; so quickly that his little press officer, Bart Slattery, seemed to be trotting along one pace behind him. Slattery carried the briefcase.

Von Braun, braking gently before his place at the top table, looked freshly laundered, a light-gray suit hanging over a mild middle-age spread. His face, with its strong jawline, cupid's-bow mouth and fair hair brushed softly back from a low forehead, had a light, healthy tan. Now fifty-seven, he looked precisely as old as he did in his wartime photographs, handsome, well fed, with the open demeanor of a scoutmaster—the kind of young man who was devoted to his mother and never pulled the wings off flies. When he spoke, he regarded his audience with a sincere, pale blue stare.

As director of the Marshall Center, which developed the monstrous Saturn, von Braun leads a hemmed-in life and few of his engagements are frivolous. It seemed likely, therefore, that his presence at the Huntsville press lunch after a number of polite refusals had an element of calculation. NASA was on the verge of another manned launch—Apollo 9. The moon was merely months away, but now there were other journeys to plan, other planets to reach. The first requirement of a good space man is that he should look many years into the future, and early in 1969 the future held many questions, including the very survival of NASA. Combined with the launch was the looming problem of the next budget session before Congress, an annual ritual in which the country's political leaders have tended more and more to sacrifice the agency's grandiose proposals to the earthbound realities of poverty at home and the war in Vietnam.

Circumstances like these tend to bring out the dogmatic in NASA officials, and no one puts the space agency's case better, in Congress or out, than the rocket man from Peenemünde, who is still, after twenty-five years, undisputed leader of The Team, the most remarkable and enduring group of engineers the world has ever seen.

Von Braun approaches his theme with the simple piety of a Bible-belt stump-preacher. He promotes rockets, as Billy Graham promotes God, with a simple rhetoric that points up salvation for the faithful and damnation for the doubters. His speeches start lightly, usually with a homely joke about his passion for hunting and his poor aim. "Hitting the moon," he says, "is easier than hitting a moose"; or, "We were in Canada waiting for the moose and we spent our time trying to drink Canada Dry."

With the joke behind him, back at the end of the queue in his speech-writer's joke file, von Braun gets down to his central theme—continued advancement for NASA's adventures in space, the glory of the American people and a pious conviction that there is no better long-term cure for the world's ailments than a healthy injection each fiscal year into NASA.

Like most busy men in American public life, von Braun has his speeches ghosted and researched. He has two full-time speechwriters, Guy Jackson and Amos Crisp, but they rarely meet him. Slattery, as head of Marshall's public affairs department, is the go-between, handing down the director's memoranda which are always written in pencil and signed with a baronial "B," followed by the date. Von Braun himself hunts restlessly for analogies to promote the space program. One of his recent memoranda underlines the point. "Quotation for a speech designed to refute wasteful space spending," it said. "I read this in a professional article on cancer. 'Cancer research in the U.S. is presently supported to the tune of approximately 350 million dollars per year. And there is not a single promising project in this field that cannot be pursued due to inadequate funding. Fight against cancer is fought without financial limitations.' "

With other members of The Team from Peenemünde, von Braun has worked hard on pronunciation and colloquialisms. His American-English is excellent (space vehicles are "space veehickles") and one of his notes approving a speech said laconically, "OK. Roll as amended."

His amendments are invariably an improvement on the draft prepared for his comments. Simplicity, clarity of style, a deft touch of Rotarian corn, set von Braun's speeches apart in an organization dominated by engineers who talk to each other—and to their mystified public—in a jargon of technical shorthand. It nearly made some NASA engineers sick when the newspapers wanted to call their lunar module "Spider"—they had, after all, made a concession by cutting down their original mouthful from lunar excursion module; but von Braun believes in human analogies and simple technological parables that make the program easier to understand. Once, when he appeared before a congressional committee and was asked what he expected to learn from going to the moon, von Braun quoted Faraday: "What is the purpose of a newborn baby? We find out in time."

The director frequently compares the problems of the space program with the confused world of growing children. Speaking to the Huntsville Press Club he said NASA had had a letter from a six-year-old girl. "Dear NASA," it read. "Please send me your Thing." Von Braun noticed, with a cool glance, that the story had evidently pleased his audience and he shifted ground almost imperceptibly to the soft underbelly of their patriotism. "NASA's Thing," he said, "is NASA's mission to advance the peace, prosperity and the freedom of the American people. NASA's Thing, the exploration of space, is only the outward manifestation of the advance of the cause of all Americans."

The mood now was thoughtful, and the director exploited it neatly, stressing the consequences of tampering with the program's income—local unemployment in Huntsville (he didn't give the figures but had them ready for question time), the superior Soviet Mars probe ("substantially heavier than ours") and President Nixon's somewhat shad-

owy plans for the future of manned spaceflights after the moon
landings. "I think personally it would be very silly to cut the program,"
von Braun said. "It's just like saying an eight-year-old child was useless because it hadn't demonstrated its usefulness to society yet." He
paused. "Man is still the fastest computer that can be produced with
unskilled labor."

A few minutes later he moved on to his next meeting, accelerating
rapidly through the crowd with Bart Slattery padding at his heel.

Although von Braun seems perfectly capable of looking after himself, Slattery hovers nervously around the director's image, worrying
about its shape and the damage that might be caused by raising old
German memories. He is a small, suspicious man, a former navy captain with a deep voice. Oriana Fallaci crucified him in her book *If the
Sun Dies* because, Miss Fallaci claimed, Slattery kept passing her
notes during an interview with von Braun reminding her to call him
"Doctor."

Slattery prowls the flanks of the von Braun convoy like a destroyer
listening for submarines, furious when reporters try to alter the mold
into which the army poured his boss a quarter of a century ago. During
the Cuban crisis the *Huntsville Times,* an inquiring and liberal-
minded newspaper, discovered that the director had ordered himself a
fall-out shelter. Slattery tried unsuccessfully to get the story killed.

Today it is possible to look back with some detachment on a war
fought and finished by the mid-1940s. A prolonged public relations
effort, conducted largely by von Braun himself, has done much to
erase the man whose bombs flattened London and create the lunar
rocketeer. But the jibes and gossip remain, and perhaps Slattery is
wise to keep on his toes. Von Braun's senior colleagues tend to send
up his lingering trace of a German accent; and it was a NASA man in
Washington who said recently, "I don't know why you want to talk
to von Braun so bad. He damn nearly blew your island off the map.
And me with it."

The fact remains that The Team's earliest work thirty-five years
ago had nothing to do with Nazi ideology. The Team members
looked on rockets much as biologists might look on mice, as objects
for research and experiment which might one day be made to yield
a revolution in man's relation to nature. In this, of course, many of
them deluded themselves. Rockets can be turned a good deal more

quickly than mice into carriers of death. The justification for the work at Peenemünde, once it was organized under government auspices, certainly did not lie in science: the motive was, understandably, to win the war. The slave-labor which built the V-2, and the wreckage which the rocket created, both bear witness to that. Nevertheless, it is something like science—the consuming search for an engineering triumph—which has kept The Team together for so many years. The skills they acquired have been available for exploitation by other men's dreams of world power. Impervious to bouts of poverty, isolation and public dislike, they have remained loyal to one man and his life's ambition. And he, in his turn, having opted for the country where he was most likely to be master of his own fate, has remained consistently true to his belief that in the end the ambition would be fulfilled.

Von Braun determined that men could reach the moon long before there was any practical chance that they would be sent there. He is not an original scientist. He has discovered no new physical truths which cast a vivid new light on existing knowledge. He works within ineluctable physical laws about the earth and the planets which were described by Kepler and Newton. But he has always had this vision, along with enough foresight to exploit a chance of bringing it closer to fulfillment.

Without the Second World War, von Braun and The Team he so brilliantly organized would have had to wait a long time for their chance. Perhaps it would never have come. Without Kennedy's decision in 1961 to send men and not merely robots to the moon, their real ambition would never have been consummated. But equally, without von Braun the warlords and politicians would have had to adopt different strategies. He was not a meekly passive element in the political process, awaiting rescue from some obscure laboratory. In 1940 and 1961 he was ready with his plans; and the fact that he was ready helped to push decisions in the direction which suited him.

He has never seriously questioned the prevailing political assumptions of his countries of birth and adoption. In Peenemünde and Huntsville, his reasoning and judgments have worked on highly specialized technological levels, until life makes sense only if it is geared to space. But he is a shrewd judge of political moods, knowing how and when to tap the veins of jingoism and fear which pervaded Congress

whenever the Russians did better in space. No one knew better than
he that the journey to Tranquility would never be undertaken out
of sheer scientific curiosity.

No press officer, and no glass offices, were there at the birth of von
Braun's ambition. The early development of German liquid-fuel rockets had all the trappings of a plot, with fiendish bangs in garden sheds,
late nights in cellar workshops below the pavements of Berlin and a
kind of optimistic guesswork in which grown men ignited their mur-
derous fireworks with hand-held torches.

They were dotty, dangerous days. The young pioneers risked their
reputations through public ridicule and pawned their lives in experiments in which, often quite unwittingly, they were on a knife-edge
between contented dreams and a slab in the city mortuary. Dr. Arthur
Rudolph, a long-serving member of von Braun's Team, now a
trembling old man living in retirement among the loblolly pines of
Alabama, nearly died in 1930 when one of his rocket engines blew
up. "But in retrospect," says Rudolph, blinking excitedly, "what a
time we had!"

Rudolph's early experiences are fairly typical of those of the first
rocketeers. Von Braun belonged to a group working in the north of
Berlin; Rudolph worked in the south with an astronomer, Max
Valier, and an industrialist, Dr. Heyland.

"We ran tests with liquid rocket engines," Rudolph said. "I was
straight from college, a young whipper-snapper. It was so fascinating
for me, I didn't mind working in the evening or even on weekends.
We didn't mind if it was cold. Once I was standing in a puddle of ice
water without noticing it. It was also very dangerous but we didn't
realize it.

"Heyland hired me for this work in back yards as assistant fabrication manager. Maxwell's rocket engine fascinated me; we measured
its thrust with a kitchen scale which you could read at once. Walter
Riedel was there, who worked on the British rocket program after the
war.

"At one time we got eighty kilos of thrust out of the engine; we
burnt a mixture of water and crude oil—very, very dangerous, only
we didn't realize it at the time. Our systems control was crude: Valier
would give a thumbs up for more pressure and thumbs down for less.

"One weekend in 1930 we started this run. A big problem was that the metal casing of the engine would start to oxidize after a few seconds which would be the time to stop. You could tell the time of danger when patches appeared on the metal, but you had to keep a close eye on it.

"I was sitting on a slope, Riedel was at the bottom of the slope and Valier was walking round the engine looking for the patches. It went OK for ten seconds and then I found myself flat on my back. When I got up I saw that our rocket motor had disappeared and there was a tremendous cloud shooting up.

"Valier was weaving back and forth on his feet and I saw Riedel run round the stand to grab him and hold him." Rudolph waved his arms stiffly, like a penguin at the back of the crowd. "When I got to Valier I noticed he was dying, bleeding profusely from the chest. I put a piece of wood under his head and I said to Riedel, 'Valier is dead.'

"The shed wall behind where I'd been sitting was plastered with holes like a machine-gun. How the pieces missed me was a miracle.

"After this the newspapers in Berlin fouled it all up, although they'd been favorable about us before that. I think this was very, very unfortunate."

Valier's death was to throw a shadow over the rocket program. Hitler had known him, and his unfortunate demise contributed to the Führer's misgivings about the future of chemically propelled missiles. But scientists, like surgeons and soldiers, accept death as a professional hazard; mourning or recrimination is an indulgence for the untutored masses. In essence, the future of rocketry rested on swift epitaphs for rocketeers who blew themselves up, and knots in the handkerchiefs of survivors to remind them where the dead had gone wrong.

Ignorance and liquid hydrogen is a deadly formula; and in Berlin in the early thirties the pioneers mixed the two with an innocence that surprises them even today. Little was known about the fundamentals of what they were trying to do, and when a problem cropped up there wasn't much alternative to lighting the blue touch-paper and making for shelter. "What was available to us?" asked General Walter Dornberger, chief of the rocket development group in the German Army Board of Ordnance. "I'll tell you: a few books, some articles in trade papers and much wishful thinking."

Like Rudolph, the rocket fanatics on the other side of town read what they could and moved on from that point into an uncharted minefield. They had before them the essays of Konstantin Tsiolkovsky, the Russian schoolteacher who had outlined the principles of rocketry in the late nineteenth century and written a series of essays on reaction propulsion, attainable velocities and oxygen supply for space travelers. Also Hermann Oberth, a German-Rumanian with a flair for publicity that brushed off on his young admirer, Wernher von Braun, had suggested a liquid-propelled bombardment missile during the First World War. In 1933, Oberth published *The Rocket into Planetary Space*.

Von Braun's mother had encouraged his enthusiasm. But his father, Baron Magnus, a severely bearded landowner who served as Secretary of Agriculture under von Hindenburg, disapproved of his son's lunar ambitions and it was perhaps not surprising that von Braun attached himself to Oberth, discovering a father-figure who listened to reason.

"My interest in this whole thing started with astronomy," says von Braun today. "I worked personally for Oberth when I was a student at the Berlin Institute of Technology. I'd sent for his book while I was still a junior high school student, and to my great dismay I couldn't understand it because it was full of maths, not my strong point at that time.

"When I left school Oberth happened to be in Berlin as a consultant to a movie company making a picture, *Girl in the Moon,* to finance some experiments. In 1930 he started some *real* experiments, and having just left high school I wrote to him and said I'd heard he was in town and I couldn't offer anything except unbounded enthusiasm for rocketry and could I help him.

"My first contribution to Oberth was helping him with a little exhibition he had in a department store in Berlin. He had a stand in one corner displaying some models of rockets. I uncrated all this equipment for him, then I stood behind that table eight hours a day answering the questions of the shopping women. I used to tell them, 'There is no question that we'll fly people to the moon.'"

When Oberth returned to his home town to teach, von Braun continued experiments in an old artillery proving ground in the north of Berlin under the sponsorship of the German Society for Space Travel, a group of civilian enthusiasts. Dr. Rudolph recalls visiting the rival group. Von Braun, it emerged, didn't think much of Rudolph's method of weighing engine-thrust on a pair of kitchen scales. "We don't *measure* thrust," he said, rather grandly. *"We* calculate it."

Like all rocketeers at that time, von Braun was whistling in the dark for the technical prerequisites of space travel. Jules Verne, among others, had sketched the broad canvas with his account of a voyage to the moon in the 1860s, but a good many eyebrows were singed both in Berlin and, later, in Peenemünde before rocketry shook itself loose from science fiction. Von Braun himself always favored the Grand Design, confident that engineers could fill in the details later. His book *The Mars Project,* written in 1948 in New Mexico, declared that the logistic requirements for an elaborate expedition to Mars were no greater than those for a military operation "extended over a limited theater of war." In 1962 he wrote a second edition of the book in which he declared that a large expedition to Mars would be possible "in fifteen to twenty years at a cost which will be only a minute fraction of our yearly defense budget."

Von Braun's optimism was based on the potential development (now still restricted) of the nuclear-powered ion engines. Ten space ships manned by at least seventy astronauts, he wrote, would make the journey, each ship assembled in orbit and three of them equipped with "landing boats" for the descent to Mars. It was by any standards a breathtaking conception; but what made it all the more remarkable was that von Braun dreamed it up ("more or less to project the technology that existed then") when, to most Americans, space travel meant Flash Gordon in the Sunday color comics.

Today, a wiser, more philosophical man after the eroding experience of twenty-nine congressional budgets, von Braun compares his "Mars Project" to Oberth's book. "Both books," he says, "showed the difference between grand ideas and what we could actually show in our back yards. In the thirties the dichotomy was even more ridiculous, when we even had a hard time soldering a nut to a piece of copper piping."

Von Braun's Team was not, of course, the only pioneering outfit in the world, and at one time during the thirties it was not even the most advanced. The American Robert Goddard, who died in 1945, is known in the history books—at least, American ones—as the Father of Modern Rocketry. Goddard had worked on the forerunner of the bazooka during the First World War and flew his first successful liquid-fuel rocket in March 1926. Supported by the Guggenheim Foundation and working in the New Mexico desert, he chalked up an astonishing list of "firsts"—first to adapt the gyroscope to guide rockets, first to install movable deflector vanes in a rocket exhaust nozzle for steering, and first to use automatically deployed parachutes for instrument recovery.

In view of the progress being made in Berlin by The Team, it was perhaps unfortunate that Goddard, a moody, suspicious man, kept so much of his work secret, hoarding his discoveries out of sight under 214 patents. One of the more open questions of the last war was whether Goddard's work could have given the Allies a rocket to match or even outclass the V-2. "When I came to the States I was really overwhelmed when I saw what that man had done," von Braun says. "Most of his work was in classified patent papers and most of it had never been built. But it really covered the waterfront of modern rocketry. He was a very sensitive individual and he resented very much that the newspapers called him 'that crazy moon professor.' He never invited the newspaper people to his launches."

Nor, for that matter, did von Braun, who began work for the German Ordnance Department in 1932, before Hitler came to power, in conditions of such secrecy that even his university thesis, written in 1934, was classified. (As late as 1941, when Professor Oberth independently suggested a two-hundred-mile range single-stage rocket and asked for a modest grant to develop it, he had no idea that his former protégé was building rockets at Peenemünde.)

Money was short even under the Ordnance Department, but at least the rocket men had acquired, for the first time, a patron—Walter Dornberger, head of the department's rocket development group.

General Dornberger was a catalyst for The Team in a climate that was, in military terms, ideal for rocket development. In Britain, rocketry was a farce because the Explosives Act of 1875 forbade rocket development; America was largely dominated by conventional militarists, who were to meet Goddard in Washington as late as May 1940 and declare themselves unsympathetic to any long-range projectile. The skies were, therefore, open to the Germans who were looking for a new weapons system not prohibited to them by the Treaty of Versailles—which had not covered ballistic missiles.

The Team owes much of its cohesiveness to those early days. The secrecy of their work, first at the Kummersdorf army proving grounds near Berlin and later at Peenemünde, isolated them until 1943 from the mainstream of the Nazi war effort; their loyalty and gratitude to von Braun, an aristocrat in a society that loved a baron, a young engineer who could talk to his elders as though they were not quite there, was unquestioning. More to the point, they drew together at Kummersdorf because only the German military would put up the cash for their work.

Dr. Rudolph, whose early cooling-jacket designs were eventually developed for the V-2, had been thrown out of work soon after the big bang in the Heyland workshop yard. "I took up teaching and writing letters for the correspondence school," Rudolph said, smiling happily as he recalled the lean years. "Then one day I bumped into Heyland, my former boss, and he said, 'Why don't you try to design your engine?'

"That reawakened my dreams. It took me about four months to design it at home on my drawing board. There was no money because no one had any, but finally Dornberger gave me and my little group a military contract. To get money you just signed yellow sheets of paper and sent them out and the army gave you a thousand marks. A very simple, a very marvelous system. Later on when I came to the U.S., where procedures were more complicated, I realized just what a simple and excellent system it was.

"Of course, it was abused too. One of my colleagues fiddled the money the army gave us and after a time I had to go and tell Dornberger, and he was furious. It made things very difficult. When we started building the engine, we'd gone to the little workshops in the cellars of Berlin, the locksmiths and precision shops. Some of them got so enthused over our project they would even do the work for half price.

"After the money was taken it was not easy, but eventually I managed to persuade Dornberger to come and look at my engine. He said, 'Will it work?' and when I said, 'Yes,' I was able to finish it. When it was ready I took it round to Dornberger's office in a taxi, and then von Braun and I took it out to Kummersdorf in an open lorry with me hanging on to a door which wouldn't close. All so primitive but also so delightful, those days."

When Rudolph got to Kummersdorf, he discovered to his alarm that there was no firing equipment available and that he was expected to ignite his own device. Dornberger shared the inventor's misgivings. While Rudolph tiptoed up to his engine holding a flaming torch in his hand, the head of Ordnance's rocket development hid behind a pine tree to watch.

When Rudolph's rocket engine fired successfully Dornberger asked him to join The Team. "At first I said no," Rudolph says. "I wanted to be a freelance enterprise, not a government employee. But then I knew I wouldn't get a contract, and I didn't want to keep on teaching and therefore to be out in the cold. I wanted to take part in this fantastic development. In those days I was convinced, despite all these difficulties, that in five years with sufficient money we would be able to build a rocket to go to the moon. I really believed it. And this is now thirty-nine years later. But when you are very young the problems all appear so small; and that's a good thing, otherwise you'd never try to do it. So I was hired by the War Department.

"Neither von Braun nor I was married and we lived in the officers' mess at the proving grounds. We didn't like to get up early; we liked to work late at night instead. Now, this is very important. In 1934 when we were living as bachelors, at midnight von Braun had his best ideas. He would expound them on a sketch pad and his ideas led to one thing: space travel. It was at that time that he developed his flight to Mars. We didn't want to build weapons; we wanted to go into space. Building weapons was a steppingstone. What else was there to do but join the War Department; elsewhere there was no money.

"The V-2, which we called Aggregate Four, wasn't even designed as a weapon; but we were government employees. In those days we were only doing what we did here first in America when we designed the Redstone rocket—another weapon. But that itself was only a steppingstone to the Saturn moon rocket. It's that simple. I've been an associate of von Braun's for nearly thirty-nine years. We are so close working together because we realized that the things we really had in mind could be done.

"To get anywhere we always had to accept, as Edison said, ten percent inspiration and ninety percent frustration. In those days this required an immense amount of self-confidence and this is what von Braun had, no matter whom he was talking to.

"One day at Kummersdorf the chief of the War Department came to see us, not only a lieutenant-general but also the most distinguished university professor in maths in Berlin. So there was this illustrious man coming to see our group which numbered only seven at that time; and there was von Braun who was very young but still our big boss. After I, the most junior, had spoken first (you always questioned the most junior first), it was von Braun's turn and von Braun talked to the General about going into space. 'Von Braun,' the General said, 'what you want to do can't be done because you can't handle the energy you'll need.' But von Braun, who was still only twenty years old, says, 'But it *will* work, for this and this and this reasons.'"

In 1937 The Team moved from Kummersdorf to Peenemünde, where in his younger days von Braun had gone duck-hunting with his father. The group's experimental station was on a skull-shaped promontory; the German Air Force settled on the skull's forehead and developed the V-1, the ram-jet "buzz bomb," and The Team worked along the back of the skull, building the V-2 rocket. In the next eight years von Braun probably learned as much about politics and interservice hostility as he did about supersonic travel. There was considerable rivalry between the V-1 and V-2 outfits, amplified in dramatic terms when one of von Braun's rockets went wild on take-off and plowed into the air force's main runway.

The Team had moved into its new quarters with only a vague idea of what it should do. "From 1932 until 1945," Dornberger recalls, "they never received any specific written requirement of any kind for a weapons system from their military superiors or anybody else. This group had to make up its own mind how a military rocket should perform. We approached the rising problems with the spirit of the innocent and the dumb. As we progressed we enjoyed our work more and more."

Von Braun, according to Dornberger, was merely "fumbling around" for a sense of direction when they sat down to discuss their future in 1936, a few weeks before the move to Peenemünde. After an hour, says Dornberger, "I planted my fist on the table and told them what I wanted and how this rocket should look."

The rocket, he declared, should carry one hundred times the explosives of the First World War Parisian gun and have twice the range —in other words it should lift 2200 pounds over a distance of 156 miles; the rocket should not be more than forty-two feet long (to enable it to be shipped through small villages by road) and it should have a burn-out speed of 3600 miles per hour.

In its way, Dornberger's declaration was as momentous as John F. Kennedy's speech twenty-five years later which launched Project Apollo. Like Kennedy, Dornberger issued a directive and left it to the ant heap to sort out the details. Rocketry, indeed, is full of eerie parallels. In the postwar years, military theorists decided that the V-2 had not been worth the time or money in terms of Germany's war effort. Many times since 1961, scientists have raised similar doubts about the manned Apollo program—what one Congressman has called "an approach . . . in which experiments and practical applications are subordinated to NASA's intention to promote at all costs immediate, extensive and glamorous manned space operations."

Von Braun and The Team learned to live with the undependable opinions of politicians from their earliest days. During the thirties Hitler showed scant interest in the work at Peenemünde, and in November 1939 he dropped it from his priority list. Not until the summer of 1943 was the program reinstated; a smiling Führer offered one of his rare apologies to Dornberger, and personally gave von Braun the title "Professor." But by then it was too late. "The deployment of this weapon," Dornberger lamented tactlessly after the war, when he was vice-president of Textron's Bell Aerosystems in Buffalo, New York, "occurred at least two years too late. The war in 1944 could not have been won by firing nine hundred V-2s a month as planned . . . Lack of foresight of U.S. potentialities in aircraft production prevented the German leadership from giving early and sufficient support to this program in order to help win the war in Western Europe."

In the end, the V-2 was rushed from development to mass production with such haste that sixty-five thousand changes were required after the design stage had been officially frozen. Even then the army's V-2 was far less efficient than the air force's V-1 "buzz bomb." A V-2 cost at least thirty times more than the smaller ram-jet and its warhead was no larger. Psychologically it was much less a terror weapon than the V-1, which could be heard approaching. No one knew a V-2 had arrived until the first crack of sound as its shock-wave hit the ground, followed by a vivid flash and explosion as the warhead detonated, then a long roar as the noise of its last moments in flight caught up with the point of impact.

Dornberger says today that the German Ordnance Department was embarrassed by the V-2's ill-founded propaganda role as a wonder weapon. In postwar speeches he liked to call his rockets "flying laboratories," including, no doubt, the one that fell on a block of flats in Stepney on March 27, 1945, killing 130 people. "Altogether," Dornberger told an American audience in 1963, "3745 of these flying laboratories were successfully launched between September 6, 1944 and March 27, 1945. Some 1115 fell on England, 2050 on targets on the continent."

As in the immediate postwar years in the United States, The Team relied heavily at Peenemünde on the patronage of the army, but even then they suffered from interservice jealousy and the Führer's unpredictable enthusiasms. Starved of personnel, the army filled the gaps at Peenemünde by raiding the frontline troops. Some of The Team's most brilliant members joined von Braun in this almost accidental way, among them Dr. Ernst Stuhlinger, a guidance and control systems expert and designer of a Mars space ship. "Someone had the bright idea," says Stuhlinger with a faint smile, "to go through the file cards. I'd been drafted as an enlisted man in the Russian campaign until one day in Berlin they looked up which scientists were still marching through the Steppes or the Ukraine. They found me and brought me to Peenemünde."

Dornberger's greatest problem as head man at the Peenemünde research center was to cope with the SS, which infiltrated and finally took over the V-2 project in the closing months of the war. In March 1944, at some personal risk to himself, he saved von Braun and two colleagues after the SS had arrested them for "treason"—they had talked about space travel during a party some weeks earlier, thus demonstrating, in the opinion of the SS, a lack of enthusiasm for the war effort.

On May 2, 1945, when Dornberger, von Braun and four hundred other scientists surrendered to the Americans at Garmisch-Partenkirchen in the Bavarian Alps, The Team had narrowly escaped liquidation by their own side. The SS motive, which was to stop The Team falling into enemy hands, would have been considerably strengthened had they but known that von Braun and a close circle of associates had long since decided that the war was lost. The Team's leading members had also agreed which way to jump next—roughly in the same direction as their proposed hundred-ton V-10, the world's first ICBM with worldwide targets already mapped on the drawing board, among them Washington and New York.

America's effort to put men on the moon began, it can be seen in retrospect, on the cratered surface of Europe shortly before and after VE Day, in May 1945. In their race to capture von Braun and The Team's documents before the Russians or British could grab them, the Americans' motive had, of course, nothing to do with lunar travel. It was far more concerned with the need to get a flying start in the event of World War Three.

Their campaign was conducted with unscrupulous brilliance. It was helped considerably by von Braun's own preference, which was to move to the States and resume his Peenemünde operations without delay. Von Braun despised the French, and saw little future for rocketry in Britain where the resources would be too meager to support the massive ambitions of The Team. When the British elected a Labour Government and turned Left toward a welfare state, the men from Peenemünde felt doubly reassured that they had chosen their new home wisely. As for Russia, into whose embrace The Team would certainly have fallen had they not moved south, von Braun felt he had had enough of the inefficiency of dictatorship.

Even so, the British worked especially hard to get their share of booty from the V-2 program. The war was hardly over before British Intelligence had moved into Europe to steal, negotiate or kidnap what they could from the battlefield scrapyards. Their battle with the Americans, until now their ally, formed an extraordinary introduction to the peace.

Advancing armies leave in their wake a political vacuum, a disordered, bewildering wasteland controlled by looters. No one really controlled the gangs of squabbling dons, civil servants, military sleuths and ambitious generals who romped around Germany looking for enemy scientists in the early summer of 1945. They were mainly freelancers engaged in what they saw as a struggle for the remains of Germany's war effort, to be carried home in the expectation that their governments might find a valuable use for the hardware. As the undignified fracas was being played out, immense decisions were being taken on the future shape of the world; but they were kept secret from the public, which believed it had fought the war to end all wars.

Von Braun, in fact, became a pawn, if a willing one, in a complex game played far below the surface of normal democratic behavior. Nearly 30,000 Londoners were killed during the blitzes, 5800 of them by V-1s and nearly 3000 by V-2s. The figures are small compared to the casualties sustained in saturation bombing raids against German cities but the public would scarcely have been in a mood to draw such a magnanimous comparison had they been told that von Braun was in London, on loan from the Americans, three months after VE day.

Yet London, ironically, was his first resting place. The rocketeer stayed in Wimbledon, where he learned to box his bedding British-army style. He was surprised by London's wholesome appearance. "Don't misunderstand me," he says, "but my first reaction was 'I don't see any bomb damage at all.' People had to point it out for you and say 'That was a building' or 'This whole city block has been razed.' It was downright amazing to me after what one had expected to see." At the Ministry of Supply, he had a cordial chat with the late Sir Alwyn Crow, head of British rocket development.

Dr. Richard Porter, who led a team from the American General Electric Company in the postwar hunt for German scientists, says today, "Of course we saw the irony of all this. But when you think of it in military terms I think this sort of irony tends to cancel out."

Von Braun agrees: "Military people, maybe, are a little less emotional about wars," he said. "I don't know what it is but I guess they take a little more of the position of sportsmen and say, 'Now the fighting's over, let's shake hands.'"

Fists rather than hands were shaken as rival intelligence teams clashed in Germany in the summer of 1945. Americans stole from Russians, Russians from the British, British from the Americans. Each party fought virulently against the other and observed only one unwritten rule: the losers didn't complain.

Dr. R. V. Jones, chief of the Air Ministry's scientific intelligence branch and now professor of natural philosophy at Aberdeen University, recalls a consignment of V-2 parts crated up and sent to London from Russian-occupied Poland. "When the stuff arrived," he said, "it was just old plane parts, much to our amusement. We thought that was very smart."

Chicanery flourished at all levels, and not only in the search for V-2s. "A lot of teams were in Germany collecting information on all sorts of projects," said a former British Intelligence man. "People were interested in all aspects of German industry—how they manufactured glass, and other highly useful things. Well, not all the information they collected went into their official reports, no doubt because they could put it to better use for themselves. I've discovered this in many cases. Human nature in the raw, apparently."

In Europe, the British considered the Americans to be an overbearing crowd and argued somewhat loftily that a country that came into the war so late should show a little more humility. But officially both parties worked together as allies, and a number of organizations were formed to scour Germany for useful documents.

One of these, the Combined Intelligence Objectives Sub-Committee, more widely known as "Chaos," purported to be a joint British-American venture. "The committee," Dr. Porter said, "was largely dominated by the British. Many of the documents we collected about the V-2 operation were supposed to go via COIS channels in London to Washington. Much of this stuff that was supposed to go via the U.K. never actually turned up in the U.S."

The allied agreement, under which spoils of war in the newly carved sectors of Germany would be left intact for the incoming tenants, was widely ignored in the case of the rockets. Night after night the air was full of the rumble of army lorries and the rattle of goods trains hijacking goods from one sector to another. The Americans shipped a mineful of V-2 papers out of the British zone and tons of V-2 parts away from the Russians. The V-2s had actually been assembled at Nordhausen, a slave-labor factory built underground in an area some distance from Peenemünde, which changed from American to Russian hands immediately after the war. It was here that the Americans pulled off a double-doublecross. Some of the rocket parts (which nominally belonged to the U.S.S.R.) should have been handed to the British. They were not.

General Holger "Ludy" Toftoy, at that time chief of American Army Ordnance's technical intelligence in Europe and the greatest postwar influence on Wernher von Braun's career, disobeyed orders and made sure that the U.K. got none of the V-2 parts. A man from the British Ministry of Supply, William Cook, now Sir William Cook, chief adviser on projects and research at the Ministry of Defence, counterattacked by smuggling away from Nordhausen several truckloads of V-2 papers. "They made it very difficult for us," Sir William says today. "God knows why. I was quite surprised."

The Americans, for their part, complained about the behavior of their British allies. Dr. Porter claims, for example, that they stole five of von Braun's rocketeers, specially nominated to develop the V-2 in the New Mexico desert. Sir William Cook, who was responsible for bringing German V-2 specialists to Britain, says affably, "I don't know what you'd call stealing. We made offers to certain Germans and they accepted them and went to work at Westcott, our rocket development place near Aylesbury. . . ."

Porter saw it differently. "I'd been under instructions," he says, "to put the five men in a place called Dustbin, an interrogation center created by the British. I didn't like the sound of this at all and when I got back to Paris I got on the classified scramble line to Toftoy. He was quite noncommittal at the time and I felt so discouraged I damned nearly went off to Cannes. It wasn't until I met him later that he explained to me that copies of everything said on that circuit were made by the British. I didn't know that at the time and Toftoy certainly wasn't going to tell me over the scramble line."

The incident finally hardened Porter to the ways of postwar Europe. When he pulled off his biggest coup—the recovery of General Dornberger's priceless hoard of personal documents, including the latest Nazi data on atomic energy and up-to-date instructions on firing the V-2, he put the cache under armed guard in Paris. "Those RAF boys," Porter said, "were snooping around doing their best to snatch those boxes and I'm sure they'd have done it without that guard. I admired those boys. I learned a great deal from them."

The von Braun Team watched the activity swirling around them with the numbed surprise of a Salvation Army band caught up in a street fight; in a way the brawling enhanced their position, giving them a kind of dignity and raising hopes that there must surely be a future if the allies were prepared to cut each other's throats for their favors. Dr. Porter looked after The Team, protecting them as best he could

from the rude soldiery who tried to steal their watches or slash their
bicycle tires. "Our own GIs," Porter said, "did tend to harass them,
and whenever this happened it would set us back two or three days.
But von Braun was very understanding."

Porter established with von Braun considerable rapport during the
early days of cross-examination. He had heard that von Braun had
been arrested by the SS and he discreetly checked the story out. He
noticed from old Peenemünde photographs that the rocketeer never
appeared at parties in an SS uniform. Porter was convinced that the
majority of the V-2 Team *had* disliked the Nazis who were, by defi-
nition, bureaucratic. There was something pleasingly derisive in the
way von Braun appeared after his capture, his arm encased in plaster
after a car accident and raised halfheartedly in a left-handed Nazi
salute.

"I always liked the man," Dr. Porter says. "He probably came closer
to understanding the world from the viewpoint of an American development manager than most people I ran into. There's a certain
language you can develop, a way of speaking, which we had together.
By the time I'd talked to him he was completely reconciled, perhaps
the word is 'adjusted,' to the situation."

Von Braun, for his part, proved to be an amenable prisoner once
he felt the Americans could be trusted. At Nordhausen, where the
scientists were waiting to be shipped out by train before the area
was taken over by the Russians, he walked down the platform with
Dr. Porter pointing out people who were not initially qualified to join
the exodus to democracy.

"When we got west," Porter recalled, "we had to sit down and sort
out who were the best men and who would be going to the States—a
board of directors' meeting, so to speak. That was the point at which
I became very impressed with von Braun's capabilities. I didn't regard him as the world's greatest scientist, or even greatest engineer,
but he is indeed one of the world's great managers of an engineering
or technical project. He has a rare ability to know his people."

Von Braun transferred his loyalty to the Americans with an easy
mind. But in one sense—since his primary loyalty was to developing
rockets—no real transfer ever took place; the king was dead in Germany but the new throne was being dusted in New Mexico. It is this
process of reasoning, straightforward enough to von Braun but trou-

bling and unsatisfactory to many outsiders, which supports his singularly amoral view of his life's work. To the question of how anyone could so cold-bloodedly change sides, he answers, in effect, that machines and not men are his idols—that it is to them and what they can be made to achieve that his primary obligation lies.

The Team's own natural desire, so the argument goes, was to send rockets into space, but they were unable to do so until the armies of the Third Reich and the allies stood aside. Von Braun's case is that he would have worked for a civilian agency from the start, had one been available. When Hitler disbanded the German Association for Space Travel in the early thirties, thus rendering private experiments treasonable, the army was rocketry's only patron. It was this which led to The Team being directed by the military men, first of Fascist then of democratic societies, for thirty years.

But the question remains: how far was von Braun prepared to go with the Nazis? The official version is that he knew little about the slave-labor force at Nordhausen, nor was he responsible for what went on there. The latter point may be true, but von Braun had unquestionably seen well before the end of the war what his work implied in terms of human misery.

On January 25, 1944, he visited Nordhausen on Dornberger's instructions, and cannot but have noticed that some ten thousand slave laborers and convicts were already at work. Sir William Cook, who toured Nordhausen shortly after it was overrun, witnessing its devastating human toll, the straw-lined bunks set up by the assembly line and smelling the stench of death, says von Braun must have known perfectly well what was going on. Any assertion to the contrary, Sir William says, was "utter balls." The Germans built a concentration camp for the Nordhausen labor force right outside the main entrance to the factory. No one going in there could have missed it.

"The problem of amorality is very, very old," says von Braun today. "Just read the history of the Renaissance and see how even the greatest architects like Michelangelo were pressed into building war machines and fortresses.

"The situation is not entirely new and I think it's always created problems and scruples. But it's always a question of 'What is a man's duty to his country?' You see, whether you build the rocket or an airplane that drops bombs there's not much of a difference, because both are basically a means of transportation. I do know, for example, that the people who built the bombing aircraft have asked themselves (and rightly so) precisely the same question that I, of course, have asked myself."

But surely the Nazi phenomenon was somewhat different? "Well, I can only speak for myself here, and let me be frank about it. When Hitler took over in 1933 I was twenty-one years old. I was wrapped up in my rocketry ideas, and as I look back at myself then, I most certainly didn't appreciate the significance of that upheaval or the evil of the rule that would follow.

"On the other hand—and whether you would consider this an apology or an excuse or an explanation, I don't know—other people, including the Prime Minister of Great Britain, Chamberlain, didn't think so very badly of Hitler in 1939 that he couldn't make an agreement with him. So I think one should not blame a twenty-one-year-old boy for not having understood the significance of such political leaders much older than himself.

"Even in the summer of 1939 I was absolutely convinced there wouldn't be a war. You can say that this was naïve, because everyone else thought there would be war. But, of course, when the war came you had a somewhat different situation. Suddenly your country is at war and whether it's right or wrong it's still your country. Besides, at that time my work had practically no significance, but only a growth potential. All of a sudden it emerged as something which became important. What really made it important was that the Luftwaffe lost the Battle of Britain. Without a rocket we couldn't get there any more, they said."

Von Braun's wartime colleague, Dr. Ernst Stuhlinger, one of the men attempting today to point American astronauts toward Mars, says, "For us, rockets were always destined for other things besides war. It's true, of course, that the first developments were brought about in Germany by the war, just as they were here in America, to a certain extent. There is an old Greek saying: 'War is the father of all things.' Von Braun once answered the same sort of question with an answer that was short, neat and inclusive: 'The V-2 was a fine rocket. The only thing wrong with it was that it landed on the wrong planet.'

"When I first began my studies in 1932, I wasn't forced to enter the Party, but I did have to take part in these student exercises if I wanted to remain a student. I became a Party member when I was an assistant professor in Berlin, which meant being an employee of the government. There was no choice. Suddenly there would be a letter in the mail which said, 'We are extremely happy that you are elected to become a member of the Party because of your good behavior. Heil Hitler, and your Party payments are due next March.' If one hadn't joined one would have lost one's job. Employment is a means of doing the work you want to do and to forgo all this would be a hard decision. Many people who joined the Party had the philosophy that you retained your own thinking even if you were a member. In that way you might even be in a position to do more good."

It was the discomfort of Party life which conclusively decided most of The Team against going east after the war. In the immediate postwar weeks they would have gone practically anywhere for a square meal, but not to Russia. "At the end of the war," says von Braun, "not only I but all my closest friends, including Dornberger my boss, had had our real fill of dictatorships in any form or fashion. For all the bad things that the dictatorship did to other people it also did a lot of bad things to the internal administration at Peenemünde. So here we had the Red Army coming in from the east, and the thought of winding up under Stalin after the years of Hitler was unbearable.

"Of course at that time it was almost naïve to hope we would be able to continue our work. But we went to the Americans to put the *idea* in the right hands. Even then, if you'd asked me who would have been the more likely to let us continue our work I would have said the Russians. I've no doubt it's just what they would have wanted. They had a big land-locked army which would particularly favor missile development, and it was pretty clear even then that there would be a future for us behind the Iron Curtain. I don't think I was ever afraid that the Russians would chop my head off or anything like that. But I wasn't hopeful at that time that I'd have a chance of continuing this work."

But what America offered most seductively to them all, in greater or lesser degree, was a stable society in which they could put down roots and start afresh after years of turmoil. "I was born in an area that is now Jugoslavia," says Dr. William Mrazek, another member of The Team. "I was released from the Jugoslavian Army and was directed to the Czechoslovakian Army. So then I had Czech citizenship, and after that German citizenship, and then there was a certain time I didn't know *who* I was. Please remember: to get all these citizenships in Europe, you didn't have to move a foot. They just rolled over you."

Today, an ordered man once more with his job in Huntsville and the most permanent citizenship he has ever had, Dr. Mrazek is grateful from the bottom of his heart. When he filled in the questionnaire asking what was the "deep reason" why he wanted to go to the United States, he had written, "To preserve the Western civilization and culture." He believes it was sound reasoning. "If the President asks me to jump in the water," he says now, "then I jump in the water."

The Team's exodus from Europe to the promised land was contrived to a large extent by the late General Toftoy, crack pistol shot, amateur cartoonist and West Point cadet who got pushed around by college hearties who mistook his name for "Tough Boy." Like Dornberger, who led The Team during the war, Toftoy was an artillery officer, widely regarded as the army's foremost mine expert. Like Dr. Porter, he established immediate and enduring rapport with von Braun. "Toftoy was the kind of man you instinctively trusted," Porter said. "I don't think he ever told a lie. He was an honest and competent man and you don't find too many of those around."

As chief of Ordnance technical intelligence in Europe around VE day, Toftoy saw in the von Braun Team a heady future for the development of American missiles, and asked Washington to import three hundred German rocketeers. Nothing much happened about his request until he returned home to become military boss of rocket research. The idea of shipping what many generals believed to be a bunch of highly motivated Nazis to the States was anathema both in the Pentagon and on Capitol Hill. There was some fear that they would be putting loyal Americans out of a job, and the best that seemed likely to happen was that the Germans would be imported for their knowledge and then exported at the earliest possible moment, the policy adopted by the Russians.

A six-month contract and a pauper's pay packet seemed to be all that Toftoy could offer von Braun. But the mild-spoken general had a way of getting what he wanted. Informed, eventually, that he would be allowed 100 scientists, he brought 127 across.

Some sources allege that the British tried to snatch von Braun during that brief visit to Wimbledon, but von Braun himself denies this. Major Robert Staver of the U.S. Army Ordnance Corps, one of the principals in the capture and discovery of The Team's Peenemünde records, was quoted in one history of the period as saying that the snatch had been attempted, verbally, by Sir Alwyn Crow, chief of British rocket development at the Ministry of Supply.

Von Braun, who regarded Major Staver as rather flash, a Californian impressed by the dramatic techniques of Hollywood, says, "When I went to London I already had my contract to go to the United States. The Americans permitted me to go to England only after there was a clear understanding that 'this man is ours.' Sir Alwyn knew this and merely wanted to know from me whether there were other first-class people left behind in Germany that could and should be approached. He never at any time asked me to work for the British. I told him that the kind of man he wanted certainly existed, but he would have to make these approaches personally because under the circumstances I didn't want to appear to any of my friends like a trigger-man putting guys' names on a list. He very graciously accepted this and that was that."

But if von Braun remained unscathed, protected by powerful men in Washington, General Dornberger, who could be said to have started it all, was not so lucky. He flew to London and was "detained." American sources have claimed that Dornberger was tricked into captivity but von Braun says this was not so. "I asked him later on if there had been any trickery," he said. "Dornberger said 'No, no. It was really very simple. The Americans never offered me a contract.'

"They couldn't do that because general officers were under some kind of taboo. They had to be debriefed first. The history writers were particularly interested in generals after the war.

"Toftoy told me when I raised the question of Dornberger with him, 'Look, I don't think it would look so good if you guys come to America under the leadership of a German general.'

"Later on, when Dornberger came to the United States, Larry Bell looked him up and said, 'Do you want to join my company?' So Dornberger became a vice-president of Bell Aerosystems and made more money than all of us."

3.

A Bauble in
the Sky

When the von Braun Team reached the United States and began to establish themselves in the unpromising Texas scrubland outside El Paso, the moon seemed almost as remote as it must have done to Galileo. They came to a country in the throes of a massive demobilization. Insofar as America was thinking of defense at all, it basked in the comfortable certainty that it alone possessed the means to destroy any enemy. The nuclear complacency induced by the atomic bombs dropped on Nagasaki and Hiroshima colored the thinking of every politician, and of all but a very few of the military.

By comparison with this doomsday machine, the V-2, the supreme achievement of German engineering, resembled a popgun. The damage it could inflict was microscopic, the deterrent influence it could exert over potential enemies had suddenly become irrelevant. The technology of supersonic ballistic missiles in which von Braun and his team led the world was demoted from the front line of warfare to an interesting but relatively speculative branch of engineering. For the next five years, the prized Peenemünde team were to spend most of their time conducting desultory experiments with surplus V-2s in the desert of New Mexico.

But they were made welcome enough. To many Americans, who had neither seen nor heard of the V-2, the war had happened a long way away. General Toftoy, of course, looked after the Germans from the Pentagon and had caught some of the flavor of von Braun's real ambition to send rockets into space. It was Toftoy who wangled them into the States legally, their first entry having been without authority from the American customs. He sent The Team over the Rio Grande to Ciudad Juarez, El Paso's sister town across the Mexican border. Then its members came trooping back as part of the normal quota of immigrants, some of them writing on their immigration forms that they had traveled in "via the Ciudad Juarez trolley line."

"It was a lively time when we first came to Texas," Dr. Mrazek recalls. "Remember, we were all bachelors and that was enjoyable. Also we had enough to eat even though we had limited resources— $4.80 cash a day."

Language was a problem. "At school," said Bernard Tessman, later to become deputy director at the Huntsville center's test laboratory, "you didn't learn languages because the soccer game came first. When I was in Texas, I was able to communicate with my hands and feet. Then I met a fellow called Tessman in El Paso, then another Tessman and we found out these guys were my cousins, one of them the son of the youngest uncle of my father who left Germany when he was seventeen. I can say we were fortunate in Texas and never had any nasty situations to face. The late General Toftoy was very much behind us. I guess he made himself a name as Mr. Missile Man or whatever they called him."

But in 1946 Mr. Missile Man was years before his time. The immediate strategic effect of Hiroshima was to persuade the Truman Administration that American defense should rest essentially on the manned bomber. With enough planes to carry what would soon be enough atomic bombs to any target in the world, it was argued, the United States would possess a force amply sufficient to deter any aggressor.

If rockets were relevant to this strategic plan, it was in an auxiliary role and at the least exciting technical level. The air-to-air, air-to-ground and ground-to-air projectiles under development at that time were, in principle, little more than advanced forms of conventional artillery—bullets, bombs and shells with greater range, tighter accuracy and larger destructive force than the weapons of the Second World War. They operated within the earth's atmosphere and were not designed in any circumstances to travel through outer space. They share the name "missile" with the Atlas, the Titan and the other giant intercontinental rockets to be developed many years later, but the usage is deceptive. In crucial military and technical respects they were a different breed.

In the mid-1940s the rockets which were to open the way to Moscow, and eventually the moon, were commonly regarded as belonging to the very distant future. A handful of military zealots were keen to start work on anything which added to their firepower. But Vannevar Bush, director of the Office of Scientific Research and Development and a leading politico-scientist of the day, speaking for many scientists, reassured the strategists when he told Congress at the end of 1945, "There has been a great deal said about a three-thousand-mile, high-angle rocket. In my opinion, such a thing is impossible today and will be impossible for many years. I don't think anybody in the world knows how to do such a thing. . . . I wish the American public would leave that out of their thinking." This kind of assertion was expected to hold true for twenty years; manned bombers, with their nuclear cargo, would still be keeping the peace in 1965.

But like not a few technological soothsayers before him, Bush was wrong. It took nothing like twenty years for the manned bomber to decline into obsolescence as the main deterrent force. Under the relentless influence of international politics, the development both of explosives and of the means of delivering them advanced with horrifying speed.

In September 1949 the Soviet Union exploded an atomic device for the first time, at least three years earlier than the Western powers had predicted. At first, Washington was plunged into uncertainty by this shattering of its nuclear monopoly. Months of bitter arguing ensued in the secret councils of the Pentagon and the Atomic Energy Commission about what response the United States could and should make. But eventually, early in the next year, President Truman was persuaded by the overwhelming pressure of his military advisers to sanction development of a weapon so hideous that it was spoken of by many atomic scientists only in a whisper. This was the so-called "super," the hydrogen fusion device with a thousand times greater destructive power than the bomb that had liquidated Hiroshima.

This of itself had little immediate significance for rocket development. The first thermo-nuclear explosion at Eniwetok in 1952 was of a device weighing some sixty tons, a load offering no obvious possibilities for ballistic launching. But it was the first of a series of events which promised to move war into a new dimension. Even before Eniwetok, the Americans knew that a hydrogen device more closely resembling a bomb, deliverable by an airplane, could be produced. When Russia succeeded with its own first thermo-nuclear explosion, the device it used was already of bomb proportions.

The swift reduction in size of the Eniwetok monster automatically had a bearing on the missile question. If it could be reduced still further, some of the theoretical objections to missiles as against manned bombers would have to be reconsidered. The most obvious and crucial of these related to the warhead's firepower. One of the drawbacks of a missile as it was conceived at that time was its relative inaccuracy; four miles from the target area was about the closest anyone was willing to guarantee its landing, even over as little as a thousand miles. With conventional explosives, even with an atomic bomb, this might seriously diminish from the missile's value. But with an H-bomb, so vastly more destructive than anything had ever been before, it was considerably less relevant.

Increasingly aware of the worldwide implications such a development would have, whoever achieved it, the air force set up a committee to examine the possibilities of long-range missiles as carriers of hydrogen bombs. The committee was chaired by the famous Hungarian-born mathematician and physicist John von Neumann, creator of the fast computers for the original H-bomb program. The question before the committee required a penetrating glimpse into the nuclear future. The group was asked to predict, seven years ahead to the end of the decade, what the ratio would be between the weight and yield of hydrogen devices: or, more to the point, how light a nuclear payload could be devised which still provided enough destructive power. In February 1954, von Neumann, enthusiastically backed by the RAND Corporation, a research outpost of the United States Air Force, reported that smaller and more powerful warheads would soon be available. The nose cones and the fuel load would come within manageable proportions. To the air force, the conclusion was irresistible: the highest priority should instantly be given to work on long-range ballistic missiles.

It took more than mere prediction, however, to persuade the Pentagon as a whole that missiles were the war machines of the future. The department was engaged at the time on a massive effort to expand

and develop the manned bombers. Only when these might be threatened was it likely that the supposedly infallible doctrine of which they were the embodiment would be revised.

Another year elapsed before the case for missiles became unanswerable. In 1955, American radar Intelligence in Turkey learned to Washington's astonishment just how far advanced the Soviet Union already was on a long-range missile program. It detected and tracked the flight of what looked like an intercontinental model from a launching point somewhere on the Black Sea.

The Russians had in fact been working hard on missiles for many years. Had the radar network been installed earlier, it might well have picked up earlier missile tests. From the end of the war, Stalin had shown an unhesitating awareness of their potential. On March 15, 1946, for example, he told a secret meeting of the Politburo, "German scientists have developed many interesting possibilities. Such a rocket [with intercontinental range] could change the fate of the war. Do you realize the tremendous strategic importance of machines of this sort? They could be an effective straitjacket for that very noisy shopkeeper, Harry Truman. We must go ahead with it, comrades. The problem of the creation of the transatlantic rocket is of extreme importance to us."

The spoils actually won by the Russians from the relics of the Third Reich were of limited value. "We defeated the Nazi armies," Stalin fulminated to Colonel Tokaty, one of his rocket experts, "we occupied Berlin and Peenemünde. But the Americans got the rocket engineers." What the Russians got were a few of the top engineers and administrators and a large number of technicians. These were sent into Russia and sucked dry of their expertise before being returned to the West. Although they did not include any von Brauns, they provided a useful basis from which Stalin's craving for rockets could be satisfied long before hydrogen warheads seemed likely to be available; before, even, the U.S.S.R. had built its atomic bomb.

Now, in 1955 the prospect from Washington was doubly grim. Not only did the Russians evidently possess great rocket power, but they would doubtless be able to arm it with hydrogen weapons. The nation which seemed so comfortably set for security based on the ashes of Hiroshima was suddenly confronted with the specter of its own nuclear bombers being blasted out of the sky, and its own cities and bases being eliminated from the map, by the missiles which Vanne-var Bush thought that no one could build.

Thus the strategic picture was completely changed. Missiles, not bombers, would be the main armory of the cold war as soon as they could be produced. Only later, after a new President, John Kennedy, had been elected partly on the strength of an alleged "missile gap," did Washington learn that the Russians had not gone ahead with large-scale missile production even though they had the competence to do so.

Another point was pardonably unforeseen. The thermo-nuclear breakthrough, in addition to its implications for war, substantially improved the chances that Americans would one day land on the moon. In retrospect this is not so difficult to perceive. Only with the certain promise of a hydrogen bomb, available to both sides, did an irrefutable case emerge for the production of missiles previously re-garded as having no clear military purpose; for neither side could remain passive in face of the possibility that the other possessed them, and could deliver H-bombs with them.

This was the justification for the great leap from conservative and uncoordinated rocket research to a crash program for production. The military missiles meant at least that the United States was likely to possess the technology capable of moving into space should she choose to do so. But this in turn meant something more. It ensured the exist-ence of a significant body of men with a vested interest in doing what they could to promote the case for space travel and with the means to prove that they were not merely dreaming. It is neither fortuitous nor uninstructive that this situation, the first serious prospect of space, should have emerged out of the bleak equations of the cold war.

Meanwhile, the heirs of Galileo had not been entirely inactive. Space as an arena of first-hand scientific investigation was being more insistently proposed in the writings of astronomers, geophysicists and other students of the planet. The absence of any rocket program which would immediately bring it within reach did not deter either scientist or soldiers from speculating rather less fancifully than Jules Verne on the usefulness of putting manmade objects into the void.

As early as 1948, James van Allen, a young man whose name was later to be attached to the single most important scientific discovery made by a space probe, outlined a possible satellite experiment at meetings of the International Union of Geodesy and Geophysics. Earlier still, the RAND Corporation had envisaged the results of a successful satellite in impressively prophetic terms.

> The achievement of a satellite craft by the United States [it reported in 1946] would inflame the imagination of mankind, and would probably produce repercussions in the world comparable to the explosion of the atomic bomb. . . . Since mastery of the elements is a reliable index of material progress, the nation which first makes significant achievements in space travel will be acknowledged as the world leader in both military and scientific techniques. To visualise the impact on the world, one can imagine the consternation and admiration that would be felt here if the U.S. were to discover suddenly that some other nation had already put up a successful satellite.

Fifteen years later such language was to become the essence of the official rhetoric of space.

The services themselves were tinkering with the possibilities. Rockets may have been inessential to American defense, but that did not mean the complete elimination of research into their potential capability. Von Braun, for one, now attached to the United States Army, was not reluctant to push the case forward. His survey in 1945 of the prospects for liquid-fueled rockets proposed an agenda for his new employers: multistage rockets, leading to satellite "observation platforms," orbiting space stations and eventually journeys "to other planets, first of all the moon." In New Mexico he was firing the modified V-2s, assembled from the parts filched from Germany, with increasing success. The first American-assembled V-2 was fired in April 1946, and soon the looted components were reaching record heights and speeds. One of them landed erratically near Juarez during a festival in May 1947, others exploded prematurely. But in general they offered encouragement to the slowly growing body of military rocket enthusiasts. In 1949, a series of anaesthetized monkeys, all called Albert, were sent aloft, most of them suffering no ill-effects from the experiment "until death on impact of the V-2."

The other services also had their enthusiasts. The navy, conscious already of the merits of diversification, was first in the field with a suggestion as early as November 1945 that satellite development be given the highest priority. The air force, much encouraged by the positive thinking of RAND, rapidly followed. Both services were anxious to establish that the satellite was a technical possibility. But in the more hazardous matter of identifying a sound military reason for attempting it, both were found wanting. In March 1948, both their proposals were effectively returned to file by the Defense Department's evaluation committee for guided missiles, which reported that neither service had "as yet established either a military or a scientific utility commensurate with the presently expected cost of a satellite vehicle."

Minor experimental rockets continued to be built and fired by all three services in competitive profusion, sounding the ionosphere, testing the multistage principle, studying high-altitude phenomena. But the prospect of actually placing a satellite in orbit rested there, with the Pentagon committee's bleak instruction to keep the question of utility under examination. Even the first allocation of money early in 1951 to groundwork for a genuinely intercontinental ballistic missile—the air force's Atlas—did not signify the advance of man into space. These were speculative studies toward an earthbound military objective which the strategic situation did not yet seem very likely to call into play. They did not raise the question of the value of space itself. Until this question was answered, the two leading groups of would-be space adventurers remained equally frustrated. The scientists thought they knew the value of the exercise, but were unable to convince anyone else that the money was worth spending. The military had some of the means to perform it, but could find no very specific evidence to justify their suspicion that American hardware should be up there.

In the eyes of both groups, the trouble at the time derived mainly from the politicians. Cost-conscious and dubious of the benefits, neither the White House nor the civilians at the Pentagon could convince themselves that a space program was anything more than a useless stunt. It was a time, according to a congressional report, when it was "not quite respectable" to talk about spaceflight. In 1952, when a group of scientists recommended after long study that a space program be seriously undertaken, the idea was "hooted down as outrageous," one of them recalled. President Eisenhower's Defense Secretary, Charles "Engine Charlie" Wilson, one of the archbishops of economic conservatism, regarded putting objects into orbit as a "nice technical trick," and told a press conference in November 1954 that he did not care whether the Soviet Union built a satellite first. The incredulous contempt with which such caution was later regarded is well summed up in a retrospective history prepared for the House of Representatives: "Some top-level people expressed the view that they did not care what is on the other side of the moon or why the grass is green."

This incomprehensible obscurantism is not the only reason for Wilson's eminent place on the roster of the damned. Along with Eisenhower himself, he has become a kind of Antichrist among the prophets of space. On the missile question, where the cost-benefit ratio was quite evidently favorable, his rigid economic principles led him to be almost as suspicious as he was of space satellites. His response to the von Neumann committee's report predicting missile-propelled hydrogen warheads was far less prompt than the air force's. While the air force immediately assigned top priority to missile development, Wilson waited more than a year before defining it as a Pentagon objective. He had, as one of his subordinates Trevor Gardner lamented, one deplorable weakness: he was quite unable to understand that maintaining technical superiority over the Soviet Union should have a higher priority than balancing the budget.

By the end of 1954, however, it was already virtually certain that an American satellite of some kind would be put into space, whatever the Defense Department thought. Plans had been under discussion for some years among the international scientific community for a great, worldwide scientific exercise, designed to advance man's basic knowledge of his own planet. The proposal originated in the belief of many geophysicists, among whom Americans were especially vocal, that the time had come for a new approach to the study of the earth as a whole and the influences upon it from outside celestial forces.

It was widely accepted that if simultaneous observations of earth could be made from many points around it, it would be possible to determine, in particular, the relationship of the earth with activity on the sun. On suggestion was for another Polar Year, emulating two earlier enterprises in which scientists from many nations had struggled to the freezing ends of the earth to record simultaneously what they could observe. But early in 1952, agreement hardened on something which promised to be bigger, an International Geophysical Year lasting from July 1957 to December 1958, a period expected to be one of maximum solar activity.

Originally the proposal for the IGY did not openly canvass the use of satellites. But now that the IGY was a firm objective, American scientists who had been vainly lobbying for action in space seized their chance. The credit for first arguing that the IGY should be marked by launching a satellite is commonly given to a brilliant young physicist, Fred Singer, who, with van Allen, was always among the most aggressive American proponents of satellites. In August 1953 he outlined to the International Congress on Astronautics a project for a MOUSE—minimum orbital unmanned scientific experiment— weighing a hundred pounds. Singer spent the next year urgently propagandizing his fellow scientists about the feasibility and unquestionable value of the MOUSE. The Office of Naval Research and Wernher von Braun were two timely recruits to the cause, von Braun eagerly suggesting that his own son-of-V-2, the three-stage Redstone missile, stood ready to push the object up within a very short time.

Already, too, considerations stretching beyond pure science were conveniently emerging. Since the IGY was an international program, it was likely to raise invidious comparisons between the technological advances it stimulated from the participating countries. Early in 1954, the National Security Council, the final arbiter of American cold-war strategy, decreed that the U.S. "should make a major effort during the IGY," and ordered the Defense Department to provide "whatever support was necessary to place the scientists and their instruments in remote locations." Again, nothing explicit was said about satellites. But at the same time, distinct evidence was coming out of the Soviet Union of a burgeoning Russian interest in space. Academician A. N. Nesmeyanov was reported as saying in November 1953 that man-made satellites could now be launched. In March 1954, Moscow Radio put out a stirring appeal to Soviet youth to be the first men to reach the moon.

The culmination of Fred Singer's energetic campaign was reached at a meeting of the steering committee for the IGY in Rome in October 1954. Before the formal meetings Singer put on a tour de force for the benefit of his unbelieving colleagues on the American delegation. He gave a comprehensive account of all the relevant factors: possible orbits, the probable lifetime of the satellite, the problems of information-retrieval and receiving stations, the effect of launching errors, the detailed scientific applications. When some scientists expressed scepticism about the likelihood of political support for the project, others moved in with confident assertions of the prestige which it would undoubtedly bring to the United States. With this assurance, the American delegation obtained the committee's endorsement for a resolution encouraging countries to mark the IGY by studying the possibilities of a satellite launch. The Russians, throughout the proceedings, said not a word.

From this moment, despite the stubborn opposition of Secretary Wilson and other economic conservatives, there was never much doubt that the satellite idea would eventually receive Washington's approval. It was now established as potentially the biggest and best bauble among the likely trophies of the IGY. It obviously accorded with the National Security Council's requirement for "a major effort." The extent of its importance—the ranking it deserved in the priorities—was not to be fully grasped by the White House for a long time. The persistently ambiguous view which the politicians took of the experiment, distracted as they were by the overwhelming need for military missile development, had a shattering consequence. But it is clear enough that when the President announced at the end of July 1955 that the satellite was going ahead, he had partly in mind the political as well as the scientific need to maintain American technological advance. He spectacularly misjudged the outcome of the enterprise. But this does not detract from the IGY satellite's status at the beginning of one of the space program's more fateful marriages, between the disciplines of science and politics.

Of course, politics was not at this stage the main propellant. It is gratifying for the legend of the American space program that the IGY satellite, its first concrete achievement, can convincingly be represented as having originated with scientists and having been pushed forward for genuine scientific reasons. What Eisenhower signed into existence seemed at the time to be a limited government investment in co-operative science.

But the irony of the legend is nonetheless unmistakable. After the decision itself, comparatively free of impure motive, events took on a quite different pattern—one rather more accurately prophetic of the true nature of the program which eventually put an American on the moon. Long before the satellite got off the ground, it became the object of political and military wrangles of the most virulent kind. When it finally reached its destination, it was no longer a triumph of science. It had been transformed from a box of technical tricks into the obsessive tool of cold-war politicians. There could have been no apter beginning to the real history of America's great space adventure.

The decision to launch the satellite posed a very awkward problem. Who should be responsible for sending the thing aloft? Eisenhower's solution, to give over-all responsibility to the Pentagon, was no answer. In these pre-McNamara days, the department's control over its different military clients was no more than fitful. The instinctive determination of the army, the air force and the navy to seize from each other the biggest piece of any action in prospect was rarely held in check by the civilians. Nowhere was this rivalry more spirited than in the field of rockets, to which all three services had devoted some energy without anything dramatic to show for it. Not surprisingly, each was inexhaustibly keen to see its own hardware pushing the first American satellite into space.

The problem had not been entirely unforeseen. Some months before the announcement of Eisenhower's decision, Assistant Secretary Donald Quarles, the Defense Department's chief of research and development, had set up a committee to review the various satellite proposals and the means of effecting them. The committee, consisting of civilian nominees of the services and the department, was chaired by Dr. Homer Joe Stewart, professor of physics at the University of California, Los Angeles.

As the committee began to survey the jungle of competing launchers in a more or less advanced state of readiness, one restraint hung over their deliberations. The National Security Council had ordered that nothing in the satellite project should be allowed to interfere with the intercontinental missile program. Although the plunge into the missile race had been seen as imperative for more than a year, the program, under Wilson's cautious hand, was experiencing serious growing pains. The Defense Department seemed to be in a state of permanent organizational revolution in the attempt to cut down the bureaucratic delay, divided responsibility and mushrooming committees which plagued missile production. Getting a Pentagon decision

was "just like putting a nickel in a slot machine," the chairman of
North American Aviation recalled to an official historian of the period:
"You pull the handle and you get a lemon and you put another one
in. You have to get three or four of them in a row and hold them
there long enough for them to say 'Yes.' It takes a lot of nickels and a
lot of time."

This was bad news for the air force's satellite proposal. The air
force, as it has never tired of explaining, deals in the air, a commodity
which would seem to have an undeniably close affinity with space.
Even in 1955 the simple logic of this argument was more than a little
spoiled by the fact that the other services had already made pre-
emptive strikes into air force territory. Both the army and the navy
had well-established air and space interests. But this alone did not
exclude the air force from the satellite struggle. Its proposal involved
using a rocket based on the motors developed since 1951 for the Atlas
missile, the earliest American ICBM to be conceived. Atlas production had been put on a crash basis since the von Neumann committee's report. To consider employing it for the satellite represented a
clear interference with military priorities.

There remained the army and the navy. They had at one time
collaborated on satellite studies, but their position before the Stewart
Committee was intensely competitive. The army proposed the descendant of the V-2 developed out of the von Braun Team's work in
New Mexico, the Redstone booster, with three additional stages. The
main advantage claimed for the Redstone was that it could get the
satellite into orbit in less than eighteen months, by January 1957.
The navy's plan was based on what was first described as an improved
version of the Viking rocket—first fired in 1949—with two additional
stages. The Stewart Committee's vote went to the navy, with their
so-called Project Vanguard, over the army's Project Orbiter.

This recommendation, publicized within a week of Eisenhower's
announcement, led the Pentagon to make one of the most catastrophic
public decisions in its history. By confirming the choice of the navy,
the department placed the entire responsibility for getting a satellite
into space on a rocket which proved to need far more experimental
work than anyone had bargained for—in effect it was a new rocket,
not a pepped-up old one. Vanguard was soon the subject of steadily
increasing delays. By the time the IGY satellite had completed its

transformation from scientific instrument into political symbol, the navy's booster was shown to be dismally unequal to the task.

Much confusion has surrounded the reasoning of the Stewart Committee. The official explanation at the time concentrated on Vanguard's greater reliability, stemming from its dependence on only two additional stages; and on military and security considerations. Whereas Redstone was a military rocket, the Vanguard engine did not impinge on prospective weapons projects. In any case, it had been declassified, and technical data about it would not have to be concealed in a way which might degrade the spirit of the IGY. It was also claimed that the navy had greater experience of putting up rockets for scientific purposes.

Homer Joe Stewart's own recollection is significantly different. He supported the army project against the majority. The broad case he made for it rested on its greater flexibility as a satellite launcher, especially within the time-span designated for the IGY. While there was a case for arguing that the nonmilitary status of Vanguard accorded better with the IGY's scientific purpose, this, Dr. Stewart says, was hardly raised by its supporters in the committee. The security problem was a still less decisive factor. Contrary to the official story, the checklist of security data on the two rockets was virtually identical.

The decisive reason for the choice of Vanguard, according to Dr. Stewart, was its "superior engineering elegance." Von Braun's original proposal used a cluster of very old-fashioned Loki rockets for the final stage. A revised version still had the appearance of a lashed-up job, with a first stage capable of lifting as much as half a ton into orbit but with upper stages which were comparatively feeble. By comparison with this clumsy contraption, Vanguard promised to be beautifully tailored to the job in hand. It therefore appealed a great deal more to committee members representing the IGY's interest, with their overriding concern for scientific potential, than it did to the dissenters, among them Stewart and Dr. Clifford C. Furnas, of Buffalo University, who happened to be the only two members of the committee with experience in developing complete rockets.

A darker factor also intruded, never openly discussed by the committee but indicative of the kind of game which rocket men were learning to play. The navy, at this time, was the scene of an intense internal dispute about the need for a full-scale naval intercontinental missile program—what was later to become familiar as Polaris. Missile men were trying to get the idea approved by their more sceptical colleagues and, says Stewart, "they were having a terrible time of it." To them, Vanguard seemed the thin end of the wedge which would let in Polaris. This attractive possibility increased the fervor with which the navy made its case and stuck to it during the devious assaults which the army was to make on Vanguard in the corridors of the Pentagon.

But in all these debates there was one fundamental defect—a stubborn refusal to perceive the nature of the game in which the United States was really involved. In retrospect it is almost touching to observe. Reading the endless barrage of doom-laden, nationalistic propaganda with which the space program was later propelled into action, no one can withhold from the Eisenhower Administration some small token of admiration for its well-meaning obtuseness.

The IGY satellite was the first, and perhaps the most critical, instance of this. At the time Eisenhower agreed to the satellite there was no lack of evidence that the Soviet Union had similar designs on space. Public reports of Russian capacity and intentions were already beginning to come in; American Intelligence, as a chastened Congress later learned, supported the hypothesis. Yet the Eisenhower policymakers doggedly refused to regard the IGY satellite as anything more than a self-justifying scientific experiment. Although the merits of achieving a great technological advance were apparent to them, the connection between this and the central question of national prestige in the cold war was not made. Above all, the President was concerned by every means possible to show that the satellite was totally separated from military objectives. It was not to be a part of any war, hot or cold.

Not unnaturally, this view infected the Stewart Committee majority and the Pentagon itself. The obviously greater speed with which Project Orbiter could be completed was discounted because being first into space was not then the overriding concern it later became. Thus the ranks of Pentagon Assistant Secretaries, whose decision led to the department endorsing the Stewart Committee view on September 9, 1955, saw no reason to alter the expert technical findings. This was the first seminal decision of America's space age. It was also the last occasion on which a strategic decision about the space effort was not made on grounds of *realpolitik*.

Not that the army lightly accepted what seemed to it to be an appalling error. It had shown itself to be fully conversant with the urgent language of national survival when it first presented its Orbiter proposals. It set to work with astonishing obstinacy to get the decision reversed.

Within days of the Stewart report, the Chief of Army Ordnance issued a categoric assertion that Redstone could perform the first orbital flight by January 1957, and without interference with the missile program. He pointed with a touch of ridicule to the fact that Vanguard required the development of a virtually new rocket within the unprecedented period of two years.

For more than a year, a series of initiatives streamed unceasingly from the army's rocket experts and their political supporters. Furnas, lately in the minority on the Stewart Committee, now moved to the Pentagon to run research and development and acted swiftly to keep Orbiter alive. He instructed the army to explore the possibility of using Redstone as a back-up to Vanguard, available should Vanguard fail to reach the pad.

Von Braun and his men had moved to Huntsville, Alabama, under the wing of Army Ordnance several years before. There a great modern arsenal had been constructed out of the relics of facilities used by the Chemical Corps during the war. The Deep South had become home for the German émigrés; they had built houses in a part of town known as Sauerkraut Hill, and been gradually accepted by the sleepy rural population as the bringers of prosperity if nothing else. Huntsville grew large and rich with the dawning of the space age. In early 1956 the Redstone Arsenal swelled, as if to emphasize the army's determination to be a rocket-powered service, into the Army Ballistic Missile Agency and prepared for battle with the forces of evil in Washington.

Despite directives from elsewhere in the Pentagon, The Team and their peppery military boss, General John Medaris, proved fully equal to circumventing the bureaucracy and dramatically improving their satellite capabilities.

They devised a ruse. Shortly after they had lost the satellite struggle, their Army Ballistic Missile Agency was instructed to start work on

one of the phalanx of military missiles designed to counter the Soviet
lead in the field—an intermediate-range specimen designated Jupiter.
Von Braun and Medaris quickly found in this a justification for continuing with firings of the Redstone, their rejected satellite launcher.

For the Jupiter missile to be effective over two thousand miles, it
was essential to establish that its business end, the nuclear warhead,
could survive the fierce ordeal of re-entry into earth's atmosphere
after the descent from space. Tests on this did not need to await
the new missile itself, which was still at the development stage. A
Redstone booster with additional stages stacked on top was capable
of projecting the warhead to the required height. This Huntsville immediately proceeded to build. A rocket was assembled, to be boosted
by the Redstone, and the whole package was given the unnecessarily
confusing designation Jupiter-C. This shrewd choice of name simplified the delicate task of continuing, in effect, to demonstrate the
superiority of the Redstone as a launcher for the fateful satellite. One
of its main results was to make available to von Braun the new launch
pads at Cape Canaveral which had been assigned to Jupiter. Ostensibly
the object was to test the future Jupiter nose cone; in fact it was to
assert Redstone's supremacy.

In September 1956, with the help of this subterfuge, the army
stated its most impressive case yet against the unhappy Vanguard
project. The first Jupiter-C, missile 27, was fired a remarkable 3300
miles down-range and 600 miles up into space. Manifestly it was capable of lifting a satellite. In fact, the Pentagon became so concerned
that von Braun and Medaris might be planning covertly to use it for
this purpose that Washington sent a specific directive ordering them
to fill the final stage of missile 27 with sand. Medaris was held personally responsible to see that there were, as the Pentagon put it, "no
accidents"—such as a fourth stage with power to go into orbit.

The triumph of missile 27 was scarcely pleasing to Washington.
When it led to yet more jubilant requests from Huntsville to be allowed to go ahead with the satellite launch, a final, silencing rebuke
was dispatched from the Secretary of the Army, who complained of
the painful embarrassment caused him in the Pentagon by this refusal
of the army's rocket men to obey orders. Draconian action seemed the
only answer to Medaris's potent demands, and the solid-fuel upper-
stage rockets of Jupiter-C were duly ordered to be destroyed. Even

now, however, Huntsville matched the challenge. It hit upon a novel method of destruction, with interesting possibilities which no one had seriously examined—destruction not by summary act but by the slow disintegration of time. It simply left the rockets on the shelf.

As Medaris reported later, his objective throughout this period had been to alert Washington to the army's capability "if they really wanted a satellite." But that was just the problem. Washington was not at all sure how badly the satellite was needed. Project Vanguard was given a low priority. No place was found for it, between the missile obsession and the economy drive, on the Pentagon's Master Urgency List. Funding was irregular and tight-fisted.

The technical problems common to all new rocket developments were causing delays: the guidance system developed serious weight problems, and the IGY committee's demand for a sphere instead of a pointed nose cone as the first, sacred orbiting object involved major changes in the rockets themselves. The manufacturers, the Martin Company in Baltimore, were also contracted to produce the great Titan military missile for the air force. This meant shunting off Vanguard, according to its director, to an airless loft in an undermanned corner of the plant. Then—the army's final insult—Vanguard was refused the use of the Jupiter launch pads at the Cape, on the grounds (curious in view of the tacit objectives of the Jupiter-C) that this would interfere with the missile program.

As the International Geophysical Year opened in July 1957, the main American contribution, the silvery orb which was intended to open a whole new vista of planetary study, was a distinctly unpromising prospect. It would be interesting to speculate on the course of future events had the history of the IGY satellite been different. For there can be no doubt that the misfortunes originating in the selection of Vanguard over Orbiter played a decisive part in shaping the American space program of the 1960s. If the choice had been different, bluntly, the United States would have been first into space. This is not apparent merely in retrospect. There is every reason to believe that von Braun and his colleagues at Huntsville were right in their assertions that they could have completed the job some time early in 1957. Had they been allowed to do so, they could have spared the American public the cataclysmic psychic shock administered by the Soviet success with Sputnik 1 on October 4, 1957.

There had been plenty of warning that Sputnik was about to fly. Hot on the tail of the announcement of Vanguard, Moscow had gloated that it would be able to launch a considerably larger satellite within two years. When the two years were up, the Soviet magazine *Radio* invited readers to listen for signals from Sputniks. Late in August, moreover, Tass announced the successful launch of a "super long distance" intercontinental missile capable of hitting "any part of the world." The only convincing official reaction came from an anonymous American general, said to have exclaimed, "We captured the wrong Germans." By late September it was obvious to Kremlinologists that a satellite launch was imminent, and the Soviet delegate to an IGY meeting in Washington made the scarcely Delphic pronouncement, "We will not cackle until we have laid our egg."

Within days, the egg, weighing 184 pounds—vastly more than Vanguard's capability—was safely girdling the earth over a hundred miles up. And overnight, America was plunged into the most profound crisis of self-confidence in her history.

If any single moment can be seen to have made Project Apollo inevitable, this was it. The moment Sputnik went aloft can be seen as the beginning of the transformation of the American space program into an arm of diplomacy, security and psychology at the center of America's international objectives. Instead of proceeding into space with the well-ordered calm of the leader in the field, the United States suddenly discovered that it had lost what appeared to be a race for that elusive and potent grail, "prestige" in the eyes of the world. It was a shattering revelation. It was to have many consequences for the economy, for foreign policy, for the military debate. But among other things it led to a restless search for some objective in space itself which would ultimately eclipse anything else which man had done there.

Even Sputnik, however, took time to move the mind of the intransigent Eisenhower. His response stands as one of the most striking bromides in postwar diplomatic history. A master of the art of political bathos, he now found a more fitting occasion for its use than any other which arose during his presidency. "One small ball in the air," he called Sputnik 1; "something which does not raise my apprehensions, not one iota." "So far as this satellite itself is concerned," he told a dissatisfied press conference, referring to the Vanguard's project, "if we were doing it for science, and not for security, which we were doing, I don't know of any reason why the scientists should have come in and urged that we do this before anybody else could do it."

The President was prepared to admit that the Soviet exploit confirmed the existence of impressive rocket power. But he was not willing to agree to any significant increase in the already swelling missile expenditure. Privately he admitted to some worry, and ordered that the administrative hold-ups on finance for missiles should be removed. Publicly, as he later wrote in his memoirs, he was principally concerned "to find ways of affording perspective to our people and so relieve the current wave of near-hysteria." Some of the help he enlisted in this process even outshone the dismissive prose of the master. Sherman Adams, his closest personal confidant, reaffirmed that the U.S. satellite program was intended to serve science, not to win "an outer space basketball game." Clarence Randall, another White House aide, described Sputnik as "a silly bauble . . . a bubble in the sky."

Exoneration also seemed apparent in the comforting words of Queen Elizabeth and Prince Philip, who visited Eisenhower two weeks after Sputnik. "You know," Ike told his resident intellectual valet, Emmet John Hughes, "when the Queen and Philip were here, they were amazed at our press reaction to Sputnik. Each one, independently, told me so. They said people in London just gave it one day of excitement, then went on about their business."

American public opinion, however, registered a quite different response. Led for so long by the Administration's optimistic line, it now viewed the Soviet achievement in thoroughly apocalyptic terms. Shame merged quickly into fear. Sputnik 1 was seen to signal unimaginable disasters, not only for American "prestige," whatever that might mean, but also militarily. Six months after Sputnik, ninety-one percent of Americans had heard of it, according to the Survey Research Center, and thirty-three percent of those who believed the American satellite program had some purpose took this to be competition with the Soviet Union.

Intolerance with the President's complacency was shared by the military and by many scientists, but it was led by the congressional politicians, especially the Democrats. No one was more prominent in organizing the congressional response than the senior senator from Texas, Lyndon Baines Johnson. As Democratic leader in the Senate, Johnson had powerful influence on the White House over a wide range of policies. Without the majority congressional support which he largely controlled, the Administration's legislative program was effectively null. And when Johnson heard the news of Sputnik at his ranch, he set the wires to Washington humming that very night. His staff began preparing next day for a major investigation which Johnson was determined to launch into America's state of preparedness across the whole field of missiles, satellites and security generally.

For Johnson personally, this was the beginning of an intimate association with the space program stretching right up to the moon landing itself. In many ways the program became his personal fief, as Senator and later as Vice-President. It took him very little time to see that space offered plausible rewards for the country, political advantage to his Party—and potential profit to himself. After all, he wanted to be President, and was already looking forward to an acclamation from the 1960 convention. Hinged on what he seems genuinely to have interpreted as a horrifying threat to national security, an all-out campaign forcing the Administration to reverse its view of space would benefit all three interests simultaneously.

Johnson suited the role peculiarly well. As early in 1949 he had vainly tried to persuade the Pentagon to start research for a space program. He had a good record in support of pure research, "unceasing, never-ending research" as he said, "endless months of trial and error following blind trials." Also he had rarely failed to vote for anything the military wanted. Drawing both these interests together with political profit, space was a natural issue for him. During the 1960s it became fertile territory for people with loud voices and a limitless conviction that it was America's glorious duty to storm every new technological frontier. Triumphalists and true believers flourished, blowing aside with one blast of patriotism anyone who dared to question the object of the exercise. The space program could hardly have survived without them. From his different seats of power, Johnson was able to ensure that nothing seriously impeded the steady march of astronauts into the sky. He quickly reached a position where not only the money for space but also the occasional top job in the program was open to his influence. And it seems a very natural consummation to find Johnson right at the heart of the ultimate decision to attempt the moon landing.

The hearings of Johnson's preparedness subcommittee, which

opened in the wake of Sputnik 2 with its canine cargo, were the
catalyst for a remarkable transformation of the national mood. Famous
soldiers, brilliant scientists, ambitious industrialists, all were brought
to testify to the sad condition of American technology. Each had his
tale of opportunities missed and dangers looming.

Johnson orchestrated the performance with consummate skill. He
was anxious not to expose himself to the charge of heightening the
danger by laying bare the gaps in American defenses, and he preferred
to dampen personal attacks on Eisenhower himself. Nevertheless, the
failure in space had to be driven home to the public. The first witness
to take the stand was Edward Teller, father of the H-bomb, destroyer
of Robert Oppenheimer when the latter's security clearance was in
question, and acclaimed by one senator present as "the greatest scientist in the world today."

Teller described America's post-Sputnik situation as a greater emergency than that which had led to the development of the atomic
bomb. America was being outpaced by Soviet technological daring.
"We are not taking the kind of risks which in war, in cold war as
well as in hot war, one necessarily has to take." Teller thought it certain that people would go to the moon, for peaceful and scientific
reasons but also for "a great military advantage." But, he added, "Don't
ask me, please, what it is. My imagination is not good enough for that."
At the end of his testimony, Teller was gravely commended by Johnson
for having described "the seriousness of the dangers that face this
nation." The nation was indebted to him: "You came and told us
what we wanted to know."

So did many, many others. The hearings were like a massive,
cathartic confessional act, in which the sins, however, were never
those of the men in the box and absolution was never granted. Their
atmosphere irresistibly recalled the Moscow Trials in the 1930s. Senators and generals vied with each other in merciless condemnation of
the one true devil, the Eisenhower Administration, with its incomprehensible refusal to admit that the country stood in mortal peril.
Czars of the aerospace industry spoke of Washington's maze of inde-
cisive committees. Leaders of technological research drew a pitiful
picture of vital advances impeded by breadline financing. General
James Doolittle, chairman of the Scientific Advisory Board, complained that it had all happened because Russians worked harder at

school: "We are making our high school courses too easy." The grim chief of Strategic Air Command, General Curtis LeMay, hinted that the end might well be nigh already: "It is doubtful in my mind whether we could catch up before we have a general war."

Naturally, too, Wernher von Braun was a leading witness. There was some danger that, although the hearings were prompted by Sputnik, they would develop into a prolonged demand by the generals for more and larger missiles, which might seem to be a more obviously desirable prop to national security than space satellites. Von Braun, solidly backed by his military chiefs, Medaris and General James Gavin, provided the necessary corrective. After a candid admission that he personally had badly miscalculated the progress of the Russian missile program, he postulated the terrifying possibility of Sputnik leading directly to an orbital bomb. Although there were, even at this early stage in space thinking, many sound reasons to doubt the capacity of anything in orbit to destroy a specific target more accurately than a warhead launched from a static position, von Braun clearly struck a good note. He described how useful an orbiting vehicle would be against moving targets, such as Soviet ships. He was "firmly convinced" that Soviet occupation of space put America close to annihilation.

The army's men all presented the case for satellites with greater vehemence than their service rivals, and for an understandable reason. A year before, shortly after the 3300-mile launch of the first Jupiter-C, they had suffered the affront of being taken out of the missile business altogether. The Pentagon had directed that operational control of all missiles with a range longer than two hundred miles (except the navy's Polaris) be handed over to the air force. It was a crushing insult, which threatened to destroy the von Braun Team and all the work at the grand new rocket facilities in Huntsville.

Satellites, however, were a different capability, still open to the service. Hence, we find General Gavin, deputy chief of the army's research and development office, telling the Johnson hearings that space exploration was "the most important thing confronting the country today," and the military satellite "perhaps the most significant thing of our times," based on any sound assessment of the strategic situation. Although Gavin was no more capable than Teller of defining precisely what military functions were unique to space, he had no doubt that there were some: "You have got to get out there first and be able to sit down in international councils and determine as to who is going to be out there and who is going to do what out there."

No rhetoric could have been better designed to win the heart of Lyndon Johnson. To him the impending missile gap, real and critical though it seemed to be, was also the emotional tool with which to open the public mind to something much grander; a belief in the conquest of space. Not content with the publicity which his hearings were getting, he set out to preach the virtues of a massive military and civilian space program organized under a new agency of government. The theme featured prominently in the private State of the Union message which he delivered to the country in January 1958, an occasion signaling the beginning of his own presidential campaign and, as James Reston remarked in the *New York Times*, the prospect that the governments of Russia and America would now have to pre-pare themselves to deal with Texas.

Johnson demanded a total re-evaluation of space in national priorities, to be conducted and subsequently enacted by scientists, with the objective of total domination. The history of other empires, as he read it, dictated no other course. "The Roman Empire controlled the world because it could build roads. Later, when men moved to the sea, the British Empire was dominant because it had ships. Now the Communists have established a foothold in outer space. It is not very reassuring to be told that next year we will put a 'better' satellite into the air. Perhaps it will even have chrome trim and automatic windshield wipers."

To Johnson, it was a simple question of good men versus bad. Was this new frontier to be controlled by the Russians, bent on gathering all men into Red captivity? Or was it to be claimed by the liberator, the apostle of freedom, the guarantor of scientific benevolence, the United States? This kind of thinking, so finely tuned to the prevailing view of the world taken by many American leaders, was to prove the keynote for much that followed on the path to the moon. "There is something more important," Johnson said, "than any ultimate weapon; that is, the ultimate position of total control over earth which lies somewhere out in space."

The woeful testimony had hardly got under way, however, before an event occurred which indicated that it might be some time before Johnson's dream came to pass. Not until Sputnik 2 at the beginning of November was Eisenhower's brass-bound coolness fractured sufficiently even to induce him to order an acceleration of the lagging Vanguard project. The event had also finally persuaded him to approve the preparation of the army's Redstone Jupiter-C for possible use should Vanguard fail. Now came the critical test for Vanguard, thrust before its time on to the launch pad and required to salvage the shreds of American self-respect.

On December 6, 1957, to a fanfare of derisive publicity, Vanguard rose a few inches from the pad before collapsing in a fiery heap. Kaputnik, Flopnik, Stayputnik, shouted the headlines in London. Moscow sent its condolences. The Senators redoubled their adjectival fury.

Seven weeks later, the IGY satellite, Explorer 1, was at last aloft, propelled by the army's Redstone vehicle which was in all important respects unchanged from the inelegant contraption which the Stewart Committee and the Pentagon had found so offensive nearly three years before. Huntsville and the army were jubilant. "The army has never let the people down" and "Move over Sputnik, space is ours" were typical of the optimistic catchlines—although General Medaris, when asked for permission to contact Washington with news that orbit had been achieved, is said to have replied, "Not yet; let them sweat a little."

In terms of the IGY, Explorer 1 was in fact an extraordinary success. Among the scientific coups of the space program this, the very first American satellite, achieved more than any other since sent up. Containing a simple geiger counter, it discovered the radiation belts outside the atmosphere, now bearing the name of the experiment's designer James van Allen, which significantly altered conventional views about planet earth.

But at the time this seemed conspicuously unimportant. Much more than the belated success of Redstone Jupiter-C would be needed to expunge the memory of Sputnik.

To Johnson and the other prophets of space, moreover, it did not seem likely that the requisite effort would be made unprompted by a man with so little sense of drama as Dwight D. Eisenhower. Quite apart from his innate refusal to be hustled, the President was now a sick man. Late in 1957, he suffered his third major illness, a cerebral spasm. Emmet Hughes reports that in private he cut a bewilderingly confused figure. When Hughes suggested, for example, that alarm over Sputnik could be marshaled into national support for a larger space effort, Eisenhower did not demur. "Quickly—almost too quickly, I felt —he agreed: 'Oh, absolutely. Anything that will get us out of complacency and make this next Congress realize how serious things are, that's all to the good.'"

Hughes was not reassured. "A year earlier, I thought, I would have heard such a remark with pleasure and would have said so. This year I no longer knew what the words meant, where any affirmations aimed. And I said nothing."

4.
The Generals Shoot
for the Moon

In Eisenhower's farewell address to the nation, the old soldier uttered a phrase which nothing in his eight White House years had caused the world to expect of him. For seemingly the first time he said something original, dramatic and durable. "In the councils of government," he warned, "we must guard against the acquisition of unwarranted influence, whether sought or unsought, by the military-industrial complex."

Ever since it entered the Washington vernacular, the military-industrial complex, or MIC, has been the subject of widely differing interpretations. Although Eisenhower coined the phrase, with its intimations of an evil conspiracy at the heart of American life, he did not define how it worked. At least two extreme positions have, in fact, evolved as to the true nature of this most durable feature of American politics. One school of thought insists that virtually no decision taken by the United States government can be understood without reference to some plot, usually secret and always sinister, between businessmen and soldiers. This school is well represented on the Left of politics, and among people who believe that all human affairs must be capable of neatly packaged description. At the opposite extreme there is the view that the military-industrial complex is a totally meaningless phrase, referring to something which does not exist. Among those most committed to this view are people who feel in danger of being identified as members of the MIC, and those most exposed to its alleged influence.

Certainly, the military-industrial complex is an elusive concept. It cannot be verified by disclosure of the usual mechanisms of conspiracy —smoke-filled rooms, illegal pay-offs, obviously guilty men. All these may feature in dealings between industrialists and generals, as they do throughout Washington life. But the complex actually describes something rather less positive. It is a satisfactory phrase only when it is seen as referring to a condition rather than a set of identifiable people: a state of affairs pervading American decisions in a number of strategic areas.

The essential feature of this condition is that it is self-generating. It grows naturally out of the American economy, and especially the percentage of the Gross National Product devoted to defense. In certain areas, the single-minded concern of the armed services to provide security, thus selflessly expanding their size and power, coincides with the single-minded interest of industry in the growth of profits. Obviously this conjunction of interest does not depend on a conspiracy. It is a natural fact of life. It is amoral, rather than immoral. On both sides, moreover, it is marked by one inestimable advantage. The separate interests of the military and of the armaments industry can be convincingly represented as coinciding with the broader interest of the nation itself: with the need for complete security, on the one hand, and the need for economic growth, jobs and technological advance on the other.

The missile program is the most obvious example of this fruitful connection at work. And among peaceful programs none has manifested the characteristics of the military-industrial complex more clearly than the space program. Eisenhower did not reveal what was in his mind when he spoke the deathless phrase, but the space business had certainly provided him with the most recent evidence to justify it. During the three years between Sputnik 1 and his retirement, he was the object of relentless assaults on his stolid common sense by men who believed it imperative that America should be highest with the mostest: that she should decide, in short, to land a man on the moon without delay. These were mainly the work of army and air force generals, a significant foretaste of the militaristic logic which, even though Eisenhower himself rejected it, was ultimately to decide the matter for his successor. In this barrage, the generals were backed by their clients in industry and their patrons in Congress. It was enough to drive any man into the language of demonology.

For a glimpse of the military-industrial complex today, at the other end of the decade, it would be hard to do better than to cross the Potomac from Washington and visit the Architects Building in Arlington, Virginia. It is a gleaming edifice, of the type which American real-estate developers build in their sleep. Tall office blocks such as this are excluded from Washington itself, in a commendable effort to preserve the coherence of the decorous federal architecture. But this does not mean that the men inside them are excluded from a full part in the life of the federal government.

The main tenant of the Architects Building, occupying fifteen floors, is the aerospace division of the United States Air Force. From here are directed the air force's own secret and extensive space activities. The sixteenth and top floor, however, is rented by a firm of management consultants, named Schriever-McGee Associates. Schriever-McGee is available for consultation on any large management project from rebuilding city ghettos to restructuring computer firms; but its speciality is aerospace. This alone might not make Schriever-McGee's co-tenancy with the air force particularly notable but for one important fact. Both Schriever and McGee are themselves recently retired air force generals. Schriever, moreover, was General Bernard Schriever, Chief of the Ballistic Missile Division, czar of aerospace in USAF, and throughout the 1950s the inspiration behind the service's extraordinarily persistent attempts to run the American space program. Lesser retired officers make up most of the staff at Schriever-McGee, assuring visitors that their continuing proximity to the service is a complete coincidence. But the firm has a large aerospace clientele, which makes fair business sense. In charting a course through the first fifteen floors of the Architects Building, any rocket contractor who did not start at the sixteenth would be out of his mind.

In the turbulent months after Sputnik, Schriever's air force had staked the fastest and most detailed claim to the moon. Committees had already been sitting, one of them under the ubiquitous Edward Teller, which recommended the service to "establish a vigorous space program with an immediate goal of landings on the moon." Already, almost unquestionably, the moon was seen as the big prize. Before

1957 was out, the Ballistic Missile Division was ordered to devise a plan to get there and produced one entailing eleven calculated leaps forward. After earth orbital missions and animal landings on the moon, Schriever said, a manned landing could take place by 1965. The approach would be "quick and dirty," with a landing at sea and the human occupant being a passenger rather than a pilot. It would cost $1500 million, or one sixteenth of the eventual price of Project Apollo.

The Pentagon cast a cold eye on these extravagantly optimistic plans, which were delivered with avenging pride six months after Sputnik 1. Perhaps the most prophetic element among them lay in the acronym derived from the most urgent of the eleven stages—Man in Space Soonest, or MISS. General Schriever, lean, solemn and fiercely tight-lipped, now experiences a moment of inadvertent candor as he looks back on the days before he joined the industrial side of the complex. There was, it seems, little military justification for the air force's pressing demand to take the moon. "No hard military objectives developed out of our early studies," he says. "There may have been some zealots with fire in their eyes who thought they could dream up things for us to do up there. But no one who really studied the matter could find military uses, especially so far as the lunar surface was concerned."

This did not deter the army any more than the air force. With a plan called Man Very High, it proposed to put man in space sooner than Soonest. Possessing the priceless von Braun, it, too, produced its own blueprint for the moon journey, the "National Integrated Missile and Space Vehicle Development Program." Once again, the language was more apocalyptic than the facts. Such a program, von Braun argued, was "not only feasible but mandatory for national security." His prospectus was no less urgent than the rival service's, promising man on the moon "as early as 1965." But it did allow of a more realistic budget: $17,000 million between 1958 and 1970.

Why, if these two plans were a military nonsense, were they produced with such a fanfare by the military services? In part the answer lies in the hysteria of the times, when it was seen as the duty of every patriotic public servant—and most of all of soldiers—to spring to the rescue of national prestige after the insult inflicted by Sputnik. Study of the finer benefits seemed irrelevant beside the need for a grand gesture.

But calculation was not completely absent. Both services had their
own vital reason for preserving the normal military decision-making
process by which the end-objective is identified and found worthwhile
before the steps toward it are begun. Superficially, the programs
founded on MISS and Man Very High appeared to lack this clearly
acknowledged objective; as Schriever says; there was no military reason
for going to the moon. Nevertheless, there were clear reasons for each
service to advance such a plan, summed up in the crude determination
by each that its own identity and importance should survive.

In the case of the air force, doubts about the future derived, paradoxically, from the unquestioned control which the service had earlier
won over the missile-deterrent force. While it was naturally proper
that the air force should be in charge of the missiles, some of the sharper
minds in the service foresaw the danger of eventually becoming a
subterranean army, noted principally for manning silos strung under-
neath the Middle West. This would be a shocking affront, only partly
mitigated by the decision to continue using manned bombers, to the
air force's belief that it was in charge of the "air." Hence it was
rational enough that the service should want to prevent any other
service, as well as any other country, from getting to the moon first.

The army was driven by a similarly compelling argument. Its prized
rocket team at Huntsville had been dealt a terrible blow by the
Pentagon directive that only the air force should control missiles with
a range of more than two hundred miles. Space would henceforth be
Huntsville's only outlet. Von Braun and his team had begun studies
for a space booster based on the principle of clustering together several
rockets in one launcher, to generate one and a half million pounds of
thrust—something gigantically different from existing rockets. The
object was to show that very large payloads *could* be put into orbit
if a requirement for them could be established. Such a requirement
might be very hard to prove, but it was essential to the survival of the
army rocket team that the case be made for it existing in a national
space program.

One result of this self-interested logic was to distort some of the
crucial facts, most of all the facts about cost. Since the air force was
bent on hustling America to the moon without scrutinizing very carefully the arguments for and against the trip, it is scarcely surprising
that its cost estimates were made to look more seductive than realistic.

Another, rather more destructive, consequence of service rivalry was
to persuade each in its different way to try to frustrate the only substantial decision Eisenhower took in the wake of Sputnik, the decision
to put space in civilian hands.

The old President, shrewder about space than about many earthly
matters, had not the remotest intention of going to the moon. He
was quite unimpressed by these grandiose plans. He did not even
see Sputnik as something requiring vengeance. But eventually he
could no longer fail to notice that he was bombarded from all sides—
by scientists, soldiers and politicians—with a deafening demand for
action in space. His concern, it soon emerged, was that if this demand
were met, the result should at least have the appearance of being a
scientific exercise. Although this intense conviction was later to be
betrayed when the Apollo program got under way, it was passionately
felt at the time. It was also passionately opposed. The birth of NASA
and the American space program proper provoked a series of confronta-
tions which were in their way as momentous as any of the technical
accomplishments on the way to the moon.

James Killian, the eminent president of Massachusetts Institute
of Technology, was the voice of the Eisenhower policy. As the President's science adviser, he occupied a far more influential position after
Sputnik than before it. So did scientists generally. They were almost
as quick as the military to take advantage of the Russian triumph, and
they had one distinct advantage: many of them thought the same way
as the President.

In a report to the nation, the President's Scientific Advisory Committee, chaired by Killian, offered a far cooler assessment than the
services. It said that progress in space was "inevitable," for four reasons.
These were: "The compelling urge of man to explore and to discover"; the defense objective; national prestige; and new opportunities for scientific observation and experiment. The committee was most
concerned with the last of the four, and outlined several scientific
schemes. It was deeply sceptical of the military value of outer space:
"Much has been written about space as a future theater of war, raising
such suggestions as satellite bombers, military bases on the moon and
so on. For the most part even the more sober proposals do not hold
up well on close examination. In short, the earth would appear to be,

after all, the best weapons carrier." The committee proposed exploration in several stages—early, late, later still. Manned flight to the moon
was classified as "still later."

This program also had implications for space organization. To Killian and the scientists there was only one way of ensuring that chimerical military objectives were not pursued at the expense of scientific
investigation. This was to separate military from nonmilitary programs:
in effect, to prevent the services separately or collectively running a
national space program.

An alternative to the services already existed in a low-budget research group called the National Advisory Committee for Aeronautics.
It was a modest body, which since 1915 had conducted basic experimental work for many crucial advances in orthodox aviation. Compared with the army or the air force its credentials for taking on a
major space program were poor. But now, to a President increasingly
daunted by the monstrous regiment of generals, it was the obvious
haven for space science. Thus, on April 2, 1958, Eisenhower announced an historic and courageous decision: to convert NACA into
NASA, the National Aeronautics and Space Agency (later, to give
it a bureaucratic fillip, Administration) and to put it in charge of the
exploration of space for peaceful and scientific purposes.

For the services it was a catastrophic moment. They may have disagreed over which of them should dominate the other, but they were
united in the conviction that civilian control would be a disaster for
them both. The air force had felt that the only supervision should
come from the Pentagon which, in the words of General Clarence S.
Irvine, should tell them what their jobs were and "provide somebody
with guts enough to hit them over the head if they don't do it that
way." Now the air force faced having no job at all after the missiles
had been perfected. For its part, the army owned the greatest rocket
man in history, but had no guarantee that he would be properly employed. The Pentagon itself was discomfited. Eisenhower planned to
give NASA alarming power to supervise space research even for potential military use.

In the end, this last point was the only major concession Eisenhower
had to make. Thanks largely to Lyndon Johnson, Congress permitted
the Pentagon to retain an untrammeled right to exploit the military
uses of space, an adjustment which helped to fashion the space pro-

[1] The secretive pioneer: Robert Goddard at Auburn, Massachusetts, shortly before the first successful test of a liquid-fuelled rocket on March 16, 1926.

[2] Birthplace of moon rocketry: The experimental area at Peenemunde where the German V-2 was developed.

[3] Twenty years before Cape Kennedy: Preparing a V-2 for launching from a train, January 1945.

[5] Smithfield Market, London, March 1945. "The V-2 was a fine rocket. The only thing wrong with it was that it landed on the wrong planet." Wernher von Braun.

General Walter Dornberger, once head of the nemunde research station, later a vice president ell Aerosystems, Buffalo, N.Y.

[6] With the paymasters: (i). A demonstration at Peenemunde, May 26, 1943. The young von Braun, in civilian clothes, is second from the right, Grand Admiral Doenitz, Hitler's successor, is in the centre wearing a dark coat. Third from the left, partly hidden, is Count Stauffenberg, leader of the July 20 plot against Hitler.

[7] New flag, same ambition. Wernher von Braun becomes a U.S. citizen, 1955.

[8] With the paymasters: (ii). Eisenhower is bleakly unimpressed. Soon afterwards he rejected Apollo.

[9] With the paymasters: (iii). President Kennedy and Vice-President Johnson during a visit to Huntsville in September, 1962. The question is no longer when, but how?

[10] Kaputnik, December 1957. The Vanguard rocket carrying the first U.S. satellite blows up on the pad. Sputnik 1 had already been in orbit for two months.

[11] The Russians rub it in. A cartoon from *Pravda* shortly after the Vanguard blew up.

[12] Konstantin Tsiolkovsky (1857-1935), the papushka of Russian space-flight.

[13] The Russian rocket that sent America to the moon. For ten years the West speculated about the giant launcher that gave the Russians their early lead in space and goaded the United States into the moon race. It was finally unveiled at the Paris Air Show in 1967.

[14] First in space. The man: Yuri Gagarin. The woman: Valentina Tereshkova.

gram more in the image offered by the magnificent Texan than the President wanted. For the rest, however, the establishment of NASA seemed to accord with the President's wish for measured, and above all scientific, advance. It was his most durable contribution to a program he never truly believed in.

Not that it signaled the end of the services' ambitions. Quite the reverse; NASA's existence seemed only to intensify their lust for the moon and heighten their imagination in devising means of getting there. Freed now from any pretensions to a scientific objective, which was safely placed in other hands, both army and air force took to stating their military objectives rather more candidly than before. "Outposts," "bases" and "strategic interplanetary systems" began to enter their conception of what space was all about. In the army, the monster rocket, genesis of the moon launcher on which von Braun was beginning work, spawned task forces specially set up to consider how it could best be used. A massive four-volume submission of evidence was made to army headquarters, showing that the earliest manned lunar landing was vital to United States interests and that Project Horizon, as it was called, provided the plan for achieving it at the earliest possible moment. Extraordinarily ambitious schedules, involving quite unrealistic use of the hardware, were incorporated in Horizon. One proposal, leading to a landing in April 1965 and a twelve-man outpost by November 1966, postulated no fewer than 149 Saturn launchings, at a rate of over five a month (as against the fastest NASA proved able to manage before the moon landing, one every ten weeks).

The air force, not to be outdone, began studies soberly intended to make a case for a moon-base from which nuclear missiles might be launched toward earth. To any rational observer, the evidence was clear even then that in no circumstances would a missile taking three days to reach earth from the moon be more valuable than earth-based missiles which took less than an hour to reach any target in the world. But that was not the point. The anticipated scenario was well described in the authoritative journal *Aviation Week*: "One premise is that if bases for exploration on near planets are established, an obligation would evolve to protect them. Coupled with this is the philosophy that scientific findings in planetary bases may bring out a prime necessity for holding these stations." Later still, in 1961 when NASA's ascendancy was unchallengeable, the air force was still at it, with

Schriever unfolding for a different President yet another five-year plan for a 1967 moon landing.

By comparison with these massive pressure groups in the services, the newly fledged NASA was small, innocent and inexperienced in the ways of Washington. It inherited eight thousand employees, but these were widely scattered round distant laboratories. It had virtually no experience of flying machines without wings. Least of all was it informed by the spirit of an international blood-feud which gave to the military planners their demonic certitude that America must be first to the moon. When the army had thrustfully advanced its proposal for Man Very High—to toss a man into space and bring him straight down—Hugh Dryden, Chief of NACA, had dismissed it as possessing "about the same technical value as the circus stunt of shooting a young lady from a cannon."

Nonetheless, NASA was not totally unprepared for its improbable responsibility. Its men had acted as consultants to the air force on spacecraft designs for the ill-fated Man In Space Soonest plan. And after Sputnik 1 some of the more ambitious figures there had stepped up work on capsule configuration, heatshield requirements, weight limitations and the other basic problems of putting man into orbit. They responded eagerly to the sonorous appeal of their first space-age chief, a staunch Republican and former college president named T. Keith Glennan, who told them, "We have one of the most challenging assignments that has ever been given to modern man."

The only trouble with this challenge was that its precise nature was uncertain, and the means for meeting it not a little obscure. NASA had a brief—to explore space for peaceful purposes—but no ultimate goals had been laid down for it. The moon itself had not been mentioned. To some extent Glennan found himself trapped by the uncertainties about space emanating from the White House itself. Eisenhower had brought himself to agree to a project for putting man into orbit, Project Mercury, but this led almost nowhere. It would not be an exploration of space, only of man's ability to survive briefly in the void. Furthermore it remained unpleasantly dependent on Pentagon support: Mercury was scheduled to be launched by the Atlas, the first and most treasured rocket built by the air force.

NASA's perplexity, however, did not last long. In the absence of goals laid down for it, its swelling band of space engineers inaugurated a practice which has served the space agency well ever since. They quickly began to define what *they* thought should be done. After all, in order to fulfil what the Space Act demanded of them it was obvious that they had to undertake elaborate forward planning. All rockets and spacecraft, for manned and unmanned flight alike, had to be conceived far into the future. They took years to develop and more years to build, and unless a working schedule was devised stretching at least ten years ahead, no coherent program could be constructed. Any such program, moreover, had to deal with not merely intermediate objectives. It had, if it was to be intelligent, to include at least a notional idea of what should lie at the very end of the road.

Thus it came about that the first material decision to go to the moon was made not by a politician but by a handful of key government officials inside NASA itself. A bare six months after NASA had come into being, they secretly selected this and nothing else as the ultimate prize to which all the agency's efforts in manned space should be seen as leading. This decision was made, and tenaciously clung to, in the full knowledge that the reigning President would not approve. Of course, political confirmation would be needed in the end; this was only an "engineering" decision, needed in order to give shape to the program which the agency was devising for itself. At the time it may not even have been seen as a truly seminal moment—Glennan, for example, now denies that he ever exceeded the known wishes of the President. Nevertheless, in the perspective of ten years this internal NASA commitment must be regarded as the first measurable step America took toward the moon. Significantly, it was not immediately mentioned in quite such clear terms to Congress.

The decision was taken in May 1959, at the first meeting of NASA's Research Steering Committee on Manned Spaceflight, better known as the Goett Committee, after its chairman, Harry J. Goett from the agency's Ames Research Center. Most of the laboratories were represented on the committee. But it was a man from NASA headquarters, George M. Low, who pressed most firmly for the moon landing. Low, a reticent, somewhat bookish contrast to many of his NASA colleagues, was emphatic on this point, where many others at that early date were pardonably more cautious. He believed that only a moon landing provided a reasonable final objective for manned spaceflight, a self-justifying achievement and not merely a step toward something more distant.

The main alternative to the moon was something less dramatic but possibly more mundanely useful, an earth-orbiting space station. This would be assembled from separate units projected from earth, and manned by scores of astronauts and scientists; it would perform many scientific tasks, and throw open many possibilities for the study of earth and the manufacture of high-precision tools in a weightless environment. In the later 1960s, the space station became the main focus of the Russian manned space program. The fact that American space went a different way can be largely attributed to the pattern which the Goett Committee, under George Low's pressing influence, imposed on future NASA studies. Certainly, as will later emerge, when President Kennedy was desperately searching for the most dramatic space goal to which the United States could beat the Russians, NASA was able to tell him that the moon, thanks to the agency's preliminary work, was the only attainable target.

Several features distinguished the Goett proposal from the extravaganzas simultaneously devised by the army and air force. It proceeded, for one thing, from different assumptions. Instead of deciding that the moon was infinitely desirable and then inventing arguments to rationalize the lust, NASA looked for a manned space program which, if the nation was prepared to pay for it, seemed to contain a logical progression. Also, the Goett Committee made some preliminary studies of the means of reaching the moon, in the process pouring very cold water on the army's outlandish Project Horizon. It proposed a landing date after 1970, instead of 1965. But the costs envisaged in this, the classified "Long Range Plan," proved almost as unrealistic as the army's. It estimated that the job could be done for little more than half the actual cost of what became Project Apollo.

Since Eisenhower had already made clear his reluctance to pay two cents for the moon, the odd billion dollar error in NASA's estimate was of small significance. Much more critical was the agency's lack of any equipment physically capable of escaping from earth. It had plans, but it did not have rockets, and the case it was building to show that the moon could be taken suffered accordingly.

When NASA was created, the greatest rocket men in the world

were elsewhere, laboring on the early studies for Saturn under the intensely possessive eye of General Medaris and the army. This was the mighty launcher which von Braun had requested, in suitably doomladen terms, during the post-Sputnik Senate hearings. Although no clear objective was set for it, he had eventually obtained Pentagon permission to start work in August 1958.

Von Braun had hardly begun his studies, however, before he and The Team found themselves at the center of the army's last stand against civilian control of space. The question was simply put: to whom did the Germans rightfully belong? Glennan's first move on taking charge of the space program had been a cool request for the transfer of more than half of them to him. He wanted all the top people at Huntsville and the Jet Propulsion Laboratory (a research establishment run by Caltech at Pasadena), who had been responsible for the major satellite success to date, Explorer 1. Medaris, predictably, was livid at this raid on what in his view was a major military, as well as space, responsibility. "I rose up in wrath," he has written, "and Wernher, eager as he was for space work, was equally perturbed at the prospect of breaking up a winning team."

Medaris's awesome rage made little impact on the Pentagon. The prospect of Huntsville's disintegration seemed, on the contrary, positively inviting to a department which had had enough of Medaris's insubordination. The Defense Secretary's office had been trying unsuccessfully to impose its ruling that only the air force had any business in the missile game; this seemed the moment to insist on enforcing it. Thus Donald Quarles, Deputy Secretary at the Pentagon, received Glennan's request most agreeably. Together they took the matter as far as the President himself, at the same time neatly preventing any army representative from alerting Eisenhower to the other side of the case. Only by leaking the story to a friendly newspaper man, Mark Watson of the Baltimore Sun—"honest, reliable, objective, patriotic and thoroughly dependable"—did Medaris prevent the deal going through on the Presidential nod.

Medaris, uncharacteristically whining, was troubled by "the essential unfairness of the situation." But it was a mere skirmish in the battle. Unknown to the army rocket men, outright annihilation was being plotted not merely for them but for their great world-beating, space-conquering machine, the Saturn rocket itself.

The idea had germinated in relative innocence during discussions about service support for NASA's Mercury project. Although this was a civilian effort, it could not be completed without military co-operation. The early trials of the spacecraft were to be made with Redstone and Jupiter, owned by the army. It was to be launched by Atlas from Cape Canaveral, both of them air force property. Recovery would be in the navy's charge. In addition, all three service networks would help to track the Mercury's flight. Immediately the jarring problem of command arose. Should it be joint, as the army and navy proposed? Or should the air force, as the dominant space force, run everything? The Pentagon, observing that there was unlikely to be work enough to justify the elephantine bureaucracy of a joint command, decided that the air force had made the best case.

In parallel with this success, the air force introduced a wholly new booster proposal of its own. Saturn, if it had any defined purpose, was seen by its builders as the centerpiece of a national booster program for the late 1960s and 1970s. But now suddenly, and without warning, the air force let it be known that Saturn would not accommodate its own space requirements, notably a futuristic "atmosphere-skipping" device it had invented called Dyna-soar. Instead, the air force proposed a hypothetical rocket of its own, the Titan-C—better known in NASA as "Saturn-killer."

The validity of the air force case for either Dyna-soar or Titan-C was obscure. Some people began to think that Dyna-soar had been intentionally designed so as to make a case against Saturn. Saturn's specific failing was that its second stage, measuring 120 inches in diameter, would be incapable of launching Dyna-soar which happened to require a 160-inch rocket. Huntsville was therefore ordered to stop work on the second stage and think again about what it would cost to change to 160 inches. Medaris was astounded by this inexplicable command. After all, the Saturn configuration had been agreed between all booster men, including the air force. The General began, as he says, "to sniff a strange odor of fish." Not only did he discover the secret air force memorandum proposing Titan-C; he found to his amazement that the rocket had already been virtually agreed to by the Pentagon research boss, Dr. Herbert York, as a replacement for Saturn. York had told his superiors that Titan could do all the military work of Saturn and more, and that the end of Saturn would also provide an opportunity to "terminate the costly operation being conducted at the Army Ballistic Missile Agency." Therefore, York concluded, "I have decided to cancel the Saturn program."

But Medaris did manage to force an inquiry. A Booster Evaluation Committee was set up to settle the rival claims. York himself was co-chairman and, true to the Eisenhower mold, clearly more anxious to cut spending than provide for the purely speculative space adventures implied by something so large as Saturn. The splenetic Medaris had no doubt that once again "unfairness" was rampant. "It seems to me," he told York, "that we are being asked to present a case to a stacked jury which is expected to give a directed verdict in accordance with the way you have made up your own mind."

But however the jury was stacked, the facts were too blatant to be ignored. In a field marked by much extravagantly irresponsible estimating, the air force proposal for Titan-C proved to be something of a record breaker. Its development costs had been represented as $218 million less than Saturn's. Yet closer examination revealed that this estimate grossly undervalued the cost of developing the engines, and omitted altogether the cost of test vehicles. The greater versatility of Saturn had been coolly ignored. No account had been taken of scheduled NASA missions for the rocket or of the large communications satellites already planned. Both Saturn's greater payload capacity and the fact that it would be available fully a year earlier had been overlooked.

This truly staggering series of falsifications produced the quick reinstatement of Saturn. At the same time, however, the question of the rocket's continuance in army hands was uncomfortably reopened. It was a considerable anomaly. Militarily, it was no improvement on existing or scheduled intercontinental missiles. Only in space might its unique capacity pay off; yet space was now NASA's, not the army's territory. A year after Medaris had spiked Glennan's secret deal with the White House, another attempt was made to move von Braun, this time by the Pentagon itself.

The German and his General were faced with a bitterly unpalatable choice. The Team might be consumed either by the air force, now the home of all military booster power, or by NASA. Their first inclination, swallowing decades of service pride, was for the air force, since they still believed that the military value of their beloved rocket would one day be perceived by all right-thinking men. But this had serious dangers for The Team. The air force tradition was entirely opposed to their way of building rockets. Ever since the German days they had not only developed their own rockets but also closely supervised production. The air force, the incarnation of free enterprise in government, rejected such methods. It had always worked intimately with private industry, positively welcoming the role of milch cow. Aerospace firms had helped sustain the service's propaganda campaigns for the moon trip. Many were not merely clients but helots, taking orders from air force generals about whom else they should do business with and being provided, in return, with a steady flow of contracts. In this suffocating climate it was unlikely that The Team would long remain a team.

So the army was forced to agree to what it had hitherto opposed by every ruse it could devise—the transfer of Huntsville to the civilian space agency. Medaris sadly observed that NASA got the greatest rocketeers in the world "virtually on a platter." For NASA, for Wernher von Braun and for all true moon men it was to prove a singularly happy arrangement. But Medaris never got over his bitterness at the perversity of things. Saturn and its builders were his children. "The child was first starved, criticized and deprived of a sense of purpose in life," he lamented. "Then when the natural parent turned it over for adoption by others, the foster parents promptly forgot all their antagonism and proceeded to satisfy all the child's wants and desires."

It was now late in 1959, and to many people who had committed their lives to space the path to the moon appeared open at last. The rocket men had been coupled with the moon planners, and both were committed to the same objective. NASA's secret moon studies were advancing swiftly. The agency's Space Task Group, the section in charge of manned space, was mapping the intermediate stages before the landing could be made; lunar orbital missions and fourteen-day journeys circling the earth were already among them. The Saturn rocket, moreover, had been taken from the dustbin, where Herbert York attempted to dispatch it and transformed into an item which actually had priority status in the budget. The public, too, were being gently prepared for the space age. The first seven astronauts had been unveiled. "Apollo," god of the sun, had been selected, somewhat eccentrically, as the designation for the moon program.

Congress, moreover, was pressing NASA for still more dramatic action. Far from being unwilling to increase the already massive bill for missile hardware, it remained a reliable fount of steaming, post-Sputnik fury. In July 1960, the House Committee on Science and Astronautics proposed a faster schedule than the space agency's suggestion of a moon landing after 1970: "NASA's ten-year program is a good program as far as it goes, but it does not go far enough. . . . A high priority program should be undertaken to place a manned expedition on the moon in this decade."

Unhappily for moon men, all their optimism ignored a single salient fact. The President was not enchanted. It could be said, indeed, that he was exceedingly irritated by his growing awareness that he was surrounded by evidently sane men producing shelves of blueprints for every step to the moon. Just as he had refused to be rattled by Sputnik, so he looked with incredulity upon the case for the moon. And once again he turned for advice to the only people he felt safe with, the scientists. In the summer of 1960, the last of his presidency, he called on his science adviser, James Killian, to make an evaluation. The questions were the same ones he had asked about the IGY satellite. Would the enterprise be scientifically justified? Would the expense, forbidding enough even on NASA's dubious reckoning, be repaid by a major scientific discovery?

The answers were a crushing blow to the would-be moon adventurers. The scientists' report, written under Donald Hornig, was fundamentally critical of the entire idea of sending men to the moon. Perhaps for this reason it has never been published. "At the present time, man-in-space cannot be justified on purely scientific grounds," it asserted. The Mercury program, designed to put a single man into orbit, was dismissed as a "somewhat marginal effort" which did not offer "a high probability of a successful flight while also providing adequate safety for the astronaut." The costs of any further manned operations were terrifying, probably over $40,000 million if a moon landing took place in 1975. Since there seemed to be scientific merit in the enterprise, Hornig suggested that the country would have to be clear exactly what the case for a landing on the moon truly rested on. "Among the major reasons for attempting the manned exploration of space," he said, "are emotional compulsions and national aspirations." On these his committee did not feel qualified to comment.

The President, however, felt no such inhibition. The Hornig report proved that NASA was engaged in a game which satisfied none of his prejudices in favor of economy and of emphasizing scientific value as opposed to drama for drama's sake. Someone reminded the President of the historical parallel most often to be found on the lips of space-men: the voyage of Christopher Columbus under the sponsorship of Queen Isabella. Eisenhower brusquely replied that he was "not about to hock his jewels" to send anyone to the moon. One of his intimates has a vivid memory of the atmosphere around the President when the decision on the moon flight was required of him. There was, he re-calls, "almost sheer bewilderment—or certainly amusement—that any-body would consider such an undertaking. Somebody said, 'This won't satisfy everybody. When they finish this they'll want to go to the planets.' There was a lot of laughter at that thought."

The laughter did not penetrate to Huntsville, where the Germans had made so many cultural sacrifices for the pleasure of fulfilling their dreams. A pall was cast on their comfortable, unspectacular lives. Al-though a few of the team had grown homesick and returned to Ger-many years before, the great majority had painfully, conscientiously, sunk themselves into the American way of life. They had believed simply that they would lead their new country to a new planet, and now they were being frustrated. Nor was there much in the news from Washington to amuse the moon planners at Langley, Virginia, head-quarters of the Space Task Group, a mini-Houston before Houston was ever thought of.

To the utter dismay of both centers, not to mention the anger of the space industry, the Administration now moved summarily to liquidate its interest in manned space. It took an ax to NASA's budget re-quest for 1962, eradicating all the carefully devised lunar beginnings which it included, in particular the crucial requests for development of the spacecraft and of Saturn's upper stages. Unmanned projects went forward, but the only money allotted to man-in-space after Mer-cury was a miniscule $30 million.

Eisenhower himself wanted to be still more drastic. He intended to announce formally in his final message to the nation that there would be no more manned spaceflight of any kind after Mercury.

He was dissuaded from this course only by the last-minute intervention of Glennan, who foresaw the damage which so unqualified a declaration would do to the morale of his men. So the President contented himself with merely rejecting Apollo, no doubt subsuming the rest of his scepticism under that unexpected warning against the military-industrial complex.

For the time being he had won his case. It was an achievement for which he deserves a more eminent place in the history of space than most people are willing to give him. His immovable common sense in the face of pressures which conventional politicians probably could not have resisted is surely one of the classic rearguard actions of modern government. He refused to believe that national prestige, in so far as it could be defined, would be advanced through space. And he was certain that the moon, scientifically, was not worth the candle. On both counts there are many people today who would admit that events have proved him more than a little prescient.

Equally, those who believe that he was negligent, the unquestioning prophets of space, must see that he served their cause as well. It was the very depth of Eisenhower's obstinacy, with the humiliations it supposedly brought the United States at the hands of the Russians, which dictated the decisions of his successor. John Kennedy was a man insatiable in his appetite for drama, unsceptical in his belief in prestige, passionate in his determination to win the cold war. The culpable omissions which he saw Eisenhower as having committed in space guaranteed that he would project America on a headlong assault on the moon.

5.
Why Kennedy Went

When John Fitzgerald Kennedy was sworn in as President in January 1961, all he knew about space was that America did not seem to be winning it. He had taken no interest in the subject as a Senator, and on the hustings his statements about it were the work of other men. Among the mixture of East Coast intelligentsia and hard-boiled politicians who were behind the Kennedy phenomenon what mattered was image-building, ward-heeling and higher diplomacy. The moon, as far as they were concerned was an unfashionable bore.

Yet Kennedy had been in office barely four months before the cause of moon travel triumphed conclusively over this unpromising beginning. In one extraordinary convulsion of statesmanship, the scene in space was utterly transformed. The real terms of the argument were laid bare, and they were seen to be quite different from those Eisenhower had determined they were for the past six years. They persuaded the new President to make a decision with arguably more enduring implications than any other he ever took. The single most conspicuous feature of this decision, to marshal all the resources of American engineering to land a man on the moon, was how little it had to do with the requirements of science. Whereas to Eisenhower science was the only dependable oracle, whose message proved consistently too ambiguous to justify so vast a venture, now, under Kennedy, it was consulted only to be ignored. To him, the intrinsic properties of the moon were of no interest. As a symbol, on the other hand, the moon had everything.

It was a symbol, first of all, of himself. The essential Kennedy had emerged very clearly during the campaign, and it consisted at bottom of a political persona in total contrast to Eisenhower. Where the Eisenhower years were inert, unexciting and full of lost opportunities, Kennedy represented himself as the man of action and drama, new ideas and new frontiers. Above all, Kennedy, with his unquenchably youthful exuberance, would get America moving again. It was a theme applied without discrimination to every issue, but to none did it relate more aptly than to space. A duly minatory campaign statement had appeared in the aerospace house magazine, *Missiles and Rockets*, under Kennedy's name.

We are in a strategic space race with the Russians, and we are losing. If a man orbits earth this year, his name will be Ivan. If the Soviets control space they can control the earth, as in past centuries the nation that controlled the seas has dominated the continents. We cannot afford to run second in this vital race. To ensure peace and freedom we must be first. Space is our great New Frontier.

The thought was Lyndon Johnson's and the words were put together by a Johnson aide, Edward O. Welsh. But they fixed space's place in the catalogue of Eisenhower's perfidy.

Secondly, the moon was a symbol of America. As his campaign indicated, Kennedy's White House would project a new picture of the world. To him, the whole international position of the United States could be judged by her position in relation to the Soviet Union. Like Eisenhower, Kennedy was never able to define "prestige," but unlike him, he believed with a compulsive passion that it was desirable. He felt that Eisenhower had perilously compromised it, thus weakening American strength. Not only was there the missile gap, Kennedy's alarming (but ultimately false) assertion that the country was gravely underarmed. The failure went wider. The Soviet Union, the candidate charged, was acquiring "an image of world leadership generally and scientific pre-eminence particularly."

Well before Kennedy formally took power, this kind of oratory had stirred many a frustrated longing among space men. The volcanos extinguished by the steady drip of Eisenhower's pessimism began once again to bubble to life. Vice-President-elect Johnson had

been put in charge of space as prospective chairman of the National
Aeronautical and Space Council, with his henchman Edward Welsh, a
loyal veteran of the Washington bureaucracy, as executive director.
Everyone remembered Johnson's angry assertions after Sputnik 1 that
space held the key to world power. It seemed likely that the space
program would be re-evaluated, and it even seemed possible that
given the shrill militaristic quality of Kennedy's speeches NASA might
no longer be in charge.

Nowhere did this prospect excite more jubilant anticipation than in
the air force, especially in the Ballistic Missile Division run by General
Schriever. Schriever went to work to deal with what he calls "this constant din from the press and the liberals about space for peaceful purposes." The din, the General recollects, had "led to the attitude that
the military had no place in space, even though the Defense Department had a clear legal duty to explore it for national security purposes." In the five-year moon plan which Schriever naturally had
ready for the President-elect, peaceful purposes did not feature even
in the rhetoric. In keeping with the note sounded by Kennedy, it
offered a moon landing by 1967 in order to prevent "unilateral Soviet
exploitation," provide a base for travel around the moon and open up
"new strategic capabilities."

Virtually the entire air force was mobilized for the propaganda effort. On December 1, 1960, immediately after the election, the
Secretary of the Air Force, James H. Douglas, sent a secret memorandum from the Pentagon to all the service's commanders and contractors alerting them to the likelihood of their getting a much bigger
piece of space. As he had read the Kennedy campaign, it indicated "a
realization at the highest levels that military supremacy in space is as
essential to our security as military supremacy at altitudes near earth."
The army was "indispensable" on the ground, the navy on the
ocean, but only the mighty air force, "the world's leading space arm,"
was equipped for the job Kennedy had outlined. The Secretary concluded, "The deadly Soviet-Free World competition for military aerospace supremacy has given urgency to the air force's efforts to advance
in aerospace achievements."

Career officers were also recruited to help win Washington's internal
space race. An intensive campaign began at all levels to prepare
industry for a major change of policy, priming them and their congres-

sional friends to back the air force against any other agency. In propaganda terms, the effort was not entirely unsuccessful. As late as
March 1961, well after the air force had in truth lost the battle, *Missiles
and Rockets* was categoric: "The best bet on who will win when the
cards are down? The air force."

One reason why the air force lost was that NASA, astonishingly,
was just as well prepared for the new regime. Kennedy was a con-
noisseur of political pressure, very experienced in the methods of
covert influence working below the surface of conventional politics;
but when he came to examine the condition of the space agency, he
might reasonably have gasped with admiration. For an outfit which
had been told categorically by the President to forget about going to the
moon, it was amazingly well-equipped for the journey.

Besides picking the moon as its own ultimate objective whatever
Eisenhower might say, it had blithely continued to build its case despite the known scepticism of the White House. In July 1960, a
massive assembly of 1300 industrialists had been collected behind
closed doors to hear NASA's original moon man, George Low, describe
the tempting pickings available from a moon program. In October, contracts for feasibility studies had been let to three aerospace giants,
General Electric, Martin and Convair. As these powerful interests
were being locked into the space lobby, the agency's own moon planners multiplied and stepped up their work. In early January, days before the inauguration, Low briefed the increasingly unhappy Keith
Glennan, Eisenhower's man at NASA, on the imperative need to
push for the moon in the forthcoming congressional budget hearings. Low and his committee on manned space had now decided that
figures could be put to their plans: the moon could now be taken before the end of the decade, they wrote in a still unpublished report,
and the job would cost a mere $7000 million.

It was altogether an inviting dish to set before the new prince. But
Glennan, using probably the last sceptical words about the moon
flight ever to be uttered by a senior NASA official, had warned Low
that he could do nothing without the President's approval. This was as
true of the new President as of the old, and Kennedy's approval was
not instantly forthcoming. The plans might sound good, but the
achievements of the manned space program so far were a dismal

sight. This had nothing to do with Eisenhower's meanness. It was a question of technical efficiency.

In the past three years, NASA's program had registered a depressingly high percentage of failures. Of twenty-five attempts to place unmanned objects into orbit, only eight had completely succeeded. Over half the launches had failed within a short distance of the ground. More painfully, the Mercury project to put the first American into space was under cogent attack. On the very first day George Low unveiled Apollo to the expectant industrialists, the first test of the Mercury capsule had ended in disaster fifty-eight seconds after take-off. Four months later the second launch went still worse. Engineers watched with incredulity as the rocket rose just four inches from the pad while the escape tower alone hurtled erratically into the air. Many NASA men despaired of the space program surviving such well-publicized failures. Mercury looked horribly like another Vanguard.

This was certainly the first view of Kennedy's advisers. The new President set up twenty-nine task forces covering the whole range of policies, and the committee on space, chaired by Jerome Wiesner of MIT found, as Hornig had before, that Mercury was a "marginal" exercise which should not be allowed to continue much longer, being "very unlikely" to put an American in orbit before the Russians. Wiesner was intensely critical of NASA in general and manned spaceflight in particular. He chided the agency for advertising Mercury as "our major objective in space activities," and urged that the exercise be put in perspective before the world got the wrong idea. The right idea, he suggested, was to cut down manned space: "We should find effective means to make people appreciate the cultural, public-service and military importance of space activities other than space travel." Military use of space, in fact, should receive an altogether greater emphasis.

The Wiesner Report was a curious document to emerge so soon after the heated rhetoric of the campaign. It pleased one department, the air force—not surprisingly, since Schriever had a hand in its composition. But as far as the space race was concerned, it seemed to declare it no contest. Dr. Wiesner, now back in the academic-industrial complex at MIT, describes the report as an attempt to "decouple from the space race." "Space was obviously a good thing," he says, "but we were not going to win the race. Therefore, was the race worth getting into? We thought not."

One explanation of the report is that Wiesner was first a scientist and only second a Kennedy intimate. Although as the President's scientific adviser he was to play a many-sided part in Kennedy's Washington, he had the scientist's inevitable doubts about the value of moon journeys by men. Such doubts were widespread in the scientific community, whose voice had already been powerfully heard through James Killian. Killian had left Eisenhower with a diatribe against manned space:

Many thoughtful citizens are convinced that the really exciting discoveries in space can be realized better by instruments than by man. The Soviets have used technology as an instrument of propaganda and power politics, but their expensive emphasis on space exploration will not be enough in the long pull to sustain an image of strength. This will only be accomplished by a balanced effort in science and technology. We should pursue our own objectives in space science, and not let the Soviets choose them for us.

Before Wiesner's report could be considered, however, Kennedy was plunged into his first international crisis, in Laos, and space was not his main concern. NASA, in deep gloom, carried on with what it had, the despised Mercury. On January 31, the program lurched a step forward when a chimpanzee named Ham was hoisted aloft. The beast was propelled further down-range than intended, but was recovered with senses and organs encouragingly intact. Besides partly erasing the memory of earlier failures, the flight at last gave evidence that the body and nervous system of something like a man could stand the strain of space. Ham had been one of a team of six "astrochimps" selected for intensive training. Each had a mock-up capsule in his quarters and, stimulated by banana pellets and electric shocks, had mastered the levers a good deal quicker than astronauts. When Ham came back to a hero's welcome, he seemed unmoved, having continued to perform his duties effortlessly during launch, weightlessness and re-entry.

With Ham's triumphant return, space men thought, *homo sapiens* could not be far from reaching his destiny. Perhaps the Russians could, after all, be beaten. So they would have been but for one surprising intervention. It came, oddly, from Wernher von Braun. Von

Braun had a longer record of space-dreaming than anyone at NASA. He had also caught from the army a compelling belief in the merit of being first. Yet now he hesitated. Ham had overshot the mark, and this persuaded von Braun to calculate the probability of Mercury, with its Redstone launch vehicle, bringing a man back alive. His sums showed reliability to be about eighty-eight percent for launch success and ninety-eight percent for crew survival. To him, it did not seem good enough. To others, consumed by a desire to prove to Kennedy that manned space did make sense, the risk seemed worth taking. But in the end, Washington sided with von Braun and the first manned flight was postponed until April 25—and it turned out to be a more momentous decision than anyone had intended.

The postponement meant, quite simply, that the Russians would be first to put a man into space. Yet another scalp would be added to the belts of Soviet rocket men. Heavier and heavier objects were being pushed out of Kazakhstan into orbit, far outweighing anything which the Americans, lacking the booster power, could contemplate. In August 1960 a veritable ark had been launched and recovered containing the dogs Strelka and Belka, as well as a wide assortment of rats, mice, plants, fungi and seeds. On March 9, another muttnik, Chernushka, was recovered from orbit, the second success in four attempts. On the face of it, a manned orbital flight seemed imminent. But no one could be sure how imminent—before April 25 or after it—and besides, the race had still not been officially declared open. The campaign rhetoric of prestige had yet to be transformed into the policy position of the new President. If Russia were first again, that would be just too bad.

One man, at least, was already planning the summary burial of these last vestiges of Eisenhowerism. At the NASA headquarters in Washington, a new wind was blowing gustily through the corridors: a hot, heavy-breathing wind, highly charged with combustible particles. Kennedy's appointment of James Webb as NASA Administrator in February, meant two things: first, some change would one day overtake the space program; and second, any question of the air force seizing it could now be forgotten. For Webb was, to NASA, a wholly unusual and even incomprehensible figure, standing in direct contrast to his predecessor, Keith Glennan.

Glennan, a competent administrative scientist, was well suited by temperament and intellect to Eisenhower's policy of caution. He was not, as he now candidly admits, a "space cadet." He believed the program should grow by gradual strides toward some truly scientific objective, and that was the program over which he had presided. This led inevitably to conflict with men like George Low who were intent on a quite different goal. As the man in the middle, Glennan was uncomfortable, constantly dampening the planners' optimism. And they, for their part, had grown unhappy with him.

Webb was a different proposition. He knew almost nothing about science, but was familiar with every important backstairs entrance in Washington. Bombastic, domineering and bullishly combative, he was a man of formidable energy and absolute commitment to whatever cause he was involved in. The true cause of space had been made unmistakably clear to him by the circumstances of his appointment. The job of finding a new NASA chief had been entrusted to Vice-President Johnson who in turn had consulted his old friend on Capitol Hill, Senator Robert Kerr. Webb was proposed by Kerr, with vintage senatorial hyperbole, as the man with "the greatest mental energy and capacity for sustained mental and physical effort of anyone I know." Webb, in fact, had lately worked for Kerr in the Senator's lush Oklahoma oil empire, and in the course of time this private connection was to prove a matter of grave embarrassment to him. But his long experience of Washington, as well as his inside knowledge of the aerospace industry (through a directorship of McDonnell Aircraft), marked him as the man Johnson wanted for NASA.

It has been said of Jim Webb that attempting to extract information from him is rather like trying to take a drink from a fire hydrant. Now, after a brief survey of his new domain, he opened the taps and drowned the Eisenhower years in a flood of political rhetoric quite out of character with the customary mutterings of the space agency.

Webb quickly came to believe that the money denied to Apollo and Saturn must instantly be restored if national security was to be protected. When the Bureau of the Budget turned him down, he went angrily to the White House with an impassioned declamation addressed to the President himself. This document has never been published before, but it is the first of a handful of secret papers which

enable us to understand for the first time what the moon race was
really about.

Composed during one feverish all-night session in early March
1961, Webb's first analysis of space foreshadowed precisely the convulsion which was about to take place. Its argument rests exclusively
on the Soviet threat, beginning with a portrayal of Eisenhower's final
decision in thoroughly alarmist terms. "His decision," Webb writes,
"emasculated the Ten Year Plan before it was one year old, and unless
reversed guarantees that the Russians will, for the next five to ten
years, beat us to every exploratory spaceflight." He goes on:

> We have already felt the effects of the fact that they were the
> first to place a satellite in orbit, have intercepted the moon, photo-
> graphed the backside of the moon, and have sent a large space-
> craft to Venus. They can now orbit seven-and-a-half ton vehicles
> about the earth, compared to our two-and-a-half tons, and they
> have successfully recovered animals from orbital flights lasting as
> much as twenty-four hours. Their present position is one from
> which further substantial accomplishments can be expected, and
> our best information points to a steadily increasing pace of suc-
> cessful effort on a realistic timetable.

The priority, as Webb saw it, was to improve American booster
power. He said that Russian rockets were now capable of 750,000
pounds thrust, compared with Atlas's 320,000 pounds. He pointed
accusingly to the underfunded work done on Saturn by The Team,
and also asked for something more gigantic still, so vast that it could
have no earthbound use. This, called the Nova rocket, would have the
almost unimaginable power of between six and nine million pounds
thrust. To justify this, Webb did not hesitate to underline its military
potential. Such an argument would have been unthinkable in the
old NASA even though, in its civilian innocence, it had already performed valuable research for the military in such fields as re-entry
physics, high-temperature structures, telemetry and data processing.
Webb was brutally candid about it: "The boosters now under development and the launch facilities to be constructed will be used directly
by the Department of Defense."

The insistent demands and the political cunning are maintained
to the end. In his peroration, a ripe pelice of international slogan-

eering, Webb shrewdly invokes Kennedy's own most famous cliché
to make his major point:

> The extent to which we are leaders in space science and tech-
> nology will in some large measure determine the extent to which
> we, as a nation pioneering on a New Frontier, will be in a posi-
> tion to develop this emerging world force and make it the basis
> for new concepts and applications in education, communications
> and transportation, looking toward more viable political, social
> and economic systems for nations willing to work with us in the
> years ahead.

In the end, this blast proved to have been exquisitely well timed.
Webb's thesis had hardly begun to sink into the President's consciousness before events proved it to be horribly convincing: the Russians
did put a man into orbit. But at first, Webb's reception at the White
House was disappointing. Kennedy, more and more deeply mired
in Laos, was preparing to intervene there with troops and the Seventh
Fleet. It was hardly the moment for urgent long-range space planning
of the kind implied in the Webb memorandum. Therefore Kennedy
took no more than a hasty, interim decision. At a meeting on March
23, with Johnson, Wiesner, David Bell (Bureau of the Budget) and
Edward Welsh present, he agreed to increase the budget for von
Braun's rocket. Saturn would now be available by 1966; Soviet rocket-
power would at last be matched.

The other half of Webb's demand, however, was left in abeyance.
Just as NASA's prudent scientists were deciding to bow to von
Braun's probability-studies and postpone the first manned Mercury
flight, the President was declining to be hustled into Apollo. The
moon, he thought, could wait until the autumn.

One single, cataclysmic event shattered that idea. On April 12, the
cosmonaut Yuri Gagarin became the first man to fly in space. His
108-minute ride, in which he completely circled the earth, was the
final, most dreaded "first" for the Soviet Union. To the world, it was
Sputnik 1 all over again. To Kennedy's Washington, it was the signal
which extinguished any semblance of controlled policy-making. Anyone examining now the secret documents and meetings of the hectic
days in Washington in April 1961 is struck by an irresistible analogy.

The capital was a city at war. The actions of its leading citizens were explicable only in terms of the same kind of panic-stricken urgency which marks the wartime condition. As in war, Gagarin's triumph left the Washington air dense with fear, crisis and recrimination. It was in this context that the decision to go to the moon was taken.

The news of Gagarin came differently to different people. Kennedy himself had a few days warning from the Central Intelligence Agency. NASA officials had been ready for it for months, although none of their long-prepared statements rang quite so true as that of Mercury's public relations chief, Colonel John "Shorty" Powers; Powers, awakened with the news at 4 A.M., irritably slammed down the phone with the words, "We're all asleep down here." But Congress and the public were not forewarned. The prospect of Gagarin "going down in the history books" rendered many people apoplectic, not to say demented. One Congressman, James Fulton of Pennsylvania, convinced that the Russians were about to go to the moon and turn the whole planet red, suggested an immediate project for America: "a blue project, to scatter blue dust so then the moon will be red, white and blue."

While Congress fumed, and Webb fed the flames with an announcement that NASA could certainly work faster than was allowed for in "the funds recommended by President Kennedy," the President himself did something very odd. On the evening of April 14, he summoned his closest adviser, Theodore Sorensen, along with Wiesner, Bell, Webb and his deputy, Hugh Dryden. Also present, remarkably, was a journalist, Hugh Sidey of *Life* magazine. Sidey was a close friend of Kennedy's, but that would hardly explain his presence at such a sensitive moment. Webb believes he was invited as a reliable newsman on whom the President could impress his deep personal knowledge of space. If that was so, then the ploy misfired: for, to judge from Sidey's account in *John F. Kennedy, Portrait of a President,** the President manifested an almost bottomless ignorance of the matter.

"Is there any place where we can catch them?" Kennedy began. "What can we do? Can we go around the moon before them? Can we put a man on the moon before them? What about Nova and Rover? When will Saturn be ready? Can we leapfrog?" Dryden replied

* Deutsch, 1964.

that with a crash program costing perhaps $40,000 million it might just be possible to land first. Then Webb, for once misjudging his moment, offered some syrupy consolation: "We are doing everything we possibly can, Mr. President. And thanks to your leadership and foresight we are moving ahead now more rapidly than ever. . . ."

> But Kennedy did not want to hear praise at this moment [Sidey writes]. He stopped Webb with a wave of the hand. "The cost," he pondered. "That's what gets me." He turned to Budget Director Bell questioningly. The cost of space science went up in geometric progression, explained Bell. Kennedy listened between questions. He tapped the bottom of his upper front teeth with the fingernails of his right hand.

Wiesner then intervened to ask for a three-month delay, on the grounds that this was no time for mistakes. But Kennedy

> turned back to the men around him. He thought for a second. Then he spoke. "When we know more, I can decide if it's worth it or not. If somebody can just tell me how to catch up. Let's find somebody—anybody. I don't care if it's the janitor over there, if he knows how."

What this meeting discloses more than anything is the sight of a man obsessed with failure. Gagarin's triumph pitilessly mocked the image of dynamism which Kennedy had offered the American people. It had, one senses, to be avenged almost as much for his own sake as for the nation's.

But it was followed by another blow, striking at the selfsame nerve. Three days after Kennedy had bared his soul to Sidey, Americans were subjected to further humiliation. This time the site was the Bay of Pigs, where the CIA attempted to launch an insurrection against Fidel Castro with a band of counterrevolutionary guerrillas. The invasion was a dismal debacle, but one of its consequences was to help bring nearer the day when Americans would mount another invasion, this time of the moon. The point was not well appreciated at the time since all the crucial moves toward space were concealed from the public. The official NASA historian claims to this day that the Cuban fiasco "does not emerge as relevant"—a statement which must be charitably taken as the ultimate example of loyalty to the agency's unreal image of the world. It is simply not credible that a man

ready to ask the janitor where to go in space would at the same time
be capable of excluding from his mind this second Communist insult
within the week.

It now emerges that at the very moment when Castro was rounding
up the last of the marauders on his beaches on April 19, the unhappy
President summoned his spaceman-in-chief, Vice-President Lyndon
Johnson, for a momentous confrontation. Kennedy's Appointments
Calendar for that morning reveals that the two men met, alone, for
forty-five minutes. Although only Johnson knows precisely what
happened at the meeting, Edward Welsh, his chief space aide,
believes it was the moment when Kennedy finally reached a personal
commitment to do something on the grand scale in space. After the
meeting, Welsh says, America "was already halfway to the moon."

At any rate, next day the President sent Johnson a directive whose
tone was that of a man willing to pay any price to avoid further disgrace. This single sheet of presidential paper has some claim to be
considered the basic charter of the mission eventually performed by
Neil Armstrong and Edwin Aldrin. It reads as follows:

> In accordance with our conversation I would like for you as
> Chairman of the Space Council to be in charge of making an
> over-all survey of where we stand in space.
> 1. Do we have a chance of beating the Soviets by putting a
>   laboratory in space, or by a trip around the moon, or by a
>   rocket to land on the moon, or by a rocket to go to the moon
>   and back with a man. Is there any other space program which
>   promises dramatic results in which we could win?
> 2. How much additional would it cost?
> 3. Are we working twenty-four hours a day on existing pro-
>   grams. If not, why not? If not, will you make recommenda-
>   tions to me as to how work can be speeded up.
> 4. In building large boosters should we put our emphasis on
>   nuclear, chemical or liquid fuel, or a combination of those
>   three?
> 5. Are we making maximum effort? Are we achieving neces-
>   sary results?
> I have asked Jim Webb, Dr. Wiesner, Secretary McNamara and
> other responsible officials to cooperate with you fully. I would
> appreciate a report on this at the earliest possible moment.
>   JOHN F. KENNEDY

Only once did Kennedy allow himself to use anything remotely like this language in public. The day after dictating the directive he told a press conference for the first and the last time, "If we can get to the moon before the Russians, we should." But to Johnson, of course, who had said such a thing many times, the stimulus was entirely welcome. It echoed his own belief, preached ever since Sputnik 1 had beaten America into orbit, that space was primarily an arena of international conflict. Ordered now to find above all a winning program, he had little doubt about what he wanted or where to look for it. In a single week of prodigious industry he marshaled the kind of support which seemed to make the case for America taking the moon unanswerable.

Three interests and three only were consulted as the Vice-President set out to restore American self-esteem. None of them was likely to resist his own preference for a moon landing, least of all NASA itself, on whom he called first. After all, had not the agency been directing all its studies, even under Eisenhower, toward that objective? Now its confidential report to Johnson was able to offer some reasonably precise estimates of the possibilities. There was no chance, it said, of beating the Russians to an orbiting space station. While the race to orbit the moon might just be won, nothing offered greater certainty than the moon landing itself. NASA was very confident that here American industry could eliminate any lead the Russians might have. It suggested 1967 as the target date, although this seems to have been named less out of technological conviction than because 1967, being the fiftieth anniversary of the Bolshevik Revolution was thought to be the Russians' own intended landing year. The cost, however, would be great, much greater than the $7000 million decreed by George Low's group earlier in the year. Webb's arrival had brought a harder head to bear on the matter; a landing in 1967 would cost nearly $34,000 million, but if the nation could wait until 1970, it could have the moon for $22,000 million.

An especially well-judged note supporting this case sped to Johnson's desk from Huntsville. Wernher von Braun knew exactly what was needed. "We have a sporting chance of sending a three-man crew round the moon ahead of the Soviets," he wrote. "We have an excellent chance of beating the Soviets to the first landing of a crew on the moon (including return capability, of course)." An "all-out crash program" could pull it off by 1967 or 1968, but this would require drastic pruning of the humbler scientific space exercises. Three decisions should do the trick: "Identify a few (the fewer the better) goals in our space program as objectives of highest national priority. Identify those elements of our present space program that would qualify as immediate contributions to this objective. Put all other elements on the 'back burner.'"

After NASA, the Pentagon. The irony of recruiting to the peaceful space program the very services against which the space agency had won so many torrid battles passed almost unnoticed as Johnson pressed forward. This was a national emergency. The air force was ordered to reopen its capacious file of rejected moon projects, and General Schriever magnanimously argued that a moon landing was vital, even though his service could not now expect to be in charge of it.

Finally, there was big business, which would have to build the monstrous moon machines. Three representative magnates were quietly brought to Washington to give Johnson their blessing. Frank Stanton ran the Columbia Broadcasting System, Donald Cook was boss of the American Electric Power Service Corporation, George Brown owned a Houston construction firm, Brown and Root. They might have had little to do with space, but they were "responsible business leaders." They were also cronies of the Vice-President; Brown and Root had done particularly well since Lyndon Johnson went to Washington as a young Congressman. Their acquaintance was not a unique privilege —"Any business leader who didn't know Lyndon Johnson in the Senate must have been on vacation," says Edward Welsh—but it was nonetheless a recommendation. All three did what was expected of them.

And that, apart from some elementary arm-twisting on Capitol Hill, was the last of Johnson's consultations. At the end of it he had emerged with what he wanted: agreement from NASA, the services and American business that it was both imperative and feasible for America to go to the moon. It is worth remarking, however, which interests were emphatically *not* consulted. One was the public at large. Quaintly enough, Welsh portrays the summoning of the three fine businessmen as representing a Johnsonian desire "to test public reaction." Public opinion, in the more conventional sense of the term, was in fact noticeably less certain about going to the moon than Johnson himself was; immediately after the President announced his decision, the Gallup Poll showed that fifty-eight percent of Americans were opposed to it.

But the most conspicuous victims of the Johnson method were the scientists, whose concern about the imbalance the moon would bring to government investment in science had been so pointedly expressed by James Killian. The reason for ignoring them now is aptly summed up in one contemptuous remark made by Edward Welsh: "If scientists had had any influence, the space program would have been about one-third the size it has been." Dr. Wiesner, nominally the President's science adviser, was allowed to attend some of the meetings but was rarely listened to. Kennedy had even asked him to dream up some alternative to the moon, something, the doctor recalls, "which could be done on earth and would be as good as space in propaganda terms. Something with an overseas impact, like desalination or feeding the hungry." But Wiesner understood perfectly that in the Washington of the time there was really no hope for anything short of the moon. "Nothing could eradicate the unfortunate, almost unspoken, fact that space had a coupling with military power."

Only one minor success did Wiesner have. It is a not insignificant detail, which helps shed a clearer light on the nature of the moon program. "I told Kennedy," Wiesner says, "that the least he could do was never to refer publicly to the moon landing as a scientific enterprise. And after he had announced the decision, he never did so."

It was now the end of April, and the announcement was not far away. Johnson had marshaled the facts and delivered the support. All that remained was to package the case for landing on the moon in the terms most likely to persuade the President himself that it was an inescapable choice which the evidence virtually selected for him.

Before this could reasonably be done, however, the fateful Mercury, that dead-end project on which NASA had labored so long, had to be seen to fly. After two postponements, the first American was due to be hoisted aloft on May 5, not into orbit but a few hundred miles down-range. His name was Alan Shepard, the number one astronaut, and his flight was awaited with trepidation around the country. The Russian flight had naturally removed some of the more alarming medical fears about man's physical ability to survive the physical ordeal of space. But confidence in Mercury was far from over-

whelming. Senator Fulbright and others, fearful of another disaster
on top of Gagarin and the Bay of Pigs, even urged another postponement.

But Shepard flew, and after fifteen minutes in space successfully
returned. Among the American public there was a surge of jubilation
which was not unhelpful to the Apollo planners. To Johnson the
signal had been given to consummate his work. He was due to set
off on an Asian tour in a few days, and was determined that before
he left he would personally present the final, unanswerable version
of his findings to the President. On the weekend after the Shepard
triumph, therefore, the principal architects of the moon plan were
assembled. They came, significantly, not only from NASA but from
the Pentagon as well, and together they composed a decisive document.

This, the summation of space wisdom in Washington at the time
the moon commitment was made, rested for years on classified file at
the Pentagon. But it is possible to publish the essence of it here
for the first time outside the *Sunday Times*. The reasons for its top
secret status are easily understood. Signed by Robert McNamara, the
Defense Secretary, as well as by James Webb, it launched the United
States into the big-time space age with a militaristic fanfare which
sounds a harshly discordant note when set beside the ostensible purposes of NASA.

The Webb-McNamara recommendations, written under Johnson's
watchful eye, were made without any profound knowledge of Soviet
space plans. These were simply assumed to be the same as NASA's,
to put a man on the moon as fast as possible. Yet, after listing the
benefits of space generally—such as weather forecasting, communications and the like—the document went on to place the lunar landing
squarely at the center of international power politics. It argued with
almost naïve directness that the road to world power lay, imperatively,
through the moon.

It is man, not merely machines, in space that captures the
imagination of the world [Webb and McNamara wrote]. All
large-scale projects require the mobilization of resources on a
national scale. They require the development and successful application of the most advanced technologies. Dramatic achievements in space, therefore, symbolize the technological power and

organizing capacity of a nation. It is for reasons such as these that major achievements in space contribute to national prestige.

Prestige was its own justification:

> Major successes, such as orbiting a man as the Soviets have just done, lend national prestige even though the scientific, commercial or military value of the undertaking may, by ordinary standards, be marginal or economically unjustified.

The nation should commit itself now to space projects designed solely, if not frankly, to achieve that objective.

The delineation of what prestige might mean in practical terms sounded chilling but, to a frightened President, possibly persuasive. Webb and McNamara did not hesitate to assign a nakedly militaristic aim to the moon mission:

> Our attainments are a major element in the international competition between the Soviet system and our own. The non-military, non-commercial, non-scientific but "civilian" projects such as lunar and planetary exploration are, in this sense, part of the battle along the fluid front of the cold war.

The words were positively mesmeric. They articulated in finer detail exactly the philosophy underlying much of Kennedy's campaign against the Eisenhower record. They were placed in his hands, fittingly, on the same day Alan Shepard arrived at the White House as a national hero, to have the NASA Distinguished Service Medal pinned on his chest by a grateful President. There was never any serious doubt that Kennedy would endorse their message, and on May 25, in an address to Congress on "urgent national goals," he did so. Little of the Webb-McNamara language obtrudes into Kennedy's, but his voice was urgent and he departed from his script to impress upon the legislators the length, cost and difficulty of the job. To some listeners he even seemed, as he faced the gigantic prospect of Apollo, to have some lingering reservations. Certainly, he asked for reassurance that the idea was right. But he had spelled out the solemn commitment: "I believe this nation should commit itself to achieving the goal, before this decade is out, of landing a man on the moon and returning him safely to the earth."

As Kennedy drove back to the White House from Capitol Hill after uttering these words, he remarked gloomily to Theodore Sorensen that Congress's applause had sounded "something less than enthusiastic." The legislators, he thought, knew plenty of better ways to spend $20,000 million. Although that may be how it sounded to Kennedy, the really astonishing fact is how trivial the opposition proved to be. The Gallup Poll was marginally unfavorable, and many scientists were troubled. But among politicians, the controllers of the budget and the representatives of the taxpayer, there was the silence of dumb accord.

The President had appealed for a great national debate, and perhaps he felt genuinely in need of the reassurance it might bring him. But no debate was heard. Perhaps Congress had been too efficiently herded by Johnson. Perhaps it was incapable of seriously addressing itself to the implications of the enterprise, or of understanding that, from small beginnings, the moon program would swell inexorably larger year by year. Whatever the reason, only minor opposition was raised in the House of Representatives. In the Senate, which thinks of itself as the greatest deliberative assembly on earth, the proceedings were almost comically inadequate to the occasion. The floor debate lasted little more than an hour. Only five of the ninety-six Senators spoke. Senator Kerr, Jim Webb's patron and now, as chairman of the Senate on Aeronautical and Space Sciences Committee, NASA's man on the Hill, dominated the floor. His only memorable point seemed a shade extravagant, given the absence of any critical pressure on him. "In my judgment," he said, "one of the benefits that will come from the program will be an increased average life span of at least ten years for each American under fifty years of age today." For the rest, the resemblance was once again to war, a time when every Senator knows that to ask too many questions is tantamount to treason. NASA's appropriation was doubled, and the journey to the moon began, without a vote being taken.

It is harder to be sure how deep a debate Kennedy conducted with himself. Did *he* consider the broader impact of the attempt to take the moon? Did he coldly examine its cost in the context of other problems? Did other considerations enter his mind, or was the Soviet threat allowed to override everything? We have Dr. Wiesner's evidence that several possibilities did occur to the President; but, after Gagarin, how real were these, how inevitable the moon landing?

Edward Welsh, one intimate witness, says that the moon decision emerged without any serious study of its place in the over-all use of resources. "We were looking at the holes in Eisenhower's budget and space was one of the biggest," he recalls. "All we were doing was putting our fingers in the dyke." The reasons such a plump finger was so readily available were twofold. First, the Gagarin flight had given a new urgency to fears which, even if that flight had not happened when it did, would have driven Kennedy to the moon one day—fears of Soviet influence around the world. Secondly, Welsh says, the moon was politically simple to push through. This was still Kennedy's celebrated First Hundred Days. Not only was it time for the promised dynamism, but the opposition to the President was not yet durably formed. He had acquired few hostages, struck few bargains, antagonized few enemies. Welsh says, "After Eisenhower, there was a demand for big decisions, any decisions. Most government decisions are made over the voices of the opposition. This one was made without such opposition, and with the further advantage of being supported by the actions of the Soviet Union.

But Welsh is perhaps a little too simply cynical. Other testimony suggests that even in the feverish climate of April 1961 some of the visible consequences of going to the moon were not entirely overlooked. Of all the people involved, none was better placed to witness the unfolding drama than the man in charge of both space and defense affairs at the Bureau of the Budget, Willis H. Shapley. Shapley, a reflective intellectual who sits somewhat oddly beside the gung-ho pioneers of space, later became a senior official at NASA itself. He is one of the very few space policy-makers now willing to admit that the greatest scientific adventure of modern times was underpinned by some formidable realities closer to home.

The moon decision, says Shapley, came at a time when demands for some major leap in arms production were being heard on many sides. "There was a conviction among military leaders, including the chairmen of the relevant congressional committees, that the country had to find some good reason for developing larger booster rockets. They held this conviction without being able to prove exactly why it

was held." Even though American rockets were adequate for all foreseeable military purposes (as Theodore Sorensen has also written in
his account of the era, *Kennedy*) no one could grasp the implications
of the other side having something bigger, something which would
operate in space itself. Shapley believes that this fear was "as compelling a reason for a big space program as any other among the
people most influential in the power structure."

But it was not merely the military who were looking ahead. With
Atlas, Minuteman, Polaris and Titan, the four main elements of
American strategic power, all moving toward completion, industry,
too, was anticipating harder times. There was, Shapley says, great
concern about this: "Could we afford the consequences of such a
decline in defense procurement?"

At this point the moon program found both sides of the military-
industrial complex at their most efficient. Kennedy faced a very real
problem: how to contain the air force and its associated parts of the
aerospace industry who were all putting in demands for yet greater
rockets? Shapley pithily describes the logic:

> People realized that space was the answer. It was a way of keep-
> ing up the aerospace economy and responding to the demand
> for more missiles without escalating the arms race. The moon
> program would produce the booster in the fastest possible time.
> By keeping the missile-makers busy on space boosters you were
> also keeping up their ability to return to military missiles if
> necessary. You were maintaining preparedness without overarm-
> ing the country.

It was not a noble argument, but then international life was not
very noble either. Without some such compelling earthly motives
as these, it is inconceivable that any nation would have gone to the
moon. As we have seen, not since Tsiolkovsky and Goddard has any
large development in rocketry occurred without military and political
encouragement; and the higher the price, the greater that encouragement must be. This is not, of course, the view taken by NASA. With
miraculous speed the space agency forgot the undignified crisis out
of which its greatest program was born. Its spokesmen are masters of
the vocabulary of adventure and scientific discovery conducted for
the benefit of all mankind. Ceaseless repetition has ensured for this

unconvincing position a triumph over its essential unreality. The position does less than justice to rational politicians. Being reluctant to admit to blemishes of any kind, it also detracts absurdly from the difficulty of the undertaking which was now, at last, underway.

6.

The Most Unexpected Way to Go

Until that transforming moment when the President dedicated the nation to reaching the moon, NASA's own commitment to the objective had existed largely in the realm of aspiration. This had been a far from fruitless exercise. The zeal of men like Wernher von Braun at Huntsville, George Low at headquarters and the visionary engineers of the Space Task Group at Langley had percolated through the agency. The basic arithmetic of the journey had been done. Many of the intermediate objectives had been set. Some of the hardware existed in considerable detail on paper. All this had bolstered the agency's confidence in asserting to the President that the landing of man on the moon was the most logical and the most attainable way of winning a space race. Nevertheless, it required a technological leap of gigantic measure. Psychologically, Kennedy's decision had removed any doubt that man did belong in space. Politically, it was all but certain that the decision would never be reversed. Now it was time for the moon engineers themselves to prove that the job could really be done.

In any flight to another planet there are essentially three technical elements, the prime factors from which all else flows. There is the rocket which provides the escape into space. There is the spacecraft, which is placed there. And there is the plan according to which these first two elements are married in order to carry out the objectives of the flight. None of these is more important than the other: they exist in an inextricable relationship: a decision about one is a decision about all three. In May 1961, such decisions as had been made about the rocket, the craft and the method to get to the moon were, understandably, in a state of some doubt.

Probably the most advanced thinking had been about the spacecraft. It was already clear that this would bear only a formal resemblance to the Mercury capsule in which Alan Shepard had provided NASA with its only experience of man-in-space: precisely fifteen minutes of it. Mercury was a minimum package for keeping a man alive in space for a day or two and getting him back to earth. Almost unable to move, the capsule wall within inches of his face, stuck in whatever orbits his temperamental launching rockets put him, the highly trained Mercury astronaut was little more than "Spam in the can." In Mercury, John Glenn was to become America's first space hero after performing the country's first orbital flight in early 1962. Gordon Cooper was to endure it for a thirty-six-hour flight. But not even the wildest fantasist imagined that this tight little box would go anywhere near the moon.

However, plans for something far more sophisticated had been maturing for some time in the Space Task Group under the direction of such men as Maxime Faget, Mercury's designer, and Robert Piland. This was already called Apollo and, potentially at any rate, Apollo was a moonship. It was not thought certain, at first, that Apollo would land on the moon; its original purpose was merely to orbit the moon and to retain—in case moon flight for some reason proved impossible—a useful capacity for earth orbit alone. But its specifications, drawn up by the Space Task Group in early 1960, were revolutionary.

It would have a crew of three. They would be able to remain in space for two weeks, ten times longer than in Mercury. It would provide a shirtsleeve environment in which the astronauts could take off their cumbersome spacesuits. It would have an engine for changing its orbit and maneuvering in space, a major advance on Mercury which could only change the direction in which it was pointing. And Apollo would have instruments and on-board computing equipment enabling it to navigate, if necessary, independently of the ground.

The Space Task Group had also developed the idea of a spacecraft constructed from a number of building blocks, known as "modules." The crew would travel in the command module, the only part which would re-enter earth's atmosphere. The engine, along with

things like the main oxygen reserves, was consigned to a separate
module, which could be jettisoned before the command module
returned to earth. In the original plans there was also a mission module to provide extra working space during the flight.

This was the kind of proposition which George Low had unveiled
to the aerospace industry in July 1960. Development of such a craft,
as opposed to design, received not a cent in Eisenhower's last two
budgets, but contracts for feasibility studies had been let to General
Electric, Martin and Convair. They had produced some exotic ideas.
All three firms, for example, suggested re-entry modules with a good
deal of aerodynamic lift, so that they could be flown like high-speed
gliders in the atmosphere and piloted to selected landing sites.
Although these speculations were put together before any urgency
was attached to the moon program, they happened to be reaching
NASA just at the moment when the moon became a top national
priority. With the industrial studies to hand, Apollo became the
obvious starting-point for moonship design.

But how was it to be propelled into space? Immediately, the other
two prime factors of spaceflight, the rocket and the method, were called
into question. As to the method, several ideas had been floated. One,
much favored by the Germans at Huntsville, called for the assembly
of the different sections of the moonship while it was in orbit round
the earth: earth orbital rendezvous. Another, seemingly so perilous
that it attracted almost no support, was for lunar orbital rendezvous,
in which the segments would split and then reassemble round the
moon. Yet another plan existed for a rocket with an upper stage propelled by nuclear power. There was even a spine-chilling proposal to
land men on the moon without the means to get off again; the return
vehicle would be delivered to the moon by a separate rocket.

However, by far the most widely backed method was a direct flight
from earth to moon, with no assembly of the parts either in earth
or in moon orbit. In NASA's paper studies and for at least a year after
Kennedy had ordered that the moon journey should take place, direct
flight was taken by the majority of people concerned to be the method
which would eventually be employed. This emerges very clearly from
the documents of the first NASA committee set up in May 1961 to
plan for an actual, rather than a notional, moon journey. The committee, chaired by William Fleming from NASA headquarters,

assumed that direct flight was the best way to go, and identified the massive rocket required by the mode as the item which would determine the pace of the entire program.

Of all the possible modes, direct flight required by far the largest rocket. It offered no possibility of splitting the load. Once the moonship reached earth orbit, the whole package would have to land on the moon and return. Direct flight would thus magnify the already extraordinary disproportion, inherent in all spaceflight, between the launcher and the tiny object perched on top of it. Because of the extensive collection of rockets needed for operations at the moon, the weight of the launcher compared with that of the capsule which eventually returned to earth would grow in the ratio of something like 1 : 1000. On a direct flight, the package would be formidably heavy. Whereas a spacecraft's return to earth can be achieved safely merely by protecting it from the searing heat produced by re-entry into the atmosphere, to land on the airless moon it needs rockets as a substitute for the braking effects of atmosphere. These rockets have to be big enough to lower gently not only the craft but the separate rockets and fuel for ascending off the moon back to earth. Stage by stage, the weight multiplies as fast as breeding rabbits. This is true of any mode of going there, but most frighteningly true of a mode which allows for no intermediate separation of the modules.

In the case of Apollo, the proposition was further complicated by a decision which had already been built into the craft, namely the size of the crew. According to some cynics Apollo was given a crew of three because it was more than two and less than four. But in fact there had been a reason for the choice. The traditional eight-hour shift seemed enough for an astronaut during a long flight; round-the-clock work therefore dictated a minimum of three astronauts. Although this made little difference to earth orbital and even circumlunar flights, on which weight was not a crucial matter, it would have a decisive effect on the moon landing.

Had the spacecraft been planned from the beginning with a 1970 moon landing in mind, the length of the astronaut's working day might well have seemed unimportant compared with the advantages of a crew of two. This would have kept down the size and simplified the construction of the spacecraft and above all of the launcher, whose weight could have been cut by at least a thousand tons.

But Apollo it was to be, and Apollo contained three men. Ironically, it was the choice of Apollo, the "obvious" spacecraft, which eventually forced the abandonment of the "obvious" plan for getting to the moon: a direct flight.

Direct flight, deeply though it was ingrained into the minds of many moon planners, depended on a rocket which in May 1961 was little more than a distant dream. The day after Kennedy spoke to Congress, Jim Webb described it to a star-struck audience of aerospace enthusiasts assembled in Tulsa, Oklahoma. It would be 50 feet in diameter at the base and 360 feet high—"60 feet taller than a football field is long." A more illuminating comparison would have been with Atlas, the greatest American rocket then in existence. Atlas had a thrust of 400,000 pounds and could put a couple of tons in orbit round the earth. The corresponding figures for the moon rocket would have to be 12 million pounds and 180 tons. Even the "big" booster which von Braun was developing at Huntsville, Saturn I, had a thrust of only one-and-a-half million pounds, one-eighth of what was required.

The rocket Webb described was, of course, the Nova, for which he had argued in his first, impassioned message to Kennedy soon after taking over NASA. It was to be built by clustering eight engines together, the engines designated F-1 which NASA had contracted with the Rocketdyne Division of North American Aviation to develop in 1959. No definitive mission had existed for these engines at the time the contract was placed, other perhaps than a desire to prove that America could if she chose do anything the Russians could do. But now their mission had been thrust upon them. Each was designed to develop one-and-a-half million pounds of thrust, as much as the total capability of Saturn I. Even as Webb described Nova, an F-1 was being tested in California.

But quite apart from its size, Nova presented other problems. If its weight was to be kept down to the 4500 tons of the version outlined by Webb, its upper stages would have to be fueled not by conventional kerosene but by liquid hydrogen, much more devilish stuff to handle. Liquid hydrogen gives, as it were, more miles per gallon; but it boils at −423° F, 136° lower even than liquid oxygen, and its tiny molecules will leak through cracks which to any other liquid are not cracks at all. Previous experience of the fuel was distinctly discouraging. A rocket named Centaur, an upper stage for the Atlas, was powered by it, and the first two ground tests of its twin hydrogen engines the previous winter had ended with explosions after a few seconds.

Nonetheless, at the end of May Nova was the notional moon rocket. NASA had its spacecraft planned, and its mode of projecting it fixed with some certainty. Nova would be a stupendous challenge, but one ideally suited to the American genius for large engineering enterprises. Clearly it would be the controlling factor in reaching the moon within the decade.

Or so the moon planners believed. The technical story of how the moon journey was ultimately accomplished consists very largely in the stripping down of this blueprint and its reassembly into a very different program. Before long it was found that the rocket and the mode had to be dramatically reconsidered. And as a result, ironically, it was to be the third element, the spacecraft, which came nearest to bringing failure on the enterprise.

The first doubts about the practicability of Nova, and with it, direct ascent to the moon, originated in a committee set up on July 20, 1961, to examine the booster program on a national scale. It can now be seen that this committee was a natural consequence of the case for going to the moon developed by James Webb and Robert McNamara in their decisive address to the President. Replete with the language of the cold war, the Webb-McNamara thesis had seen the space program as being closely bound up with defense and the need for continuing missile production. It was logical, therefore, that an attempt should be made to develop a moon rocket which would also fulfill the needs of the Pentagon: to create, in fact, a national launcher program around a single family of machines.

The committee charged with studying this possibility had a chairman representing each interest, Dr. Laurence Kavanau from the Department of Defense and Dr. Nicholas Golovin from NASA. But it is known, after its dominant figure, simply as the Golovin Committee.

Golovin, a Russian-born mathematician, was not a newcomer to NASA. He had first joined the agency in 1959, bringing with him some highly theoretical statistical techniques used to improve reliability in the missile program. But he soon clashed with the more down-to-earth Mercury engineers of the Space Task Group, who tended to refer contemptuously to his approach to reliability as "the numbers game." After a year he had disconsolately resigned and joined the White House science staff. His experience had yielded an undying suspicion of NASA's standards of reliability, and this was later to be of considerable significance. But he returned, briefly, to lead its side of the booster study.

The Golovin Committee was the last attempt to create a unified national launcher program, and in this it was a failure. The discussions resumed, in effect, where Medaris had left off. Once again the attempt was made to resolve the competing claims of von Braun's Saturn I and the air force's Titan 3, the so-called Saturn-killer. Titan 3 was a version of the Titan missile, with two "strap-on" solid-fuel boosters to raise its performance. The air force wanted it, among other things, to launch its Dyna-soar space glider. Although the performance of Saturn and Titan was much the same, Saturn was closer to completion. Nevertheless the Golovin Committee was unable to agree on a launcher to serve both purposes. The air force was adamant that Saturn was unsuitable because its liquid hydrogen and oxygen fuels had to be put on board at the last minute; Titan, with its storable propellants and much smaller launch crew, was better suited to service requirements. The air force was ready to pay for Titan 3, and next year it got the green light. Never again would an attempt be made to make NASA and the air force use the same rockets.

However, this aspect of the Golovin Committee, dealing with medium-size rockets, was only marginally relevant to the moon landing. Far more important were the committee's views on Nova and its alternatives.

Golovin's main source of advice was, not unreasonably, the greatest team of rocket experts in the Western world, von Braun's Germans. And Huntsville, peopled by engineers of normally limitless horizons, did not like Nova. Among other counts against it, Nova was a concept which suffered from having been invented elsewhere. The Germans felt it was such a large jump from existing rockets that it might well not be ready for a moon landing by 1970. The Golovin Committee agreed. Other people thought Nova could be built in time, but the advice of von Braun's engineers was the beginning of the end for Nova, and for a direct flight to the moon. Why were they so cautious?

Behind the genuine technical doubts, deep forces were at work. For more than thirty years the Germans had been dreaming about spaceflight. Through military missile programs, German and American, they had established an unrivaled reputation. But they did not want to be rocket builders only. They had their own plan for landing men on the moon which envisaged rockets far smaller than Nova, and which would also allow them to diversify into the spacecraft side of the business. This plan was for earth-orbital rendezvous.

The concept of rendezvous—linking two spacecraft together in orbit—had been known to space men for many years, mainly as a way of assembling permanent orbiting space stations too big to be launched with a single rocket. In the Huntsville moon-landing plan the seventy-five-ton Apollo moonship would be split into two packages, each to be launched by rockets roughly half the size of Nova and joined together in orbit round the earth before setting off for the moon.

True to the tradition established in the fifties—when the von Braun satellite launcher was usefully confused with the Jupiter missile—the rocket conceived for this moon plan was given a name which implied an organic connection with Huntsville's existing work. It was called the super-Saturn. But in truth it had far more in common with Nova than with Saturn I. Where Nova used eight of the huge F-1 engines in its first stage, the Huntsville earth-orbital-rendezvous rocket used four, giving it a thrust of six million pounds. It was a big step beyond Saturn I, but not as big as Nova and therefore less likely to cause a stumble. Earth-orbital rendezvous, using two four-engined super-Saturns, consequently became the method of getting to the moon recommended by the Golovin Committee in its final report in December 1961.

Of course, earth-orbital rendezvous had disadvantages. Big rockets were notoriously unreliable. Long holds during countdown at that time seemed part of the natural order of things, and even when the button was finally pressed something went wrong with one launch in ten. The super-Saturn was only half the size of Nova, but it would still have ten times the power and complexity of Atlas. To get one off the ground on time seemed a formidable enough undertaking, but rendezvous required two to be counted down simultaneously and launched within a day or two of each other: half a moonship could not be left suspended in orbit for weeks, steadily deteriorating, before the moon journey even began.

Besides being on time, the two launchers must be on target. Changing orbit consumes a lot of fuel, so for a successful rendezvous the two spacecraft must be put into similar paths and not too far apart. Even the same orbit is not good enough if they are on opposite sides of the earth.

Another difficulty was breaking the Apollo moonship down into two packages of roughly equal weight. It could not be done neatly, and the best solution seemed to be to put the partly fueled spacecraft into orbit with one rocket and to use the other as a liquid oxygen tanker. But liquid oxygen was difficult enough to handle on the ground, let alone in space with weightlessness as an additional complication. On the ground a liquid can at least be relied on to flow out of a pipe in the bottom of a tank. Weightless, in orbit, a liquid could not be relied on to flow anywhere. Nobody knew quite what it would do. It might, depending on its characteristics, float like a ball in the middle of the tank without touching the walls, or cling to the walls leaving empty space at the center, or break up into a dense mist of tiny droplets. None of these possibilities was likely to make pumping liquids from a tanker to an orbiting spacecraft any easier.

Above all, no one had ever attempted, let alone achieved, a rendezvous in orbit. It had been studied on paper at Langley and Huntsville, but it was low among NASA's priorities for action. Whatever the people who had studied rendezvous thought, to the uninitiated the difficulties looked horrifyingly formidable.

Besides its uncommon demands on timing and accuracy, the business of mating two craft in space has another dimension, one much less readily intelligible by analogy with conventional locomotion. Then normal procedure for catching up, on the road, at sea or in the air, is to head for the target and step on the accelerator. In orbit that is precisely what not to do. If an astronaut points his spacecraft at another located, say, one hundred miles ahead and fires its engine, the effect will be to push him into a higher orbit where he will travel more slowly and fall farther behind than ever. The correct course is to do the opposite: to use the engines to slow down, thus moving the spacecraft naturally into a lower orbit where it will travel faster and gradually overhaul the one ahead.

When the two spacecraft finally begin to approach each other, precise control becomes vital. They must come together very gently if they are not to be damaged. Would astronauts be able to judge speeds, angles and distances accurately enough? If not, would radars or optical range-finders? Would the spacecraft's small control motors respond with the necessary delicacy?

Difficult as rendezvous appeared, the difficulties diminished rather than grew with increased familiarity. Those who had studied it closely were convinced it was perfectly feasible. The demands on the launchers were no greater than for other missions. The back-to-front procedures of the chase were unfamiliar, but based on the three-hundred-year-old laws of Newtonian mechanics. A human being using his earth-trained reflexes might be put off, but a computer would not. The final approach was well within the scope of the electronic art, even if astronauts could not manage it. The counting down of two big boosters simultaneously remained a major problem, but it was not enough to alter von Braun's conviction that earth-orbital rendezvous was the way to go to the moon.

Although von Braun had support in Washington, when NASA embarked on Project Apollo its headquarters' organization was comparatively weak. The only other center whose views counted for anything was the Space Task Group at Langley, the embryo of the Manned Spacecraft Center which moved to Houston late in 1961. (The circumstances of the move were somewhat bizarre, as will be recounted later.) Huntsville would be responsible for the launcher, but they would be also responsible for the spacecraft.

The Space Task Group in the middle of 1961 favored direct ascent. It was the method they had all assumed would be used when they started to talk about moon landings in the late fifties. Most of them were former aircraft men, and direct ascent fitted in with their straightforward, no-nonsense approach. They did not relish the demarcation disputes which would inevitably arise with earth-orbital rendezvous. Direct ascent gave them as much control over things as possible.

But as the Space Task Group began to study the direct ascent mode in detail during the second half of 1961, they confronted unexpected problems. The rocket for direct ascent was already recognized as a major difficulty. Now it emerged that there were hidden traps in the moonship itself. The main one was beautifully elementary: how would the astronauts see what they were doing during the moon landing? The landing itself was the one part of the flight where the astronauts would clearly have to be ready to act like real pilots. Computers could not be expected to steer the craft on to the most favorable site. Yet the men would be perched on top of a lighthouselike structure which might be ninety feet high. By giving the spacecraft two braking stages, the first of which would be abandoned in lunar orbit, this could probably be reduced to forty feet, but that was still a very remote distance from which to direct a landing on an unknown surface. And how would the astronauts be able to see what they were doing, lying on their backs in a capsule whose walls sloped inward over their heads? Even if they landed safely, could they be expected to climb in spacesuits with cumbrous back-packs down a forty-foot ladder which might well be leaning backward if the landing site were not level?

Earth-orbital rendezvous raised the same problem, since the moonship it demanded would be of similar size. As 1961 wore on, the Space Task Group became seriously worried about these difficulties. At one stage there was actually talk of landing the pencil-shaped spacecraft on its side. Eventually the moon planners, hitherto blinkered by the argument between direct ascent and earth-orbital rendezvous, admitted the need to find an alternative. They found it in the ideas of a man who had been hovering on the fringes of the scene for some time, talking volubly, but hardly listened to. His name was John C. Houbolt.

Houbolt, at the time of the Apollo triumph a white-haired but youthful forty-nine, with a voice which still rises with excitement as he talks about his ideas of many years ago, has now left the space agency. But in 1961 he was a middle-grade engineer, head of the theoretical mechanics division at Langley, though not a member of the Space Task Group. For some time he had been running an informal extracurricular study group on rendezvous.

To the members of the group, rendezvous at first seemed interesting purely as a way of building a big space station. But even in 1960, when direct ascent still held sway, it began to be contemplated as something bigger, conceivably a way of getting to the moon. At one meeting of the moon planners late that year they discussed every possible way rendezvous might be used—on the way there, on the way back, or in lunar orbit. "I felt intuitively and at once that this was the answer," Houbolt remembers. After the meeting he did some quick back-of-an-envelope calculations and convinced himself that rendezvous in lunar orbit was the way to get to the moon.

For Houbolt it was like the conversion of St. Paul on the road to Damascus. He had seen the light and he had to spread the word. For more than a year he worked with obsessional zeal as a solitary propagandist for his conviction. At first he was regarded as a nuisance, but eventually people began to listen. In the end, after a long struggle, they were obliged to agree.

The mechanics of lunar-orbital rendezvous are now familiar enough. A three-part spacecraft, consisting of a command module in which the astronauts travel, an engine section called the service module, and a lunar module, is put on course for the moon. The complete spacecraft goes into orbit round it and two of the three astronauts crawl through from the command module into the lunar module. The lunar module separates and descends to the surface while the mother ship remains in lunar orbit with the third astronaut inside it. After their stay on the moon the two explorers take off again in the lunar module, rendezvous with the mother ship and transfer to it for the return to earth. The lunar module is then abandoned.

Although Houbolt and his colleagues did not know it at the time, this was not a wholly original conception. The basic calculation had been made by a self-educated Russian mechanic named Yuri Kondratyuk fifty years before. And on November 13, 1948, H. E. Ross had read a paper to the British Interplanetary Society in which, backing his argument with diagrams and figures, he suggested a journey to the moon using both earth and lunar-orbital rendezvous.

The most telling merit of lunar-orbital rendezvous over any other method is the enormous saving in weight, and hence in rocket power, which somewhat paradoxically results from carrying a complete extra spacecraft for the lunar excursion. With this extra craft, neither the fuel for the return to earth nor the protective heatshield nor any other item irrelevant to the lunar landing needs to be taken down to the surface. So the rockets for descending and ascending can be dramatically smaller, and their fuel lighter. The weight saved here more than offsets the weight of the lunar ferry itself. It means that the package can be launched from earth by a rocket which is a whole order of magnitude smaller than that required for direct ascent. Where Nova would be needed for that, and twin rockets more than half Nova's size for earth-orbital rendezvous, lunar-orbital rendezvous could be done with a single such rocket.

Along with economy in rocket power go savings in time and money. Along with reduced complexity goes a smaller chance of accidents. But for the spacecraft designers, lunar-orbital rendezvous clearly offered another great advantage. The ferry would be designed solely for landing on the moon. Good visibility and easy egress could be built into it from the start. It would be of manageable size, far more appropriate for landing on an unknown surface than the huge spaceship hitherto envisaged. These were the arguments on which Houbolt based his campaign.

His first presentation was made in December 1960 to colleagues in the Space Task Group. It was a Sunday and the weather was stormy, but everyone turned up. However, they were not very impressed by Houbolt's case. His calculations simply were not believed. After the meeting someone was dispatched to go through them, but according to Houbolt he was incapable of following them intelligently.

More presentations followed, to the Administrator a couple of days later, to the Space Exploration Council in January, to an intercenter meeting on rendezvous in February. (At one of these early meetings Maxime Faget, the designer of the Mercury spacecraft, is said to have let out an impassioned cry. "Your figures lie," he shouted. The words sound more appropriate to Victorian melodrama than to a meeting of American space engineers, but Houbolt swears that was the sense of them.) Throughout the summer, Houbolt labored to convince Washington that he was right. He was much in demand as an expert on rendezvous generally and lost no opportunity to put in a plug for lunar-orbital rendezvous.

Autumn began, Apollo was starting to take shape, and he had got nowhere. He had given nine major briefings without apparently producing any effect whatever. Once he had been rudely told to cut out his commercials. The idea of a rendezvous in orbit round the moon was a nightmare which most people preferred not to think about. At least if something went wrong with a rendezvous in earth orbit the astronauts could easily be brought back to earth. A quarter of a million miles away they would not stand a chance.

Almost in despair, he got together with his few supporters to prepare a detailed report on lunar-orbital rendezvous. On November 16, he sent it to Dr. Robert Seamans, NASA's Associate Administrator and most senior engineer, with a covering letter beginning, "Somewhat as a voice in the wilderness . . ." But unknown to Houbolt things were already starting to move his way.

By the end of 1961, the Space Task Group was badly alarmed by direct flight and definitely moving away from it. In addition, the scene at NASA headquarters had changed. One of the first effects of the moon decision had been to stimulate Webb to push through a major reorganization. Among the strongest of the new men brought in to run the swiftly expanding agency was one named Brainerd Holmes, director of the office of Manned Spaceflight.

Holmes came to NASA from industry, where as general manager of RCA's Major Defense Systems Division he had accomplished the almost unprecedented feat of completing a big military contract on time and on budget. This was the Ballistic Missile Early Warning System, the three giant radar stations, one in Alaska, one in Greenland, one in northern England, which give the United States the notorious fifteen-minute warning of a missile attack.

Brainerd Holmes describes his skill as lying in his ability to get people to work together. This is thoroughly misleading. Holmes was one of the first sophisticated managers ever to enter NASA, and far from being the tactful committee man, he was single-minded and ferociously energetic. Inevitably this eventually led to bad relations between him and the ebullient Webb, and Holmes left NASA after two eventful years. But in 1967 he was sufficiently fascinated by the challenge to take a salary cut from $50,000 to $21,000 in order to help beat the Russians. As Holmes said recently, "I thought the Russians were going to the moon too and I wasn't going to be second."

Holmes arrived with no preconceived ideas about the mode but with an overpowering conviction that the debate should be settled without further delay. At first he inclined to earth-orbital rendezvous, the front-runner at the time. But as a device to cut the Gordian knot which Huntsville and Langley had tied for themselves, he determined to establish his own study group at headquarters. To replace the unclubbable Golovin, the man qualified to run it as the successor to his own study of Nova, Holmes brought in another outsider, Dr. Joseph Shea. Shea, a brilliant and jocular fellow, was only thirty-five, but he had already run the development of the inertial-guidance system for the Titan missile. He also belonged to that new breed of men, the systems engineers: analysts who understood the workings of complete technological organisms in their many interrelated parts.

As Shea, under Holmes's direction, began work at the end of 1961, he confronted a balance of pressures something like this: Huntsville was firmly for earth-orbital rendezvous; the Space Task Group, frightened by the problems of landing the complete Apollo spacecraft on the moon, was becoming increasingly interested in lunar-orbital rendezvous; headquarters itself tended to earth-orbital rendezvous, though without Huntsville's strong commitment.

Direct ascent had only one breath of life left in it. The Space Task Group, originally its main supporters, was deserting the cause, and the Golovin Committee, whose final report appeared in December, came out against Nova mainly on the grounds that it could not be built in time. In the same month, however, an all-NASA committee on launchers under Milton W. Rosen, Holmes's Director of Launch Vehicles and Propulsion, rather eccentrically disagreed. Although it had the benefit of the Golovin Committee studies, it actually recommended a direct ascent using Nova. It pressed its case on Seamans. But Seamans, with both the main field centers now against direct ascent, would not buy it. Although Nova remained in the background during 1962, its prospects were steadily diminishing to nothing.

The Rosen Committee's main contribution was in suggesting the configuration of the "super-Saturn" which became the Saturn V, the moon rocket of 1969. A strong minority of the committee favored earth-orbital rendezvous and the report recommended it as a back-up mode. Von Braun's original outline of it called for a rocket with four F-1 engines, but this allowed little margin for any increase in the spacecraft's weight. For this reason, and because it kept the lunar-orbital rendezvous option open, the Rosen Committee suggested that the super-Saturn should have five engines instead of four. (The fifth fitted neatly into a hole in the middle.) Early in 1962, official word reached Huntsville to start work on the five-engined super-Saturn.

[15] The Original Seven in 1959. Ten years later they were (left to right): President, Regency Corporation, Denver, Colorado—Wally Schirra; Chief Astronaut, NASA—Alan Shepard; Director of Flight Crew Operations, NASA—Deke Slayton; deceased—Gus Grissom; President, Royal Crown Cola International, New York—John Glenn; Astronaut, NASA—Gordon Cooper; Aquanaut, U.S. Navy Sealab Program—Scott Carpenter.

[16] NASA Administrator James E. Webb with his patron Lyndon Johnson. "Total control over earth lies somewhere out in space," said the President.

[17] General Bernard Schriever: An Air Force blue moon for one and a half billion dollars.

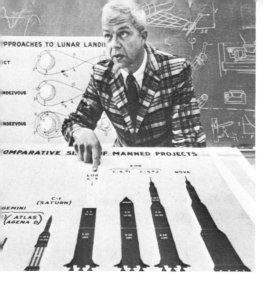

[18] John C. Houbolt, prophet of the bug: "A voice in wilderness."

[19] Joseph F. Shea, systems chief, later spacecraft manager: the computers said lunar orbital rendezvous.

[20] Jerome B. Wiesner, Kennedy's science adviser: A mistake in the sums?

[21] Brainerd Holmes, manned spaceflight chief: getting people to work together.

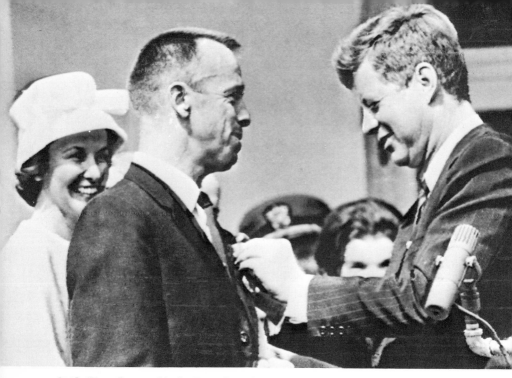

[22] "But I was first": President Kennedy pins the NASA distinguished service medal on Alan Shepard after the first U.S. spaceflight.

[23] John Glenn: "I did not want to be the oldest, permanent, used astronaut."

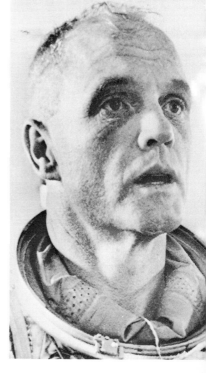

[24] Scott Carpenter: "I've got the sunrise to worry about."

C
O
P
Y

April 20, 1961

MEMORANDUM FOR THE VICE PRESIDENT

In accordance with our conversation I would like for you as Chairman of the Space Council to be in charge of making an overall survey of where we stand in space.

1. Do we have a chance of beating the Soviets by putting a laboratory in space, or by a trip around the moon, or by a rocket to land on the moon, or by a rocket to go to the moon and back with a man. Is there any other space program which promises dramatic results in which we could win?

2. How much additional would it cost?

3. Are we working 24 hours a day on existing programs. If not, why not? If not, will you make recommendations to me as to how work can be speeded up.

4. In building large boosters should we put out emphasis on nuclear, chemical or liquid fuel, or a combination of these three?

5. Are we making maximum effort? Are we achieving necessary results?

I have asked Jim Webb, Dr. Wiesner, Secretary McNamara and other responsible officials to cooperate with you fully. I would appreciate a report on this at the earliest possible moment.

/s/ John F. Kennedy

[25] Apollo's charter.

[26] The picture that brought the moon home to earth: the crater
Copernicus photographed by Lunar Orbiter 2 on November 28, 1966.

[27] Human Satellite: Ed White making the first U.S. spacew
during the Gemini 4 fli₃

[28] The confinement of space: the can opens on Neil Armstrong and
David Scott after Gemini 8.

Now at last both the spacecraft and the rocket for the moon had been firmly chosen. But the mode still remained an open question. Saturn V ruled out direct ascent, but it could equally well be used for earth- and lunar-orbital rendezvous. It was between these two that the final choice rested, a choice which it was Joe Shea's job to make.

One of Shea's first calls was on Houbolt at Langley, who for all his industry was still something of an outcast. After a rapid briefing on lunar-orbital rendezvous, Shea contracted with an outside firm to study it in detail and provide a dispassionate assessment. Simultaneously renewed examinations were undertaken by all three of the NASA principals—Langley, Huntsville and Shea himself. All were directed toward three essential questions. Which mode was the safest? Which offered the best chance of a successful mission? And—rather less important—which would deliver the goods soonest and for the lowest price?

Calculating the comparative probability of failure of rockets and spacecraft not yet designed, and of maneuvers never attempted, may sound like a black art. In fact it is a surprisingly precise science. Take, for example, the launching rockets. Both Nova and Saturn V used the same engines. Even before the engine existed it was possible to make a reasonable estimate of the chances that any particular engine would work. It was then a simple matter to calculate the chances of a number of identical engines working correctly. Direct ascent required the correct functioning of eight engines in Nova, lunar-orbital rendezvous five in Saturn V, earth-orbital rendezvous ten in two Saturn V's. So it was possible to make a perfectly valid comparison of the chances of success of the launch segment of the mission by each of the three modes. By breaking down the flight step-by-step over-all comparisons could also be made.

Estimates became more hazardous when like could not be compared with like. Rendezvous in lunar orbit, for example, could not be compared very directly with anything. It merely seemed to be highly dangerous. But even the perils of this maneuver began to fade under analysis. Rendezvous depends first on getting into the right orbit and second on making a successful approach. The guidance accuracy required to get into the right orbit turned out to be actually less than for the return to earth, when the craft must slot into exactly the right keyhole if it is to avoid burning up or skidding off the atmosphere back into space. Moreover, the chance of failure could be made smaller still by duplicating radars and other vital equipment and arranging for the main spacecraft as well as the lunar module to have the power to maneuver into rendezvous.

To begin with, the final debate continued to favor rendezvous in earth orbit. Von Braun seemed to be winning. His mode even went some way toward formal selection, and during the congressional hearings in the middle of June on NASA's 1963 budget, Webb, Seamans and Holmes all gave the impression that it would be adopted. But a week before the hearings began an event momentous and rare in the history of the space age occurred: Wernher von Braun changed his mind.

On June 7, Shea and others from headquarters visited Huntsville to be briefed on the German's present thinking. Several of them spoke, indicating by no nuance in an adverb that there had been a change of heart. Von Braun himself, claiming, as he said, the privilege of all bosses, spoke last. To veterans of the debate it was a shattering moment. The great rocketeer began to list the merits of lunar-orbital rendezvous and went on:

> We readily admit that when first exposed to the proposal of the LOR mode we were a bit sceptical—particularly the aspect of having the astronauts execute a complicated rendezvous maneuver at a distance of 240,000 miles from the earth where any rescue possibility seemed remote. In the meantime, however, we have spent a great deal of time studying the modes and we have come to the conclusion that this particular disadvantage is far outweighed by the advantages.

What had converted von Braun? There was strong pressure from the Space Task Group, and studying lunar-orbital rendezvous in detail was certainly the best way of comprehending its advantages. But it is not hard to imagine von Braun's reluctance to sacrifice the diversification into the spacecraft business offered by earth-orbital rendezvous. Happily, his dream of the moon was stronger than that. His studies had simply convinced him that lunar-orbital rendezvous was the best mode. They showed that it would be just as safe as the others, more likely to succeed, cheaper, and that it would make a landing possible at least six months earlier. (There may well have been another inducement, too. In due course, Huntsville, not Houston, was given responsibility for the major post-moon spaceship, the Orbiting Workshop, in which a manned space station will be constructed from empty rocket stages.) Although this unexpected conversion settled NASA's own argument, the debate was not quite dead. There remained the ubiquitous Golovin, now back at the White House once again and unable to forget the shoddy attitude to reliability he had detected in his association with the space agency. As one of Jerome Wiesner's lieutenants, he was determined to keep the President's Science Advisory Committee in close touch with goings-on in NASA.

Golovin had done some private analyses of lunar-orbital rendezvous and emerged a strong opponent. He was convinced that it was the most dangerous method and the one least likely to succeed. When it came to his ears that NASA had chosen it, he interested Wiesner in the matter. Wiesner regarded the Science Advisory Committee not as a body whose function was to give gentlemanly, generalized advice but as one which should be closely involved in all major national technical decisions. The method of getting to the moon clearly fell into the latter category, and Wiesner demanded that NASA disclose to him the full details of the decision.

This led to one of the most bizarre incidents in the entire episode. On June 20, NASA sent to the White House the results of three analyses of the different modes, one carried out by Shea's own group, one by Huntsville, one by the Space Task Group. Golovin went through them figure by figure, equation by equation, and found his worst suspicions confirmed. According to one set of figures, probably those from Huntsville, lunar-orbital rendezvous emerged as considerably more dangerous than the other modes. Golovin told Wiesner, who got on to Webb. On the evening of July 3, Webb called Shea and asked him to go over and calm Wiesner down. After two hours' intensive persuasion, Wiesner was still not convinced. Golovin seemed at last to have won the day against the sardonic moon engineers.

There is still no agreement on how this strange miscalculation occurred. Shea claims that when he rechecked the figures, he found an elementary arithmetical error which, once corrected, removed any evidence for believing lunar-orbital rendezvous to be the most dangerous mode. Wiesner, on the other hand, asserts to this day that there was no simple error in the figuring but a basically false assump-

tion which NASA, thanks to Golovin's vigilance, was forced to correct
in order to maintain its case.

Either way, the discrepancy was an extraordinarily careless one to
make in a presentation to the White House, which NASA knew
very well was instinctively opposed to their chosen mode. It solidified Wiesner's hostility. The Science Advisory Committee began to
contest the decision as fiercely as it knew how. Wiesner seized on the
possibility of reviving the deadest duck of all, direct ascent. He picked
up a suggestion from North American Aviation, contractor for the
Apollo capsule, for a flight scaled down to two men, which could
reach the moon directly under the power of the Saturn V. North
American did not like the thought of the actual landing being made
with a lunar module built by a different manufacturer. They saw
their chance in the split between NASA and the White House, and
even persuaded Wiesner and members of his committee, one of whom
was actually a North American consultant, to visit their plant in
California for a briefing.

But NASA was united now, and determined not to budge. On
July 11 it announced its decision publicly, saying that lunar-orbital
rendezvous provided a higher chance of success than other modes,
with "essentially equal" safety. It would also be between 10 and 15
percent cheaper, and the first attempt with it could be made some
months earlier. It called for tenders for the machinery of the mode,
the lunar excursion module, at the same time seeking to mollify the
White House by buying yet another mode-study from another outside firm.

The dispute, which continued for some months, was conducted
mainly in private. But on one occasion it flared into the open, to give
an unmistakable taste of its bitterness. As summer ended, President
Kennedy set out on a tour of NASA's burgeoning installations. His
decision to take the moon within the decade was more than a year
old. Ostensibly the tour was to allow the President to observe for himself what progress had been made, but privately he had another motive.
He wished to inform himself about the background to the row between
his adviser Wiesner and the top management of the space agency.

On September 11 the President and his entourage arrived at
Huntsville, where von Braun showed them a model of the Saturn
moon rocket and went on to explain how it would be used. Listing the

merits of lunar-orbital rendezvous, he spoke with all the enthusiasm of the recent convert. One member of his audience, however, was unimpressed. Despite the presence of Vice-President Johnson, British Minister of Defense Peter Thorneycroft and many reporters, Jerome Wiesner started to argue loudly with von Braun's claims. Lunar-orbital rendezvous was, he insisted, more likely to fail and more dangerous. The discussion became heated and threatened to develop into a public brawl. Only a timely quip from the President brought it to a close.

Next month, NASA felt strong enough to demand a decision. Webb went to the White House and coldly informed Wiesner that the agency was going ahead and placing a contract to build the lunar module unless the President himself objected. The visit was well-timed. It was made on October 24, at the height of the most perilous of all Kennedy's presidential days, his confrontation with Khrushchev over the placing of Soviet missiles in Cuba. It was no time to bother him with the moon. So NASA sealed its choice of the way to get there by placing a contract to build the lunar module with the Grumman Aircraft Engineering Corporation of Long Island, New York.

7.
Carving Up
the Spoils

Although they were not to build the complete moonship, the employees and shareholders of North American Aviation Inc., did not starve. The decision to make the moon journey via lunar-orbital rendezvous meant that another vehicle would be hitched on to the smooth contours of Apollo; and this, the grotesque little landing ferry, would be constructed on the opposite side of the continent. Some of the sheen inevitably faded from the satisfaction of California's greatest aerospace giant—it could not now describe itself as *the* moon corporation. But neither could it complain of neglect. With the contract for Apollo, the firm became by a single stroke the largest beneficiary from the space age.

The most immediate earthly benefit of the moon program has clearly been the one which Willis Shapley described when he disclosed the reasons underlying Kennedy's decision: the pumping of jobs and money through the aerospace industry into the economy at large. In no branch of the economy did the pump work such an inflation as at North American. The spacecraft was much the most costly of all the tools for reaching the moon; the total contract would be worth over $3500 million, many millions more than was envisaged when North American's tender was accepted. But the firm was also contracted to build the second stage of the rocket itself. Altogether, it was committed by the end of 1961 to space work which would bring in more than $6000 million by the time men landed on the moon.

The chairman of North American's Space Division, Harrison

"Stormy" Storms, greeted the award with a ringing message to his men. "We'll all have to grow an inch taller round here or lie down and let them throw dirt in our face," he announced. "The secret of this business is that you have to be a little afraid—afraid you'll forget something." Noting the zest with which Apollo had imbued North American workers Storms added, "They don't believe the days of fairies are over."

But the destination of Apollo's billions was not fixed by fairies, nor by any other supernatural intervention. Before the decision was taken, it was seen as one of the utmost importance. It later proved to have even more distinctive consequences for the space program than anyone expected. No intelligible account of how America got to the moon would be complete without some examination of the circumstances in which North American and not some other corporation were given Apollo to build.

The Apollo contract was, after all, rather more than routine government business. It was the biggest civilian contract in American history and the centerpiece of a program on which a large slice of the national destiny was seen to be riding. The contract would guarantee a long and prosperous future to any aerospace firm facing the prospect of a decline in military spending. To the success of the mission, the choice would be even more decisive. The main reason for going to the moon was to make manifest American technological supremacy: it was from this display, the policy-makers had argued, that inestimable admiration would accrue to the United States among all the nations of the earth. In no other government program, therefore, had it been quite so crucial that American industry should not bungle the job.

Obviously, no corporation could promise this. The moon was not only expensive; it had to be reached within a tight deadline, and made many wholly novel technical demands. The years of work were certain to be marked by disappointment at many stages, whoever undertook them. But equally, it was not impossible to make a judgment. There were criteria by which a rational decision could be reached concerning the corporation which could produce the most encouraging credentials.

To examine how this rational choice was made in the case of the Apollo spacecraft is to do far more than compare the voluminous proposals made by North American and their rivals. It plunges one instantly into the vortex of Washington life. It could not do otherwise. In a city where the location of a single dam or a minor railroad crossing can be a blue-chip stock on the political market, no one would expect a $24,000 million program to be somehow protected against the bulls and bears on Capitol Hill.

No one, that is, except the space agency. From the moment it was set on course for the moon, NASA established certain basic rules about the image of its affairs which had to be put across to the taxpayer. One precept was that the moon mission, for all its urgency, was not an exercise in international power but a scientific adventure for the greater glory and improvement of man. This was supported by a second decree, that no identifiable worker in the space program ever made a mistake; at worst, any error was to be explained by the perverse and unaccountable failure of machinery. Also among the laws of image-building was the need to believe that NASA floated as high above the Washington murk as its rockets streaked above the clouds. Obsessed by the mission to promote technological perfection, the space agency displayed an apparently sincere conviction that its world was unflawed by bargain, concession, venal profit and the other common coin of politics.

The picture is unconvincing and the facts are untrue. The moon program gave birth to its own political underworld, which was never more active than in the early years when the big money was being handed out. Alongside the cool technical geniuses of NASA, profiteers and power-brokers flourished. In Washington the species is as immovable as the Lincoln Memorial, as unavoidable as politics itself. These men, far from intruding apologetically into space, as if it were a world too sterile for them to inhabit, grew to a scale commensurate with the pork-barrel off which they fed.

The consequences of North American's Apollo contract provide one illuminating instance of this. Like the real story of Kennedy's decision, the case gives some idea of the inevitably political context in which the mission to the moon got under way. It brings into focus a series of unexpected figures, chief among them the chairman of the Senate Committee on Astronautical and Space Sciences, Robert Kerr, and a shadowy character named Fred B. Black, one of the most successful manipulators of business-in-politics in modern times. The names will rarely be found in official histories of the journey to Tranquility. As the advance to the moon progressed, they were expunged from memory as surely as loose talk about the fluid front of the cold war. Yet in their way they were as inextricably involved as Wernher von Braun and George Low. As representatives of a certain kind of moon man, they have much to reveal about lunar life on earth.

The formal process of selecting the main Apollo contractor can be swiftly described. It had begun, as we have seen, well before the decision to go to the moon was taken. The invitation for design studies in 1960 had alerted the entire aerospace industry, and several firms had begun detailed work on possible moonships. But by July 1961, two months after Kennedy spoke, the number of potential spacecraft builders had been pared to twelve. Each of these was asked to bid on the basis of elaborate guidelines laid down by NASA. The guidelines dispatched to the twelve weighed over 250 pounds, a formidable package which soon reduced to five the number of serious contenders.

In October, five proposals to build Apollo, each at least two thousand pages long, were received by the space agency. Besides North American, they came from Martin-Marietta of Baltimore, builders of the Titan missile, and three consortia which together absorbed most of the larger fish in the pool of aerospace: General Electric, Douglas, Grumman and Space Technology Laboratories; General Dynamics and Avco; McDonnell Aircraft, Lockheed, Hughes and the Vought Astronautics Division of Ling-Temco-Vought. Their proposals were put before a Source Evaluation Board, 192 experts drawn from NASA and the Department of Defense, who shut themselves away on the top floor of the Chamberlain Hotel at Old Point Comfort, Virginia.

For three weeks the complex evaluation went on, through committees and subcommittees and back to committees and back to the main Board. A final recommendation was agreed, and submitted to NASA headquarters. There it was studied by James Webb as well as his two chief deputies, Robert Seamans and Hugh Dryden. The Board was interrogated on its choice. After a seemingly smooth and conventional procedure, Webb announced at the end of November 1961 that negotiations would begin with North American Aviation.

This bald but unexceptionable account was as much as Congress knew of the selection of the Apollo contractor for several years. If all had gone well with North American and its associates, it is unlikely that anything more would ever have been disclosed. No industry going into business with government could ask for a more scrupulous guardian of its privacy than Jim Webb. Not even several billion dollars of public money has altered Webb's conviction that the public has no legitimate interest in knowing about the internal workings of the space agency and its prime contractors. Webb, alone, would have said no more. But all did not go well with the spacecraft. In 1967, a fire in the first manned Apollo killed three astronauts, and in the aftermath Webb was compelled to disclose what for six years he had hidden: namely, that North American had not been the first choice to build Apollo among the 192 experts of the Source Evaluation Board.

Neither this nor the tragedy which exposed it, of course, meant that North American was unqualified to build the most complex vehicle ever conceived. Although the accident was caused by negligence of an impressive order on the part of NASA as well as the contractor, Apollo's later triumphs were to prove that ultimately North American had sufficient competence. Nevertheless, some of Webb's statements when he was finally compelled to divulge the truth cast significant doubt on the streamlined account of events as they appear in NASA's public documents. They provide the best starting-point for an inspection of the way in which the ethereal space program fitted into the habitual pattern of Washington life.

Webb's most suggestive statement was a false one. Soon after the fire, one curious Senator chanced to ask him whether North American had been the first choice of the Source Evaluation Board. Webb replied without hesitation, "Yes. It was the recommended company." He added, in typically fulsome self-defense, that he had since asked members of the Board if they had ever had any doubt about the selection made by Dryden, Seamans and himself, and, Webb said, "No one of them has ever raised a question that we applied the facts that they had so carefully worked up to make the right decision."

Three weeks later, under more detailed questioning, Webb had to retract this bland misstatement—although he was never asked to explain why he had uttered it in the first place. He admitted that North American was not the company recommended by the Board, which had found Martin-Marietta better qualified on several counts.

What happened in 1961 was this. Comparing the technical approach, technical qualifications and business qualifications of the three consortia, the Board rated McDonnell at 6.4, General Electric at 6.4, General Dynamics at 6.6. North American also scored 6.6; Martin-Marietta scored 6.9. But because, taking technical criteria alone, North American was higher than any of the consortia, it emerged as the single competitor to Martin. And the Board found for Martin by a decisive margin. Webb, however, supported (as he constantly emphasized) by Dryden and Seamans, found that the Board had wrongly measured the experience of the two firms, by taking into account not merely the work of the divisions which would build the spacecraft but the output of work companywide. They also felt that Martin had been unduly credited for its work as one of the three companies contracted to produce the 1960 design studies.

Webb therefore ordered the record of each company to be recomputed, with the exclusion of most of Martin's work on missiles and some of North American's rockets and conventional aircraft. On this basis, said Webb, "the ratings became slightly less than two-to-one in favor of North American." In particular, it seems that North American's experience in building the X-15 rocket-aircraft, designed to operate sixty miles above the atmosphere, weighed heavily with the administrator.

There was also the matter of cost. Webb now disclosed that according to the Board North American's proposal would be about 25 percent cheaper than Martin's. It was perhaps an odd criterion to employ on work which, as NASA knew better than anyone, was virtually incapable of being accurately estimated. (The irrelevance of preliminary figures is aptly illustrated by the fact that on its original tender North American put a figure of $400 million, one-ninth of what it was finally worth to them.) Nonetheless, summing up the reasons why the contract was switched to North American, Webb cited the firm's "greater technical competence" and its "lowest cost proposal." He had used his executive right to overrule the Source Evaluation Board, and, after four days' study, to overturn its conclusions.

Belated though it was, this explanation, too, had a plausible engineering logic. Most administrators would argue that it was their job to avoid being dictated to by technicians. Yet there were some unarguable oddities about the choice. It was all very well for Webb to say

that only the relevant division of the prospective contractor should
be evaluated, but North American as a whole was already burdened
with a large piece of the space program which required it to expand
its corporate size at a speed to tax any management. Having already
begun development of the J-2 rocket engines, it had been given a
"directed" or uncontested contract for the second stage of the Saturn.
Apollo would require it to quadruple its payroll within a year, a
problem which not even the X-15 experience had prepared it for.
At least one man was disenchanted with the selection on these grounds.
Just as the contract was sealed, Brainerd Holmes arrived at NASA to
run the Office of Manned Spaceflight, which carried direct executive
responsibility for beating the Russians to the moon. Looking back on
the spacecraft contract now, he says, "It was not a sensible choice."
Holmes felt that Apollo would prove too large a slice of the pork-
barrel even for North American's voracious appetite.

"Pork-barrel" was, in fact, the one element left out of account in
Webb's explanations. It is a term peculiar to American politics
describing a condition which exists there in greater sophistication
than anywhere else. No single synonym does justice to it, but what
it refers to, simply, is government money, available for carving up
between the States and the industries of the Union. Space was a most
generous pork-barrel, with pickings for middlemen as well as prime
contractors. This may not explain why North American got the
contract. But given Jim Webb's Byzantine network of connections in
Washington, it suggests why, in the first place, he attempted to conceal his overruling of the Space Evaluation Board.

Webb was a protégé of Senator Robert Kerr's and he could scarcely
ever forget it. Kerr had recommended him for the top NASA job,
having developed an intimate respect for Webb's organizational
talents. The relationship ripened after Webb had become a director
and "assistant to the president" of Kerr's vast oil and uranium empire,
Kerr-McGee Oil Industries Inc., based in Oklahoma City. Webb had
got to know Washington as director of the Bureau of the Budget and
Under Secretary-of-State in the Truman Administration. When
Eisenhower came to power, Webb, a loyal Democrat, moved West
to join Kerr. This gave him a close acquaintance with oil politics; simul-

taneously, a directorship of the McDonnell Aircraft Company involved him in aerospace.

Throughout the period, Webb made a lot of money, mainly thanks to Kerr. Not only was there oil, there were also banks. The generous Senator had eased Webb's way into a major stockholding in the Fidelity Bank and Trust Co. of Oklahoma City which was, in effect, Kerr-McGee's private bank. When Webb took the NASA job he divested himself of all holdings connected with aerospace. But the Fidelity Bank continued to run his affairs, and as late as May 1962, he still held nearly $800,000 of stock in it, according to a study by the House Banking and Currency Committee.

Kerr himself was not at all distracted from his senatorial duties by his huge business interests. Indeed, he had found early in life that business and politics had a way of getting on very well together. Already the most powerful man in Oklahoma, Kerr became in 1961, after Lyndon Johnson's departure to the vice-presidency, the uncrowned king of the Senate, with cumulatively more muscle at his command than any ten of his colleagues. A huge man, with a rumbling laugh, a passion for gin rummy and an uninhibited enjoyment of power, he held by virtue of longevity crucial positions on a number of important committees. But for a few golden years none was more fruitful than the Space Committee, whose chairmanship was bequeathed to him by Johnson. From this position Kerr ran space politics like everything else he touched, with an eye to the maxim which is his own best epitaph. "I represent myself first," he once declaimed, "the state of Oklahoma second and the people of the United States third, and don't you forget it."

Standing never very far from this legendary senatorial boss when the Apollo contract was in the air was the Washington representative of North American Aviation, Fred B. Black. Black, the son of a dry goods merchant from Carterville, Missouri, had been around the capital for many years. He had been a dry-cleaner salesman and an apprentice cotton-classer as well as holding one or two minor jobs in government departments; but since before the war he had been in business as a lobbyist.

The trade of the lobbyist is everything and anything—public relations man, mediator of influence, broker of power, mercenary at large in the great gray area where politics and commerce intermingle.

Every firm with aspirations to a government contract has to have one. The lobbyist is the man who knows who to go to and how to get things done, or prevent their being done. He is the fixer *par excellence*, and at his best a truly formidable custodian of the pork-barrel. By 1961, Fred B. Black was a very big lobbyist indeed, after small beginnings picking up what he could from insignificant firms seeking a piece of the Second World War. "During the war," Black recalls now, "people like me became part of a thing that was growing and growing. A lot of fly-by-nights came to Washington in those days, the sort of people who sat around hotel lobbies and made remarks about reaching so-and-so for $500. I established myself for two reasons. In those days Washington was a very small town, and the grapevine wasn't so complicated. You became known for what you were able to do, whether you did it correctly or whether you did it with political influence or by paying for that sort of influence. Secondly, I never told anyone I could do anything that I couldn't do."

Quite soon, Fred Black began to make money. It was not so much a matter of crude influence, he shrewdly noted, as of "an *aura* of influence." In Washington the appearance of power was as good as power itself. The prescription for success was deceptively simple and it never changed: "The most worthwhile service you can perform for an organization in the capital," Black says, "is first to know who makes the decision in the case, and second to be able somehow to get enough time to tell your story to that person." Black's description of the way such contacts are effected could serve as any visitor's introduction to the totality of Washington life: "There are several ways you can get the interest of the man who makes the decision. First, you always have the political help that you could ask for from someone you know. There are very few people in the executive departments of government who will refuse to answer a United States Senator's telephone call, or a Congressman's call if he has influence in the House. And one thing that every member of the executive branch loves to hear from a Senator is 'We don't want any favor. We just want you to listen with an open mind.'

"If you know a person, that person knows someone else and introduces you because he likes you. So pretty soon you have a small group of friends and once you meet one group, you meet another. It is just a never-ending daisy-chain."

Among the more brightly blooming daisies in Black's chain when the moon program began was Senator Bob Kerr, chairman of the Senate Space Committee. The lobbyist kept a grand house round the corner from Lyndon Johnson, chairman of the Space Council, but on space contracts Kerr, a Svengali in the lives of many men, was the crucial link to be cultivated by anyone known as Mr. North American in Washington. That was Fred Black's unofficial title, for which he received $230,000 a year to pay his staff and himself; his own cut was $90,000. He believes he certainly earned it. "I was actually a policy adviser," he says. "I handled all the introductions myself. The guidance system for the Minuteman was worth $700–800 million. The B-70 program was worth $700 and some million. The F-108 program was worth an awful lot of money although it was canceled rather early." There was also, many times bigger than all of these, the Apollo program itself.

It is Fred Black's firm contention that the mediation of Senator Kerr played a decisive part in removing the Apollo contract from Martin-Marietta and granting it to North American. Of all the "some-ones" whom Mr. North American could reach, none was bigger than the Senator. Black, like Webb and another equally feline figure, the notorious Bobby Baker, was close to Bob Kerr's affections. He watched the Senator's tentacles reaching out across the capital, and also observed the way North American's success profited the Senator, the Senator's circle and himself, Fred Black. Tactically, the critical point for the lobbyist, as he observed the Source Evaluation Board's findings, was that North American was high on the list: and that Webb, with Dryden and Seamans, had power to change the decision. Ploy 1 of the lobbyist's code was clearly successful: "Know who makes the decision in the case." Ploy 2, reaching him with your own story, was not very difficult for a man with Senator Kerr's support. "I know the usual story about how they switched the contract," Black says. "I know they say it was because we had done so well on the X-15. But from my own point of view I think it was a little more practical, a little more political. I think Mr. Kerr asked for it to be done that way."

Not unexpectedly, Jim Webb always insists that Kerr's opinion influenced him no more than that of any other Senator. "A lot of Senators and Congressmen talked to me about the Apollo contract," he has said. "I was willing to talk to everyone about it. There are a lot of people who have tried to give the impression that I was not independent, and that I was in Senator Kerr's pocket because I had worked for the Kerr-McGee enterprises." But, Webb added, he had worked only part-time for Kerr-McGee in the year before he became NASA's administrator.

Since the Senator has been dead since 1963, it may never be possible to measure exactly the influence he exerted on North American's behalf. But two facts are unmistakably clear. One is that the blessings which descended on Bob Kerr in the wake of North American's success were, as will be seen, mightily bountiful, proving that it was not merely science, technology or national prestige which would profit from the moon. Secondly, the breadth of the Senator's influence was so great that it would scarcely be nullified simply by a part-time association with him. To those whose lives he had touched the Senator was not a friend so much as a constant presence. As a wielder of patronage he was one of the few modern politicians who matched the Duke of Newcastle, the renowned purchaser of governments in eighteenth-century England. Not even Presidents could ignore him, let alone executives dependent every year on his committee for money to stay in business.

Fred Black tells a story which nicely illustrates the point. It concerns, almost inevitably, a bridge. After dams, bridges are the commonest small change of Washington. This particular bridge was in Poteau, Oklahoma—Kerr territory. It was Kerr's bridge, which meant automatically that it was not the bridge of Kerr's only rival for power in Oklahoma, Governor Edmundson, John Kennedy's chief lieutenant in the area. It was also a bridge which connected no roads at the time it was built. Shortly before the bridge was completed, Kerr announced that it would be dedicated by President Kennedy. Whereupon Governor Edmundson, who had fought many a battle for Kennedy against Kerr during the presidential election, flew to Hyannisport in a fury to talk the President out of it. But Kennedy gave him a political lesson. "I'll tell you why I'm doing it," he said. "I'm going down to dedicate that bridge and kiss Bob Kerr's ass." Kerr could make or break a series of Kennedy's measures and that was enough for the President.

According to Black, Kerr was equally explicit in the terms he laid down to North American: "He asked me if we, North American, wanted the Apollo program. Then he said, 'If you get it, what can North American do for Oklahoma?' And I told him that I'd put plants in Oklahoma to build parts of Apollo or other type of work, so that Oklahoma would have less unemployment."

After getting the contract, North American duly did provide some jobs for Oklahomans. But much the most striking evidence of the watchful relations with the Senator maintained in this cause by Webb and the space agency is to be found in a snatch of conversation which took place within weeks of the Senator's death. It is recorded in the files of the Federal Bureau of Investigation. On February 11, 1963, the Bureau, then investigating Baker, tapped Black's telephone in a Washington hotel and listened to an exchange between Black and Dean McGee, the surviving half of Kerr-McGee Industries. The Senator's body is hardly cold, and already the lobbyist is worried by the turn NASA's decisions seem to be taking. Proposals put forward by North American for siting plants in the state are evidently not receiving from NASA quite the attentive co-operation of the old days.

Black is apologizing to McGee for the recession this may threaten to the economy of Oklahoma. "Two things," Black says. "First of all, since the old man died, this fellow Webb has gotten weaker and weaker where the State of Oklahoma is concerned. We sent them [NASA] several things before the Senator died—OK—when we got them back and got back an OK on a third of what we wanted to put there. He's just not going to do anything for us. I'm getting concerned about a few things in Oklahoma City itself. NASA is not helping us. When the Senator was alive, he'd be helping."

"I want you to know," Black concludes, "North American and Fred Black aren't backing up one inch."

There were not only jobs for Oklahomans. Before the Senator died, there was also profit for himself to be thought of. It just so happened, for example, that his company owned some unused land outside the second city of the state, Tulsa. The land lay along the course of a proposed navigation canal for which Kerr had conducted a long battle in an attempt to link Tulsa with the Mississippi River, thus greatly improving the commercial prospects of the city. Soon after Apollo began, part of this land was leased on option to a company planning to lay down plant in the city for manufacturing space hardware. The hardware in question was for the Apollo spacecraft, and the company, of course, was North American Aviation.

Still more profits from the moon accrued to the Senator's circle through the activities of his most notorious protégé, Bobby Baker. Baker was nominally the secretary to the Senate Democratic Majority. In practice he was the personal political leg-man of the Democratic Leader, originally Lyndon Johnson, who once described Baker as "my strong right arm . . . the last man I see at night, the first I speak to in the morning." When Johnson moved to the vice-presidency, Baker passed to Kerr, for whom, according to Black, he played an even more versatile anatomical role: "Kerr loved Baker, Bobby was his ears, eyes, nose, throat, hands and feet in the Senate. Kerr was dedicated to making Baker a millionaire, the same as he'd made Jim Webb a millionaire."

Kerr's gift to Baker was less obvious than the debt he imposed on Webb. Webb has been given a lucrative, but orthodox, job. Baker was given influence and openings, and he knew how to exploit them, as he had done under Johnson. Often the deals Baker got himself into grew well beyond the space program. But a significant number of them began with Kerr and the fact that North American had somehow won the Apollo prize. They show very clearly the truth of the Senator's maxim: whoever profited from them, it was not the people of the United States.

The first public awareness of the fall-out quietly raining upon selected private citizens from the Apollo contract began to dawn two years after North American's bid was accepted. The owner of a firm dealing in vending-machines, Capitol Vending Company, issued a writ against Baker, his lawyer Ernest Tucker and Fred Black. The writ alleged that Baker, Tucker and Black had obtained for Capitol the concession to place its vending-machines, selling food, drinks and cigarettes, in the plant of one of North American's small subcontractors, Melpar Inc.; and that the three men had later had Capitol removed from Melpar when Capitol's chairman refused to sell his business to them.

Capitol's suit stated a grave charge, which raised uncomfortable questions, not least for North American. Referring to a company owned by Baker, Tucker and Black—Serv-U Inc., another vending-machine operation—the suit said, in part, "As partial return for the services performed by Fred Black and Robert G. Baker, North American entered into an agreement to permit Serv-U to install vending-machines in its plants in California." Subsequently, the suit went on: "Fred Black and Baker assisted in securing contracts between Melpar and North American. In partial return, Melpar has agreed to enter into an agreement with a vending-machine operation in which the defendants, Fred Black and Robert G. Baker, have a financial interest."

In addition, Capitol complained, Baker had demanded money for putting them into Melpar in the first place. Capitol's chairman said Baker originally asked for $1000 a month; this was reduced by hard bargaining, but in seventeen months Capitol had still paid the Secretary to the Senate Democratic Majority $5600.

The case set Washington alight, and ultimately put the Senate in the distasteful position of having to investigate the affairs of one of its own employees; and also, by implication, those of one of its members, Senator Kerr, lately dead. In the course of this investigation, more of the consequences of Apollo seeped into the public realm. It emerged, for example, that Serv-U Inc. had been formed by Baker and some friends, and that Black had been given cheap shares in it on the understanding that he would help Serv-U into North American. This he very quickly did. Serv-U's first contract with North American was signed only three months after NASA had allocated Apollo. Within the year, the existing holder of the vending-machine concession had been ruthlessly ousted from all North American plants, and more than forty thousand employees were buying their lunch from Baker-Black machines.

Tucker's name had been used to conceal the interest of Baker and Black, and before the Senate investigators, North American's chairman, Lee Atwood, and its public relations chief, Leland Taylor, both denied on oath any knowledge of Black's large financial stake in the vending firm he successfully pressed upon them. Black's recollection is somewhat different, and accords more convincingly with the removal of a franchise-holder whose performance had, so the company records say, been "completely satisfactory." "Lee Taylor certainly knew about my connection," Black says. "As a matter of fact I carried on Serv-U's business at North American in Mr. Taylor's office with him sitting beside me."

One man who unquestionably knew the truth about Serv-U's stake in North American was Senator Kerr. According to Black, it was the Senator's idea in the first place: "Baker had talked to Bob Kerr about his new company and Kerr, who wanted to make Baker a rich man, suggested that he talk to me about it with the idea of perhaps getting him into North American for vending." Kerr backed this suggestion very forcefully. In a sworn statement to the Senate, Black disclosed that the money to finance the huge vending undertaking was supplied by the Fidelity National Bank in Oklahoma, the one in which the tireless Senator had large interests, after a single telephone call from Kerr to the bank's President while Black was sitting beside the Senator. In time Black and Serv-U borrowed over half a million dollars from the Fidelity National, often with no security—other, perhaps, than Black's infallible reputation, where the space program was concerned, for turning business and politics into a profitable combination.

Kerr presided over these mushrooming outgrowths from Apollo with the benign pleasure of the impresario. His reasoning has a universal validity: he wanted to remain ahead of all his clients in the favors game, always ensuring that they owed more to him than he owed them. "He always did more for other people than he asked other people to do for him," says Black. "It was his philosophy, and naturally it did put people in his debt."

Probably the most startling favor Kerr ever did Fred Black, after Apollo was safely in North American's hands, was to teach him how to buy a piece of a bank for himself. The tale has all the expansiveness for which Washington has never forgotten the most generous chairman the Senate Space Committee ever had. "He invited me round to his office," Black remembers, "and we played some gin rummy. Then he asked me if I'd like a bank. He told me to write a check for $175,000. When I said I didn't have it, he said he hadn't asked me that. He told me to write the check on the Fidelity National in Oklahoma City and then he took out a private telephone from his bottom drawer and called the Bank President. He told him he had a new customer for the bank, and that the bank had just loaned me $180,000 and that I was giving him a check and a note simultaneously. With that he instructed the bank to buy 10 percent of the stock in the Farmers' and Merchants' State Bank in Tulsa and to forward it to me. And that was how I bought my way into the Farmers' and Merchants'. I'd borrowed the money, bought the stock, and then put up the stock to secure the original loan. It makes sense if you look at it long enough."

It made sense to Fred Black, and likewise to the Farmers' and Merchants' Bank. The accounts held with it began to grow, notably those maintained by Kerr-McGee. Also counted among them was the business put down on Kerr-McGee's land near the proposed navigation canal in Tulsa: the main Oklahoma outpost of North American Aviation, and the living evidence that the aerospace giant from California stood ready to do its duty by the chairman of the Senate Aeronautical and Space Sciences Committee.

No one remotely familiar with Washington can suppose that this kind of activity flourished just because North American got Apollo. One fact might have changed: had the Source Evaluation Board's recommendation been accepted, Martin-Marietta would have got the contract. But a number of other facts would not have changed. Bob Kerr would still have been chairman of the Space Committee, still an addict of power, still a shameless collector of money, admirers and jobs for Oklahoma. Nothing would have altered the fact that it was he whom NASA had to satisfy, and he who had done much for the career of NASA's top man, Jim Webb. Through their attachment to Kerr, Webb and Baker would still have known each other, and Fred Black, it can be said with some confidence, would not have faded from the Washington scene. The Kerr court was formed, and its leading courtiers defined, without the assistance of North American. Any other company with designs on the moon would have had to take account of that.

But the Baker investigation gave the American public its first glimpse of the underbelly of the space business. North American, as the prime contractor, was touched at a sensitive point. It had obeyed the political rules, and been found out. Immediately, it invoked another well-tried principle: instead of the corporation suffering, a scapegoat would be found. Fred Black was fired from the payroll.

The lobbyist's next few years were to be spent in a welter of court cases; he brought a $9 million suit against North American for breach of contract, and in turn was prosecuted by the federal government for income tax evasion. The sacking was an act of remarkable hypocrisy. It is clear enough that senior executives of the company knew very well of Black's connection with Serv-U and his simultaneous employment by at least two rival outfits in the aerospace industry—the pretexts on which he was removed. But more than that, Black's entire operation in Washington had been dedicated, with enormous success, to the corporation's benefit. The point was well made by a judge who tried Black for tax evasion. "It sounds," said Judge John Sirica of the United States District Court in Washington, "as if these companies are making Mr. Black the scapegoat to cover up their own slimy trail. If these companies hired this man to do their dirty work, they should be here in the courtroom with him."

Black, after a lifetime of Washington, is a little more philosophical. His tax conviction was thrown out by the Supreme Court on the grounds that evidence obtained by wire-tapping is not admissible. He is still not welcome in the smoke-filled rooms on Capitol Hill, but he is back in business, with a permanent suite at one of the most expensive hotels in New York City. Far from being defensive or apologetic, he sees the building of Apollo by his old employers as a supreme example of the well-oiled business of democracy. "North American was five times as large as Martin," he reflects happily, "so when they got the contract you had five times as many happy people as you had unhappy people. That's democracy in its finest form."

It is a plausible thesis: more plausible, certainly, than the NASA thesis that space was conquered in a political vacuum. The machinations of Kerr and his friends illustrate the cardinal point that the completion of the moon program was as dependent as the decision to begin it on the emollient power of politics, Washington-style. The first year of the mission to the moon saw the biggest outpouring of government money in the history of the civilian economy—the first stage of the Saturn V booster to Boeing, the third stage to Douglas, the advanced Saturn I to Chrysler, the lunar module to Grumman, as well as the Apollo and the second stage of Saturn V to North American. From these prime contractors flowed a stream of subcontracts which spread the money and the jobs from California and the Deep South around the nation. If a single bridge can represent patronage enough to send Governors flying to Presidents, what can be expected of a pork-barrel as large as space?

Many more instances of the power of the moon to move business as surely as it moves the tides could be exhumed from the early years. But one shows more graphically than any other that politics, whether or not it was manipulated by Bob Kerr, was capable sometimes of overriding even the most manifest technical imperative. In the case of North American, the technical case was at least arguable. In the selection of Houston, Texas, as the command headquarters for the moon journey, it was unambiguously empty. Of all the earthly artifacts of the moon, Houston will surely stand as the most impressive monument to the political context of the enterprise.

The space agency had already selected Cape Canaveral (now Cape Kennedy), on the ragged tip of the Florida peninsula, as the launch site for moon rockets. The acreage it owned there was far more than it needed for anything short of the day when jumbo spaceliners set off for the planets. The Cape could very easily accommodate the spacecraft and command center as well, with obvious benefits to smooth management and intimate co-ordination. But that was too simple a solution. It would overload Florida with installations which other states and their Senators would bitterly envy. NASA therefore dispatched a team of officials to find a site outside Florida which combined a permanently sunny climate, access to the sea and a large labor force with an atmosphere which would be culturally attractive to scientists.

The team searched the nation from Boston to Seattle, but nobody had much doubt that it would quickly succumb to the attractions of Texas. Lyndon Johnson had not lost his interest in the place. More strikingly, the Congressman in charge of the appropriations subcommittee with responsibility for space funding was Albert Thomas, and Albert Thomas was a power in the city of Houston. To risk the capricious stubbornness of Thomas when so obvious a method of soothing him existed would have been the depth of folly; it might have impeded the entire course of the space program. It was not long, therefore, before Administrator Webb announced that a squashy tract of land twenty miles south-east of Houston and one thousand miles from Cape Kennedy had been chosen as the site for the Manned Spacecraft Center.

Thomas's constancy ever afterward was only one of the ramifications of this decision. Whichever site had been chosen, someone would have made money from it, and in the case of Clear Lake City, as the space municipality came to be known, the beneficiary was the powerful Humble Oil Company. For the sake of appearances, some attempt was made to conceal Humble's participation in the business. The land was said to be a gift from Rice University in Houston, a donor who endowed the space program with a suitable modicum of scientific respectability. But in fact Rice itself had received the land as a gift, from Humble; and Humble had imposed a condition that the gift would be void if NASA did not settle there. It was Humble, moreover, which most obviously profited: its gift was not so much a donation as an investment with a swiftly increasing yield. For to Humble the site provided for the Manned Spacecraft Center was only a fraction of the land it owned in the vicinity. When the moon men moved to Clear Lake City, they settled on Humble land and lived in communities developed by Humble, which have never ceased to rise in value.

This is very satisfactory to the Humble Oil Company. But one feature common to the choice both of Clear Lake City and of North American, apart from their political penumbra, was that neither brought unflawed benefits to the moon program. Before Americans landed on the moon, in fact, both decisions were to contribute to the space age's most avoidable disaster.

The part played by North American in the capsule fire in which three astronauts died is well established. It is described in a later chapter. As the race to the moon accelerated, the company's performance deteriorated so badly that NASA might have had grounds to consider replacing it as the builder of Apollo.

Rather less well-known is the contribution which Houston, situated so far from the scene, made to the tragedy. When the illogicality of Houston is raised with NASA officials now, they can be persuaded to admit the part played by the late Albert Thomas, but they do not agree that it has made any difference to the space program. The conventional view is that Houston is as good a place as any other, and has proved very agreeable. But a little-noticed passage in the investigations which followed the fire reveals a harsher truth. Here the chairman of the official board of inquiry attributes some of the errors which led to the disaster to "the interface between the Manned Spacecraft Center and the Kennedy Spaceflight Center." Some duties tended to slip between the interface. Sometimes neither center knew where its responsibility ended and the other's began. A few things, as North American's space chief, Harrison "Stormy" Storms, feared, got "forgotten."

With great delicacy, the chairman of the inquiry, perhaps torn by the fact that he was a NASA employee himself, designated the problem as one of "cumbersomeness." To the colleagues of Gus Grissom, Ed White and Roger Chaffee, who died, that may have sounded a little inadequate. The astronaut's life was hard enough already. He had been chosen and trained for unknown danger; his life was dedicated to the improbable feat of representing the human race on the moon. He made personal sacrifices and suffered professional tortures enough without being exposed to further careless and unnecessary hazards. To the astronauts preparing for their own flights into space, death by cumbersome management must have seemed a high price to pay for politics.

8.

Bureaucrat
Heroes

Long before NASA was sent to the moon, it had chosen the men who would go there. Man, in the space agency's eyes, had always been the critical item in the cargo. Scientifically his presence might have limited value. Technically it would multiply by ten the complexity, and the cost, of the exercise; for although man was the best computer in the world he was also the most vulnerable machine, and he had to be guaranteed a safe return. Nevertheless he was what the romance of the moon, and hence its political value, was all about. It was of him and not machines that people dreamed when they contemplated the occupation of another planet. NASA knew this when it was making its own secret plans, and it prepared accordingly. Kennedy endorsed it when he launched Apollo. If prestige was the quest, man alone could bring it.

But what kind of man would it be? By what combination of cells and reflexes would this new breed of creature, the astronaut, be identified? What kind of life should he have led before, that it would qualify him for the freakish work of moving out of his natural environment and inhabiting the alien world of space? Once chosen, what could prepare him for hazards which could never all be anticipated?

Like so much else on the journey to Tranquility, the configuration of the astronaut was fixed in the early days. When NASA was working out the methods by which he would be selected, trained, tested and preserved at the beginning of the decade, it was settling a pattern which would survive essentially to the end. The men might come and go; the idiosyncrasies might be different; the shaping of human fallibility into mechanical perfection might become steadily more refined. But the basic stereotype would remain as NASA first defined it.

When the space agency began looking for astronauts at the end of the 1950s it defined the sort of man it wanted as between twenty-five and forty years old, less than five feet eleven inches tall, in perfect physical condition, willing to accept hazards "comparable to those encountered in modern research airplane flight," and able to react adequately under conditions of stress. Originally that was the complete profile. It might be filled, NASA thought, by a multitude of well-motivated people, including mountaineers, scuba divers, balloonists and polar explorers as well as test pilots. The moon planners were anxious only to exclude the mentally disturbed; they stipulated that applicants should be sponsored by some responsible organization.

But the field was later limited by President Eisenhower, who ruled that selection must be confined to test pilots, and military test pilots at that. He thought it the best way to ensure that the classified details of the space program remained secret. This decision, typically inconsistent with Eisenhower's insistence on a civilian-run space program, narrowed NASA's scope but greatly simplified its task. Military men did not need to volunteer: they could be drafted. And that, curiously, is how the preliminary selection was made. The records of over 500 military test pilots on file in Washington were scrutinized, and 110 men were told they had been nominated for service in space. Happily, very few of them demurred. After a series of written examinations and medical tests, thirty-two went forward to the final inquisition.

What followed was probably the most rigorous physical inspection ever made of any collection of human bodies. The heart, brain, metabolism and senses of every candidate were charted in the finest detail. They were subjected to every kind of stress which doctors and engineers could invent: tests of each man's ability to sustain extreme acceleration, extreme vibration, extreme noise, heat and cold, tests by loud noise, tests by spinning and tumbling until they were sick with dizziness. Endurance was proved on treadmills, on tilt-tables which suspend the blood circulation to the point of heart failure, with balloons which had to be blown up to the point of exhaustion. There were also, at a rudimentary level, tests of personality. "Who am I?" the candidate was invited conscientiously to answer. "Why do I want to go into space?"

All this was surprisingly unhelpful. The candidates were in such impeccable condition that they proved impossible to rank in order of performance. Of the eighteen who came out equal first in bodily and mental perfection, seven were selected. But the decisive criteria reverted to their technical qualifications. These were laid down, on a pattern which was to endure throughout the decade, by a committee dominated not by doctors but by engineers. Two engineers, Charles Donlan and Warren North, worked with a single flight surgeon to identify the men who could be expected to augment the machines most faultlessly—as well as satisfy military sensitivities. Originally the seven were meant to be six; and officially the reason for the increase was said to be that no six could be found who excelled over the seventh. A more plausible explanation, given the plenitude of talent, is that seven made a neat equation: three from the air force, three from the navy and one from the marines.

Shepard, Glenn, Grissom, Schirra, Cooper, Carpenter and Slayton were names out of any telephone directory, albeit one with an obvious imbalance of Anglo-Saxons. The more recent strains of immigrant American were not represented, nor were Negroes. These men were slightly shorter than the average American male, and fitter in every respect. But they were in the main the epitome of the clean-limbed WASP.

Captain Yossarian, the anti-hero of Joseph Heller's classic examination of the military condition, *Catch-22*, would surely have deemed them mad. But if they knew that space flight was mad then, like the unfortunate Yossarian, that very perception certified them as sane. They knew with utter clarity the risks which were entailed. Coldly and without doubt they wished to undertake them, to travel, as Wally Schirra nonchalantly said, "higher, farther and faster" than was previously possible. They were professional aviators who had flown many hundreds of hours in advanced aircraft and did not want to be left behind on an old frontier.

But the Original Seven, as they inevitably became, were more than superb pilots. They were the founder members of a new and exclusive brotherhood, for which staid military routine scarcely provided a clear body of rules. They were recognized instantly by press and public as a new species of hero, and this fact was not lost on them. Although NASA, with its tradition of faceless triumph, did not at first approve, nothing could be done to prevent this. Soon, in fact, the agency came to see the value, as well as the penalties, of possessing ready-made public figures who would form the emotional connection between the space program and the nation. It was not long before the Original Seven astronauts began to whet the American appetite in much the same way as the royal family whets the British.

Lurid stories about the training these awesome figures underwent became instant folklore. Some of them were true. There were, for example, prolonged sessions in the centrifuge, a whirling arm on which the astronaut could be accelerated at a rate as high as 16gs. "Even lying down," wrote John Glenn after one such experience, "it took just about every bit of strength and technique you could muster to retain consciousness." Another centrifuge inflicted not merely acceleration but simultaneous rotation in three axes at once. The first astronaut to set foot in one of these, Alan Shepard, quickly turned green and pressed the "chicken switch" to signal it to stop.

More noise, vibration and orientation tests were devised, but this time their purpose was not, as it had been earlier, to sort out the men from the supermen. The chosen seven now had to teach themselves how to continue performing efficiently in the buffeting conditions which might be expected in rocket-powered flight. Through simulator training, they slowly prepared themselves for the ordeal of capsule life. Academic studies were not so popular, but the new and wide-ranging field of space science had to be absorbed by the men who were to use it at closest quarters. Likewise, regular visits to the factories where their craft were being put together became a more normal part of life than it had been for any conventional aircraft pilot.

In every respect, therefore, the seven astronauts chosen for the leap into space were given the attention due to celebrities who had volunteered for almost unimaginable danger. The final accolade, proof that they would be showbiz legends as well as nerveless technicians, was an exclusive contract with *Life* magazine for their "personal stories." *Life* got the contract not only because it was the highest bidder —$500,000 split between the seven of them—but also proved a thoroughly reliable image-builder. Given the *Life* treatment, astronauts have emerged from the beginning as lovable freckled heroes with sons in the college football team: reassuring commercials for white teeth, God and baseball hats.

The only trouble with *Life*'s interpretation was the lack of life it breathed into its subjects. There was also much irritation among other reporters, who took a dim view of the astronauts' doors being banged in their faces when the American taxpayer was spending $24,000 million to get to the moon. But that was a minor problem by comparison with the fact that all astronauts began to sound alike: machine-men, cheerfully facing torture, danger and perhaps death for their country.

In fact this picture did them little justice. Some of the Original Seven astronauts were far more interesting than that. As test pilots, they were uniquely well qualified for work which demanded bravery, stability, endurance, team spirit and a sharp mind in blurred conditions. But they were also flesh and blood. As the space program developed, they disproved the science fiction that they were robots programed to live and work like expensive machines.

Of the seven, only three remained with the space program as far as the moon, and only one of these, Alan Shepard, was still a fully operational space man. Another, Donald K. "Deke" Slayton, a tigerish Air Force captain, proved after only four months as an astronaut that the extraordinary trials he had survived were not quite rigorous enough; he was grounded with a murmuring heart, and given an office job as director of flight-crew operations. Well before the last assault began, Slayton was to acquire great authority, especially over crew-selection, but he never quite got over his displeasure at the doctors' refusal to let him go into space himself. The third survivor was another Air Force man, Gordon Cooper, who flew longer in Mercury than any of them but whose taste for racing cars was said to have relegated him below junior men in the race for seats to the moon: it is one of the many frustrating facts of astronautic life that there are always more men than flights to send them on.

The other four came to very different ends. One of them, Gus Grissom, died in the notorious capsule fire. Two, John Glenn from the marines and Wally Schirra from the navy, left to go into business, Schirra being so anxious to get out that he even spurned the exotic chance of being the first admiral-astronaut. He became president of a company formed in Denver, Colorado, to lease industrial equipment. Glenn, untempted by the prospect of being what he calls "the world's oldest permanent used astronaut," left soon after his first and only flight, and later became president of Royal Crown Cola International in New York. Finally, there was Malcolm Scott Carpenter, the handsomest man of them all but the only one who made a human hash of his flight. Carpenter eventually left space for the ocean deep, to become a pioneering navy aquanaut.

It was not only at the end of the decade that these men went different ways. From the moment they joined NASA, they were divisible into subgroups. United in dedication and well-tested skills, they were singularly different in character. If there were archetypes, these were most clearly personified by Alan Shepard and John Glenn.

Shepard and Glenn were equal but opposite embodiments of what America demanded of her astronauts. Shepard, a tough, prickly character, had the timeless arrogance of the fanatical pioneer. He was remote and untouchable, in the way one kind of hero ought to be. John Glenn was a hero of different stamp: the sincere all-American boy next door, the kind of man whom the people could easily admire and with whom they and their sons could identify as some kind of Ideal. This earned Glenn the derisive title "Mr. Klean" among some of his colleagues, after the glowing character in a series of detergent commercials. But he had his disciples too, notably Scott Carpenter, for whom, according to one NASA official, he served "as a sort of mother-and-father figure." A mutual distaste developed between these two on the one hand and men like Deke Slayton and Gus Grissom, men in the Shepard mold, on the other.

The rivalry between Shepard and Glenn was woven right through the decade of the moon. It began when Shepard, not Glenn, was judged to possess the slightly greater reliability for the first, the most hazardous, American spaceflight. It continued as Glenn became the first authentic hero of the space age, after performing the first orbital flight; when NASA laid on a ticker-tape parade for Glenn in New York, Shepard and Gus Grissom were less than happy. At the end of the decade, when President Johnson gave a dinner for astronauts past and present after the first orbital moon flight, Glenn was omitted from the company. One convincing explanation of his absence was that plans for the White House junket were shaped in Houston, in the office of the chief of all the fifty-two practicing astronauts, Alan Shepard.

Much can be learned about the temptations and demands of the astronautic life from a closer look at the careers of these two men. For although they were very different characters and positively hostile to each other's outlook, they had a similar understanding of one large fact which is common to all astronauts: the fact that they are exceptional people doing an exceptional job.

Three years after that first momentous flight, Alan Shepard was grounded, as Deke Slayton had been, by a physical disability. He was found to be suffering from Ménière's Syndrome, a condition of the inner ear which causes dizziness and nausea. For a time it prevented him from flying even aircraft, let alone a spaceship.

This did not, however, make Shepard any less of a celebrity. None of the Original Seven were unaware of their scarcity value, but no one saw more clearly than Shepard that the dollars from *Life* magazine need not be the only commercial result. Soon after reaching Houston, he had found himself a patron, later to become a business partner, named Bill McDavid.

McDavid was a self-made Texan car dealer whose Oldsmobile dealership, the third largest in the world, supplied all the early astronauts with cost-price cars. McDavid is now dead, but his nephew, Dan Boone, who took over the business, put the matter succinctly: "Mr. McDavid was very good at capitalizing on opportunities, not on people but opportunities."

In Shepard, McDavid evidently saw a longer-term opportunity. Their meeting is well remembered by Boone. His account, given against the background of a tall neon rocket unceasingly launching and aborting its flight over the freeway traffic, nicely catches the kind of atmosphere, reminiscent of Gold Rush days in the Yukon, which developed in Houston as the astronauts moved into town.

"Right after Shepard made his flight," Boone says, "it became known they were moving NASA to Houston. The astronauts stayed at the Rice Hotel and naturally they got to know a lot of people, including the sales manager of the hotel who introduced Bill to Alan Shepard.

"First time I ever met him, Uncle Bill had invited him out to a barbecue. Uncle Bill called me and says, 'Dan, bring the kids. We're having Alan Shepard out here. You may never see him again. Here's a guy just been in space, and incidentally bring your camera.'"

"We didn't know whether we'd get to know him after that or not," Boone added. "But later there were two or three other parties that involved all the Original Seven. Course, we knew *him* best because he later became a business partner of Uncle Bill."

Shepard's career as the part-time Midas of space travel really began when McDavid decided to take over a bank in Daytown, Texas. "Mr. McDavid was smart enough," Boone said, "to know Alan wanted to get in on the same kind of financial matter, so he brought him in. Shepard, of course, had some notoriety and this was a situation where they had to be careful not to capitalize on his public image."

But the name Shepard proved mysteriously magnetic. "At the time he went into the business the First National Bank in Daytown had reporters from *Life* and *Time* and, hell, television cameras and the whole works. So they immediately got public notoriety for their bank and they had stock offers and people writing from all over the country wanting to buy stock. So that was a $20 million bank in Daytown and to cut a long story short all of them recently made a *ton* of money out of it. I know Uncle Bill made half a million dollars at least."

Shepard's bank dealings grew a little complicated, if quite different from those of Fred Black and Senator Kerr. At one point he and Lee Brazefield, President of the Daytown bank, bought a controlling interest in the Fidelity Bank and Trust Company in Houston, which they later sold to McDavid. The chief astronaut subsequently sold his interest in the Daytown bank, but retains an important role in a company formed to build its grand new headquarters. With McDavid he also bought a $200,000 private plane, and before the old man died they used to fly off together to conventions of the National Automobile Dealers in Detroit and Las Vegas. Another expanding interest was the oil business: an enterprise Shepard was involved in had the remarkable luck to strike four wet holes out of six drilled.

All this sounds far removed from the dedicated world of the astronauts. But Shepard did more than enliven his NASA desk work by accumulating a small fortune on the side. He kept himself in trim for a future flight which only he thought he would make; and he dug himself deeply into the space agency's hierarchy, dominating his colleagues by force of character, alarming them with his

rudeness, pleasing them with opportunities to buy cost-price Olds-
mobiles.

Behind his back he was still Professor Al, from the early days at
press conferences when he insisted on fielding all the questions,
leaving his fellow astronauts (at the best of times never a loquacious
crowd) sitting in dumb rows behind him. He wore his authoritative
chainmail without much humor, and seemed impervious to jibes. In
1962, for example, when the second group of astronauts was being
introduced to the press, Mercury public relations chief, Shorty
Powers, first presented the Original Seven in reverse order of their
flights. Coming at last to Shepard, Powers said, "And finally this is
Alan Shepard, the man who's been screaming for years 'But I was
first.'" The audience roared with laughter but Shepard stared back at
them with a face of stone.

In the end, however, the laugh was on everyone but Shepard. A
Christian Scientist who cursed the medical profession, he spent six
years refusing to accept a disease which, he was told, would eventually make him deaf and make it difficult for him to keep his balance.
Then suddenly he slipped away for an operation and returned to
Houston cured. In May 1969, he got himself put back on flight status.
Not many months later he was named to command Apollo 14. With
two novice astronauts, this extraordinary man with only fifteen minutes
of suborbital flight behind him—and that nine years before—would
make America's fourth flight to the moon, sometime in 1970.

Shepard, at forty-seven, would be the oldest man on the moon. He
would also be the first millionaire. And at least in his ambition for
money he had something in common with John Glenn. They set
about accumulating it, however, in different ways. Whereas Shepard
stayed in the program, his talents being well suited to the larger-than-
life risk-takers of Texas, Glenn moved north to the polished society
of the East Coast, there to make his own fortune. He was NASA's
most durable ambassador, the perfect image of middle-class American manhood; he also proved to be an effective envoy for the soft
drinks business, orbiting thirty-four countries in three years with
some very effective sales talk.

Glenn's remoteness from many of his colleagues was founded on a
marked combination of hauteur and sensitivity. Temperamentally he
was a loner in a job which demanded teamwork, and Shepard was

not the only man he clashed with. Wally Schirra, perhaps the most independent-minded of all the Original Seven, felt after his six-orbit Mercury flight that Glenn had been ignoring him and refusing to cooperate. He said as much to a reporter, and when the news appeared Glenn went away and began filling page after page with notes, apparently making a list of all the things he could say in public about Schirra. Glenn called it his "don't-push-me-too-far" speech and kept it in his inside pocket, which he patted menacingly whenever he watched Schirra get up to address an audience.

Politics was one of Glenn's ambitions. When he left the program early in 1964, he set out to run for the Senate from his home state, Ohio. After his heroic orbital flight, he had been taken up by both President Kennedy and Robert Kennedy, and this connection proved more enduring than his own political fortunes. Three weeks after beginning his campaign he knocked himself out by slipping in the bathroom, an accident from which it took him a year to recover. But when Robert Kennedy was assassinated in Los Angeles in 1968, Glenn was there. It was he who broke the news to some of the Senator's children before taking them home.

Now, comfortably installed as the president of Royal Crown Cola International, Glenn remembers with some bewilderment the furor created by the transactions of the Original Seven. These were managed by a lawyer named Leo De Orsey, who did the job without fee. "Leo," Glenn said recently, "thought we might be able to keep some of the *Life* magazine money together and invest it as a group and do better than if we went off and made a little investment of our own. Most of us wanted a guarantee that we could keep enough of it and give the children a decent college education when the time came.

"So Leo did look into a number of things. We took some of the money and had a part interest in an apartment house in Washington. And we had a hotel at the Cape, just a very small interest in it. But then there got to be such a hue and cry, although *we* didn't feel there was anything wrong in it. But it was felt we were trying to get favored treatment at the Cape and that we were insisting people stay at our motel, though no one did that, of course."

Another deal misfired rather more comically. As if to excel Bill McDavid and his automobiles, a Houston property speculator, Frank Sharp, offered the Original Seven free houses in his new suburban development called the Sharpstown. According to Glenn, the Houston Home-Builders Association was making the $245,000 gift out of the goodness of its collective heart. "Leo stewed over this one for a couple of weeks," he says, "trying to get some official advice. He couldn't get it, so he accepted the offer on our behalf and then the roof fell in and everyone who'd been noncommittal jumped on Leo's back."

The offer was torpedoed, unwittingly, by John Glenn himself. He was sent to Washington to put the astronauts' case for accepting the property before a small committee convened at NASA headquarters. Glenn made a formidable case, according to another man who was present, and as the committee wrestled with this compelling problem all day he seemed to be winning his point. Only at the very end did someone naïvely inquire what the astronauts intended to do with their Sharpstown homes. "Well," said Glenn, "we don't intend to live in them, because they're too far away from the Center. We'd reckon to keep them a year and then sell them."

The Original Seven had to give up their $35,000 homes. They had, however, one peculiarly valid reason for wishing to make the future safe for their families. Private investment was the only kind of insurance they could buy. The best premium any astronaut was ever to be quoted was $360 a month, or a quarter of his official earnings, for cover of $70,000—and that was only after NASA had demonstrated over many years the validity of its claim that flying a spacecraft was at least as safe as flying a jet plane.

At the beginning, the cost of insurance was immensely steeper. Before Glenn's first orbital flight, De Orsey tried every company without success before finishing up with an offer—"I think it was from Lloyd's of London," says Glenn—of $100,000 cover for the four-and-half-hour flight at a premium of no less that $16,000. In the end, De Orsey himself grandly wrote a $100,000 check for Glenn's wife in case he did not come back. Congressman Albert Thomas once tried to pass a bill setting up a special insurance fund for the astronauts, until it was pointed out to him that soldiers in the fields of southeast Asia were taking equal risks without insurance.

Spaceflight did get safer after the early years of the Original Seven, and in any case insurance was eventually included in the arrangement with *Life* magazine, joined now by an equally munificent literary contract with World Books. Other things, too, began to change on the astronautic front. As new groups of men entered the program, subtle mutations were observable in the breed.

The selection process was still dominated by engineers; Charles Donlan and Warren North, who had made the final choice of the Original Seven, never concealed their suspicion of psychiatric criteria. Naturally, there continued to be great emphasis on a man's capacity to withstand extreme bodily torture. The new men, like the old, took a wet-browed pride in pushing the frontiers of pain. At the School of Aerospace Medicine in San Antonio, Texas, the crew manning the centrifuge drew up the Order of the Elephant. The Order was awarded to men who "by design, default or sheer stupidity allow themselves to be exposed to acceleration of more than 15gs on the centrifuge." Whirling round at that speed, the citation noted, a man "couldn't breathe, chest pain was moderate to severe, vision faded or failed, his tongue was impossible to manage and survival was uppermost in his enfeebled mind."

But the experimental space doctors at San Antonio had been examining the Mercury flights, and taking a closer look at the qualities of the Original Seven. In 1964 it published a report which cast some doubt on the methods employed in their selection. Through the dense sociological jargon it emerges fairly clearly that some refinement was needed.

> In general [the report said] crew members have been selected in the past on the basis of their ability to do an assigned task, with little or no attention to the type of social or non-job oriented interaction they might have within the group. With aircrews, this has worked well, not only because competence is an important factor in crew satisfaction but because ample opportunity exists for social interaction outside the crew. When personality clashes develop, crew changes were possible.
>
> However, with flights measured in weeks and months rather than hours, crew members will be restricted to each other for job as well as non-job related interaction for prolonged periods. Hence it becomes more important to consider the effect of personality variables on interpersonal reaction.

Two examples of the professional conduct of the Original Seven aptly illustrate the kind of difficulty NASA had in finding the right

148   JOURNEY TO TRANQUILITY

kind of machine-like performer in the early days. In their different
ways they reveal features of astronautic behavior which later became
virtually inconceivable.

The first debacle was the three-orbit flight of Malcolm Scott Carpenter in May 1962. Carpenter's problem was, quite simply, the
intoxicating view from space. Unlike the ice-nerved Batman he was
meant to be, he behaved like an erratic tourist taking in ten capitals
in a weekend. He received repeated warnings from ground control,
but kept hosing precious fuel away as he maneuvered for the best
camera angles on irrelevant sunrises. At one point he even declined
to help with recordings of his blood pressure because, as he said, "I've
got the sunrise to worry about. I've a beautiful sunrise through the
window. I'll record it so you can see it."

On the second orbit he confessed, "I've gotten badly behind with
the flight plan now." So concerned did control become about the fuel
supply that it almost decided to abort the flight and bring the craft,
Aurora 7, down early.

Stowing his gear ready for splashdown, Carpenter noticed the same
little fireflies outside his capsule that had puzzled Glenn on the first
orbital flight. Actually they were particles of dumped urine reflecting
the sunlight—Constellation Urinus, as they later came to be called—
but Carpenter didn't know that and once again took out his camera.

From then on, pretty well everything went wrong. Absentmindedly
the astronaut tried to fly his craft on manual and automatic systems
at the same time, making it impossible to handle. Beginning to panic,
he forgot to lower his helmet faceplate until reminded twice to do so.
One fuel tank was empty, the other only 15 percent full. "I hope we
have enough fuel," Carpenter gasped as Aurora 7 hurtled into the
atmosphere. Listening to the astronaut's anguished cries, one NASA
official asked, "Does he think he is changing his sex?"

Nor was that all. Carpenter landed safely, but 250 miles from the
scheduled spot in the ocean. Although the mission controllers knew
exactly where he was, the word went out that he was lost and the
resultant public excitement conveniently clouded interest in the far
more alarming events which had happened in space. In the end, a
navy destroyer in the vicinity was sent to pick him up—in preference
to a very unstreamlined tramp steamer which was much closer—and
Carpenter returned to a hero's welcome.

In his official report, the astronaut admitted his errors as hand-somely as a Communist official repenting some deviation from the party line.

The spectacular novelty of the view from space challenged me to make the most of my opportunity [he wrote]. It lured me to an unwise expenditure of fuel early in the flight. I understand that many were concerned while waiting on word from me during re-entry and after landing. However, from my position there was no major cause for concern. The spacecraft was stable during the critical portions of re-entry and the parachute worked perfectly. For me, this flight was a wonderful experience and I anxiously await another space mission.

But Scott Carpenter waited in vain. Not only had he endangered himself, he had placed the whole space program in public jeopardy. It was not enough that he had found the flight a wonderful experience and evidently wanted to record as many sunrises in four hours as Turner had done in a lifetime of painting. After a few years flying a Large Steel Desk (LSD in the Houston vernacular), Carpenter left space and joined the navy SeaLab experiment on the ocean bed, where, no doubt, he could enjoy the view at greater leisure.

A second episode illustrating the unprogramed foibles of the Original Seven happened years later and involved one of the most case-hardened of them all, Wally Schirra, the only man to fly Mercury, Gemini and Apollo. Schirra was commander of Apollo 7, the first manned Apollo flight, and the first to be made after the fire which killed Gus Grissom. Oppressed by the tragedy, Schirra applied himself fanatically to the condition of his own spacecraft. He was especially annoyed about the inclusion of television equipment on board, regarding it as one more item which could go wrong. At one point he even had the TV wiring ripped out.

NASA insisted on television, but Wally Schirra became very unco-operative when he was requested to switch it on in space. The acrimony did not subside even when Deke Slayton himself, a man few astronauts disobey, came on the line, as this exchange with ground control (CAPCOM) indicates:

SCHIRRA. You have added two burns to this flight schedule, you have added a urine water dump, and we have a new vehicle

JOURNEY TO TRANQUILITY

up here, and I tell you this flight TV will be delayed without further discussion until after the rendezvous.

CAPCOM. Roger, copy.

SCHIRRA. Roger.

CAPCOM. Apollo 7, this is CAPCOM. Number 1. [Slayton].

SCHIRRA. Roger.

CAPCOM. All we have agreed to do on this is flip it. Apollo 7, all we have agreed to do on this particular pass is to flip, flip the switch on. No other activity associated with TV. I think we are still obligated to do that.

SCHIRRA. We do not have the equipment out, we have not had an opportunity to follow setting, we have not eaten at this point, I still have a cold, I refuse to foul up our time lines this way.

No such noisy insolence was ever to be heard from later recruits to space. Moon flight would expose deficiencies in patience and self-control much more dangerously than short flights round earth. They simply could not be allowed to happen. A moon journey made it imperative that the crew get on with each other and run an equable ship.

The School of Aerospace Medicine had already reached conclusions which might have done something to explain an outburst such as Schirra's. It had tested the behavior of people during long spells in the spacecraft simulator and reported:

It was noticed that on all flights crew members felt relatively at ease in expressing hostility toward the control monitors in contradistinction to their inhibition of expressing hostility toward each other. Frequent derogatory comments which they were well aware would be heard by the control monitors seemed to be a major avenue for releasing hostilities actually derived from close association with their partner.

But equally, the school possessed graphic evidence of what might happen if any prospective moon voyager was not carefully screened for antisocial habits.

Jabber, jabber, jabber [wrote one of the cabin guinea pigs after a week entombed with a companion]. It'll be nice to sit down at a well-set table with cloth and silver, and to eat with someone who doesn't talk with his mouth full of food, who doesn't slurp his coffee, who doesn't smack his lips, who doesn't belch at the

table. Are good manners necessary? Most certainly. They keep us
one step above animals.

The only thing that grates my nerves is a sloppy eater, no matter where he eats. Slurps his coffee, smacks his lips, belch, scrape
the dish, clear the throat. He never misses a one. He also has
the dropsy. Everything he picks up he has to drop.

I'll have to say he works with gusto. He's in everything up to
his neck. He tries hard. Too much spirit physically. He hasn't
learned that a person can be enthusiastic and yet be outwardly
calm.

After the Original Seven, some evident concessions were made to
this kind of thinking. Psychiatrists and doctors still occupied a humble
place in the NASA hierarchy; one thing for which Dr. Robert Gilruth, director of the Manned Spacecraft Center, had never forgiven
the medical profession was its attempt to delay Shepard's first flight
(originally scheduled before Yuri Gagarin's) for more medical checks.
But the new entrants tended to be not quite such cantankerous figures
as the pioneers.

They were still predominantly military officers. The second group
included men who were to become as celebrated as Alan Shepard and
Wally Schirra, but their style was distinctly John Glenn's. Among
them were Frank Borman, perhaps the most reliable machine in the
entire astronaut corps, who was later to take Apollo 8 round the
moon at Christmas, accompanied by a reading from the First Book of
Genesis. Also there was one civilian named Neil Armstrong, destined by a series of many strange chances to become the only astronaut
assured of a place in history books.

There was never any shortage of volunteers, not least from civilians.
Sailors, marines and air force men continued to take most of the
places, but in 1965, when six places were made available for potential
scientist-astronauts, 422 people applied for them. In 1967, the market
was even fuller. Then no fewer than 750 applicants put in for eleven
posts, which might or might not propel a physicist, a geologist or an
astronomer into space. Slowly the breed was changing, even though
for many of them disappointment loomed as NASA's prospect of
sending men anywhere beyond the moon receded. Nothing cast the
scientists into deeper gloom than the selection of the old chief of all the
astronauts to command Apollo 14. To these highly educated men,

festooned with doctorates and bursting to bring an expert eye to the moon at close quarters, the choice of Alan Shepard seemed to confirm what they had always suspected: that the role of science in the American space program was distinctly secondary.

To meet an astronaut now, as is still possible despite *Life* magazine, is a consummately barren experience. The arrangement is made strictly on NASA's terms. The agency makes its men available every Friday: not any particular man but, as if to emphasize their production-line identity, any man who happens to be available.

The meeting takes place in Building Four at the Manned Space-craft Center, where the space men share capsule-size offices and dictate letters to secretaries in long mini-skirts. The circumstances would not be out of place on Death Row. The visits start at bleary hours, usually around 8 A.M.; the visitor is under escort and has thirty minutes to plumb the soul of the specimen in front of him.

The astronaut turns out to be a calm, polite man with short hair, a powerful handshake and the strange pallor of a gymnasium athlete. He sips black coffee from paper cups, and is demurely well-motivated about life with NASA—the chance of a flight, the ordeal of training, the prospect of being killed, the meaning of landing on the moon. The interview bores him—and why not?—but he looks at his big wristwatch rather less often than the NASA spokesman whose job it is to abort the interview on time.

At the end of half an hour one realizes that he has said precisely nothing. The blameless chat has faithfully preserved the carefully constructed image of the modern astronauts as unselfish, modest and rather dull human beings. For the astronaut himself, the questions must seem tediously familiar. For the interviewer the answers are totally predictable. It has been an extension of the routine life in the spacecraft simulator. Both there and in conversation, the space man is equally aware of the danger of indiscretion, and his mind seems programed, technologically and verbally, for a faultless performance.

The impression of extreme control is confirmed by men who have lived and worked alongside astronauts for years. Paul Haney, formerly chief of Public Affairs at Houston, says they tend to run to a clear pattern, particularly the ones who come from the military academies. "With a few exceptions, they're extremely disciplined people with an almost tunnel-vision ability to look onto a problem and never let go," he said recently. "They become so disciplined they can almost dial up the emotional commodity that's needed. If they're going to a cocktail party they'll dial up to where it says, 'We're going to be light and gay.' They might even muster up a slightly off-color story. They're extraordinarily well-ordered people who don't panic easily. On the other hand, they don't react to much either."

They are also conspicuously confident characters. "They're very intelligent," said a military psychiatrist who sees a lot of them. "Most of them fall into the top two percent of the population intellectually. They're aggressive, competitive people. They've got very good opinions of themselves, for one important reason; the good opinion is based on reality. Indeed, they can be rather pleasant to work with because they've less to prove than the next guy. Perhaps they're not very imaginative; you don't get poets up there. Well, you've only got to listen to them about the view, 'Gee, it's beautiful!' "

The background of the modern astronaut has been checked with rather more thoroughness than it would have been in 1959. It is improbable that anyone would be let in, as Scott Carpenter was, without having formally graduated from his university. Like all civil servants, the space agency's desk men are obsessed with the neatness of human life and its adaptability to little green folders in long black filing cabinets. They have gone to much trouble to ensure that the pattern is not spoiled. Not only the doctors and teachers, but also the neighbors of a candidate for the astronaut corps are visited by government agents inquiring into his domestic habits in case he drinks too much or beats his wife. Even when he has been chosen, an astronaut who gets involved in public scandal risks being grounded, however long he may have trained and proved his value in space.

Relatively few such scandals occur. Some of the men have established heroic reputations with women during the long trips away from home. The endless circuit between Houston, the Cape, Huntsville and Arizona, where the moon walks are practiced, would put any marriage under strain. And after any flight there is plenty of jubilant drinking, just as there was after RAF sorties in the Second World War. Some astronauts are even superstitious, paying calls on a mesmeric British witch called Sybil Leek, who lives on the Florida coast. "I got back at four one morning," Mrs. Leek recalled recently, "and the

phone was ringing. It was one of the astronauts. He said 'Where have
you been. I've been trying to reach you all night.' "

But the divorce rate is low—only one broken marriage among the
forty-eight astronauts, in a part of America where the average rate is
30 percent. Despite the constant throb of tension under the surface,
daily life is almost painfully normal in the Spanish and olde-English
houses of Clear Lake City, with their mock-Tudor shopping parades
and their addresses kept secret by government order.

These men, it is clear, are a comforting symbol of those who live
around them. To the middle-class families of the South, they have
come to represent what America might have been without hippies,
negro militants and the Poor Marchers. They are famous men who
came from hick towns and still retained the values of Sunday church
and ordered family routine. Like Superman they can easily be seen
as clean, hard-working, patriotic and honest, dodging into cupboards
to change the double-breasted suit for the glamorous gear of space.

As such, they are much-sought-after guests at Houston's expensive
social events, and they pose with their wives for the society pages,
sharing jokes stiffly in their impeccably white shirts. Betty Ewing,
society editor of the *Houston Chronicle,* wrote as follows of one
such occasion during the flight of Apollo 9:

> While astronaut-husband *Jim McDivitt* was orbiting the earth
> on the 7th day of the 10-day Apollo flight, charming wife *Pat* was
> whirling around the Emerald Room of the Shamrock Hilton.
> Pat was a guest of the Strake Jesuit Mothers Club's scholarship
> benefit, "An Evening with Marguerite Piazza," along with *Astro-
> nauts James Lovell, William Anders* and *Frank Borman* and their
> wives and pretty *Pat (Mrs. Ed) White,* widow of the astronaut.
> They were guests at *George Strake's* table where in the ab-
> sence of her mother (in the hospital), *Suzie (Mrs. Robert) Dil-
> worth* acted as hostess.
> Astronaut Lovell said he was off to Cape Kennedy on Monday
> so he and Marilyn departed early from the party.

For the wives it is a strange world in which to build a home. Although they, too, are carefully inspected before their husbands are
chosen, there is no exhaustive training for *their* job. Many of them
married men who were junior military officers, and humdrum barracks
life was no preparation for the occasional glamour of space. Very

often they find difficulty in doing it justice. Surrounded by a crowd of reporters at the front of the house, all they can think of to say is what they remember the last astronaut's wife saying during the last flight: "I certainly am proud of John."

But spaceflight confers status, inside the group as well as out of it. A certain social rivalry develops between families which have been up, families which haven't and families which might never. There was even a time when this was commemorated by the arrival on launch day of Marjorie Slayton, wife of the astronaut's boss: an occasion which had more than a touch of the state visit about it.

The least avoidable feature of the life, however, is the wife's involvement in her husband's work. This can reach an intensity even greater than that commonly found among average middle-class careerists of American society. In no wife, perhaps, is it manifested more devotedly than in Jan Armstrong, a fittingly ambitious representative of the female moon breed. When Neil Armstrong was testing the X-15 rocket plane, long before he was asked to go to the moon, Mrs. Armstrong would be up on the roof watching him through binoculars. When his Gemini spacecraft began to tumble toward near-disaster, she demanded to be let into mission control. The door was barred, but Mrs. Armstrong nevertheless neatly upstaged the space agency. One of the critical tapes recording what happened just before the trouble started was missing; Mrs. Armstrong traced it, using the other tapes and her own tracking map, and found out which piece was missing before NASA admitted that it was.

Some troubling questions remain poised over these exceptional, yet exceptionally ordinary, men and their families. They relate not merely to the occupational doubt about how many of them will get the flight for which they have spent so long preparing themselves. It is more a matter of what will happen when they do. Future flights, if Congress provides the money, will last longer than the eight days of a moon journey. They will involve weeks in earth orbit, or possibly a flight far beyond the moon to Mars, a proposition measured in years.

The point is well made by a psychiatrist who has been associated with space research for many years. "Long-distance space flight," he says, "is going to require a different kind of man in many ways. You're just going to have to get some people who are more, well, introspective. It will require men who have settled a great deal of inner turmoil, who understand themselves and are comfortable with themselves. I don't think there's anyone who cannot be broken, with one qualification—and that is the man who's willing to give his life. If a man is unwilling to do this under any circumstances then the weight of psychiatric evidence is that he can be gotten to and may retire into a psychosis defensively."

There is little evidence of solitary introspection among modern astronauts. One of them sculpts, another paints in oils. But they have been chosen by engineers to do an engineering job, and the most conspicuous of all the demands made on them is an ability to function as part of a generous-spirited, even gregarious team. They are better at this than the Original Seven. There are fewer prima donnas. Their rarity value has sharply diminished and the descent from legend has been marked by a substantial fall in the interest of *Life* magazine.

They will, however, remain the critical link in the drama. That is the way the space program was planned. That is what gave the project of a moon landing the peculiar aura of public excitement which Kennedy hoped would stun the world.

And once up there in the spacecraft, the astronauts have insisted on maintaining a significant modicum of control. Among other things their work seems to them a guarantee that the life of the pilot, in an age of computered flight paths and remote-controlled landings, has some kind of future.

A long time ago, shortly after being chosen as one of the Original Seven, Deke Slayton vehemently defended the pilot's role. "Objections to the pilot," he said, "range from the engineer, who semi-seriously notes that all problems of Mercury would be tremendously simplified if we didn't have to worry about the bloody astronaut, to the military man who wonders whether a college-trained chimpanzee or the village idiot might not do as well as an experienced test pilot. . . . I hate to hear anyone contend that present-day pilots have no place in the space age and that nonpilots can perform the space mission effectively. If this were true, the aircraft driver could count himself among the dinosaurs not too many years hence."

The point was made for modern astronauts with equal sharpness by Commander Joseph Kerwin, a man who, if he gets a flight, will be the first doctor of medicine to be placed in the arena which his profession has for so long lost to the engineers. "We've designed the spaceship so it can't be launched unmanned," he said. "We can't send an unmanned flight on a lunar landing. Astronauts, particularly those who've gone before me, have insisted on maintaining significant prerogatives in responsibility in the crew rather than on the ground. Of course, it's a co-operative venture. But you don't go up there feeling like a canned pig with nothing but a computer and a red button."

9.

What
Race?

The first and most truly heroic phase of the space age ended in the summer of 1963. Two years had passed since President Kennedy's commitment to the moon. They were, to the public eye, the years of the astronaut; a period when this strange new breed of man was established as something larger than ordinary human life, with gallantry and nerve beyond the common experience.

This was partly due to the sheer novelty of the Original Seven, and the ruggedness of some of the characters among them. But partly, too, the nature of the Mercury program was responsible. Somehow one man in a capsule, alone in the totally unfamiliar void, more easily acquires heroic status than two or three men facing the ordeal together. By himself he bears some resemblance to the old adventurers, opening their solitary paths through jungles and deserts. Teams of astronauts are less compulsive. They spoil the illusion that a spaceflight is the work of one frail mortal against the elements, instead of a massive corporate enterprise. The last flight of the Mercury series, by Gordon Cooper in May 1963, was the last appearance of the astronaut-as-superman.

But the date has a more telling significance. That summer marked, as well as the end of Mercury, the first substantial public awareness of what the moon program really meant. For two years the nation had seemed to be mesmerized by Kennedy's dream. NASA had gone about its work in a suitably unworldly atmosphere of public consent and mute congressional approval. The decision about how to go, who should go, and in whose machine they should travel to the moon had been taken. The basic lines along which the gigantic undertaking would move forward had been fixed beyond alteration. Nothing had impeded the course the agency chose for itself; hardly anyone had heard of Fred Black or Bobby Baker, John Houbolt or George Low.

Even now it was not on men such as these that attention focused. Rather, it was on the very concept of Apollo. At last the great national debate for which Kennedy had appealed began to be heard. Being, extraordinarily, two years late, it was badly placed to change the course of history. But as Mercury gave way to new advances on the moon, the political climate grew subtly cooler. The technology continued to move swiftly forward, but against a counterpoint of argument. The space program began to be seen for what it was: an enterprise which made distorting demands on skilled manpower, economic resources and moral effort.

Was it really worth doing? Did the Russians really have to be beaten? How great was the chance that science would profit from this more than any other effort? Was NASA traveling too fast? The President himself was not immune from self-doubt. The space agency became not a little bewildered by the unfamiliar experience of being forced down to earth.

Mercury was a narrowly limited project. It proved that men could endure the g-loads of launch and re-entry, and retain full use of their faculties while weightless in space. It was not designed to show very much more, and this, coupled with the fact that Yuri Gagarin had survived in space before the first Mercury flew, later led to it being regarded as somewhat unrewarding: the stunted child of Eisenhower's ambiguity.

Certainly, Mercury had no great relevance to the moon. But it did not lack durable advantages. Besides producing heroes, led by John Glenn, the first man into orbit, it produced successful machines. For any country with designs on the moon it was obviously not enough to know that a foreigner could be placed in space and returned safely. The two suborbital and four orbital flights performed by the Mercury spacecraft, on Redstone and Atlas rockets respectively, proved that American industry could be marshaled by the space managers and forged into a successful team, all contributing to an immensely complex enterprise. Above all, the program brought self-confidence to a country which had for too long believed in its inferiority in space.

Not that Mercury was a flawless accomplishment. No other flight was fraught with the tragi-comedy of Scott Carpenter's, but most of them revealed troubles large or small with the hardware. In Shepard's craft, leaks appeared in the thrusters which reduced capacity on the only maneuver of which Mercury was capable, alteration of its attitude in flight. Gus Grissom almost drowned when the hatch of his craft blew off after splashdown. Glenn's flight was postponed several nerve-racking times, partly because of bad weather but also because of the discovery of fuel leaks and a broken bolt on the hatch. It was a time when prelaunch check-outs were less efficient than they later became, and holds on the countdown a routine happening.

Much was learned, however, from the engineering failures. Most of all, it was established that astronauts could not only survive but positively contribute to a mission's success. Glenn's flight, like Shepard's, was marred by failure of an attitude-control jet; more seriously, his heatshield, the vital protection against burning up on re-entry, was thought to be in danger of dropping off. In each case the work of the astronaut himself, making his own decisions with guidance from the ground, helped prevent the damage from being fatal. Similarly, Gordon Cooper, in his day-long flight, successfully by-passed the consequences of a serious electrical fault.

By the time of Cooper's return, the astronaut had become less of a passenger and more of the pilot he had been before deserting conventional aircraft. With the program completed, it was with an air of patently exultant relief that the Mercury Flight Director, Christopher Columbus Kraft, was able to retort to critics of man-in-space: "Man is the deciding element. As long as Man is able to alter the decision of the machine, we will have a spacecraft that can perform under any known conditions, and that can probe into the unknown for new knowledge."

But the critics had at last found a voice. Hitherto constrained by the solemnity with which the President had committed every man, woman and child in America to an exploit of patriotic importance, scientists and politicians alike now began to look more deeply at what they were about. Mercury, after all, had cost $400 million. Plans for the moon could conceivably consume one hundred times more than that. None of this had been put to the voters. The program demanded a more certain, extended and consistently rising level of funds than any other on which the country was engaged, yet no consensus on its behalf had been established. Scientists, in whose name the venture was supposedly being undertaken, had been coldly brushed aside during the hysteria of April 1961. Kennedy had pleaded for the decision to be taken "as a nation," and the decision had indeed been made. But the nation had not spoken.

It was known by those who cared to find out that what NASA's official Mercury history calls "a substantial portion of the scientific community" was sceptical. It probably agreed with a much-publicized statement made by a leading atomic physicist, Alvin Weinberg, who argued that "most Americans would prefer to belong to a society which first gave the world a cure for cancer than to the society which put the first astronaut on Mars."

To scientists, the question raised by Apollo was essentially one of priorities. Few of them were wholly opposed to a manned landing on the moon some time. But many were concerned by the headlong speed at which the enterprise was propelled from its nonscientific origins.

In the summer of 1963, shortly after the climax of Mercury, the validity of scientific opinion received its first formal recognition when a number of scientists were invited to testify before the Senate Space Committee. The occasion was cautiously stage-managed; eight of the ten witnesses were astronomers, physicists or academic administrators whose institutions drew funds from the space program. Many, not unnaturally, were willing believers in the space agency's policies. Nevertheless, a forum was provided in which the scientific values implicit in the space program were placed before Congress for the first time, and in the context of the biggest budget request NASA had yet made. For the fiscal year of 1964 the agency was demanding almost $6000 million; Apollo alone would cost three times more than the previous year.

Opening the testimony, Dr. Philip Abelson, director of the Geophysical Laboratory of the Carnegie Institution of Washington and the first American to split the uranium atom, cited a straw poll he had recently conducted among scientists not connected with NASA's work. He was editor of *Science*, the journal of the American Association for the Advancement of Science, and a survey of readers had produced

110 votes against the manned lunar landing program, with only 3 in favor of it. This, Abelson said, was a result he was loathe to trust, but it was supported by the tone of his correspondence. Most scientists did not believe that manned landings would advance the cause of science in a way which would even begin to justify the cost.

Abelson himself agreed, and went on to outline the common reasons for the scientists' concern. Much, he said, was already known about the moon: its size, its weight, the density of its rocks. It was already certain that nothing of economic value would be brought back, nor any material which was dissimilar in composition from earth rocks. Such questions as remained obscure could be investigated at infinitely smaller cost by unmanned vehicles. Automatic probes would be entirely competent to retrieve evidence leading to greater understanding of the origin and history of the solar system, the principal general question to which the science of deep space was directed. The really important practical science was already being done not in deep space but in the vicinity of earth; this, too, was the work of unmanned satellites.

It was not true, as Kennedy had claimed, that man was the finest computer. On the contrary, he was a very poor instrument, unable to observe X rays or solar flares, for example, and incompetent without the ten-thousandfold increase in his natural ability provided by electronic equipment.

The manned space program, then, was a scientific indulgence. It also made intolerable demands on manpower which were doing critical damage to other areas of science. Physicists, especially, whose innovative powers could not be spared elsewhere, were being drawn into space. Admittedly, the country was training thousands of scientists, partly under the stimulus of the space program; but only two or three hundred scientists were really creative, capable of making "the tremendous advances." Too many of these were being drained artificially into the NASA pool, attracted by the glamorous challenge of working on something designated as a national goal.

"I believe," Abelson argued, "that diversion of talent to the space program is having and will have direct and indirect effects on almost every area of science, technology and medicine. I believe that the program may delay conquest of cancer and mental illness." More demonstrably, it was drawing scientists away from weapons development. The only attraction of this grim work had been the 25 percent salary increment it carried because the work was being done on government contract. But NASA, too, unlike universities or commercial firms, could offer this bonus plus a happy release from the constraints of weapons-research: "The weight of secrecy is removed, the scientist becomes socially respectable, and he can enjoy publication of his research results." Thus, far from improving the defenses of the nation, the rush to the moon was positively detracting from national security. It did not make sense to seek pre-eminence over the Russians in one area when "we are in competition with them on a thousand different fronts."

Abelson's statement, undeniably representative of a significant body of scientific opinion, met with a certain fuddled amazement among the Senators. It caused one of them, Senator Bourke Hickenlooper, a very conservative Republican from Iowa, to say something which epitomized Congress's unhappy disability when dealing with the space program. The Senator seemed uncommonly grateful to the sceptical scientist. "My concern," he said, "is whether we, who are unschooled in this, may not be led into appropriating vast sums of money which have really no presently ascertainable development, as compared to many other things which have really constructive results." When it came to space, Senator Hickenlooper fretfully observed, "We are indeed babes in the wood."

Some other witnesses agreed with Abelson, notably the chairman of the Physics Department at Columbia University, Dr. Polycarp Kusch, a Nobel prizewinner. When Kusch was asked whether he believed that the lunar landing should have a priority for achievement during the decade, he replied abruptly, "I do not." He discerned a number of features of American life which seemed to him to be worthier of a major national effort than reaching for the moon. Water supply was one. "The water table in the West has been disastrously falling for a couple of decades, perhaps more. The underground waters of the continent have been used at a prodigal rate." Pollution was another. It was a national disgrace which scientists, backed by a major national commitment, could do much to eradicate.

Again, oceanography and the exploitation of marine raw material could do far more for the population problem than a putative colony on the moon. As for the "adventure in science" represented by the space program, it was in danger of being very short-lived; the program had a magnetic attraction to people who might otherwise be teachers of science, without whom future generations would have no introduction to the subject. Kusch's testimony in fact seemed to indicate that the space program, instead of sponsoring a multiplication of the scientific elite, might well diminish it.

Even Dr. Simon Ramo, not only a distinguished scientist but vice-chairman of a corporation, Thompson, Ramo, Wooldridge Inc., which was a large industrial benefactor from NASA's activities, expressed alarm. He saw a growing fanaticism in the American belief that the Russians must not be allowed to reach the moon first. Interestingly, Ramo's fear of this was less for its scientific than its military and economic consequences—arguments which the Senate might be expected more readily to understand.

Too great a commitment to the moon, Ramo said, could well interfere with more mundane security objectives. It meant that the space program "would have to go on, even if new facts turned up indicating that it was a foolish decision, because our investment would have become too great to turn back. We would exaggerate and kid ourselves about every reason for carrying on the program." Moreover, if the race were not slowed down, an equally frightening specter loomed for the free-enterprise economy which was meant to be demonstrating that it, rather than a socialist system, was the best medium for technological advance. The present headlong space program would gradually eat into the economy: "It would create government control over so large a fraction of our technological and industrial effort as to permanently impair free enterprise, and, by making it impossible to give proper attention to other uses of science, would stunt our economic growth."

Many of the scientists called to the stand had more comforting words for the committee than this. Whatever Dr. Abelson's straw poll might have revealed, the profession proved that it included some strong proponents of the manned lunar landing program. And none offered firmer advocacy than one of the deans of scientists-in-government, Dr. Lloyd Berkner. As a young engineer many years ago, Berkner had accompanied Byrd's first expedition to the Antarctic. It was an experience which predictably led him to sympathize with the purely adventurous aspect of the moon mission. Still more to the point, he had been chairman of the Space Science Board of the National Academy of Sciences at the time when the decision on the moon landing was being prepared in Washington. To Kennedy, then, he had offered a scientist's rare support. To the Senate now he provided a powerful and shrewdly worded buttress against scepticism.

This may not have been very scientific; but it granted the imprimatur of science to a venture in need of academic respectability. Berkner made it very clear that he knew why America was going to the moon, even if his colleagues could not understand it. And he approved of what he knew. The enterprise was a contest, ". . . a genuine test of technological capability, in the sense that the peoples of emerging nations size up the developing potentialities and inevitably back the winner. The implications of allowing our technology to fall to second-rate stature, with respect to space, are a matter of technological posture in a 'cold war'—a posture that is recognizable on all sides." The program was essential to national defense because of the "technological dexterity" to which it testified. The plan to land within the decade represented progress at "the optimum rate."

As for the scientific objectives of putting men on the moon, Berkner saw these as impossible to disentangle from the political and military aims. He implied that the answer was not to be found by narrowly examining the intrinsic interest of the moon. The test should be more generous; in fact, it lay, to judge from Berkner's evidence, very close to the Everest-syndrome, the profoundly unscientific notion that because something is there, it must be done. Science was served, therefore, by any forward movement. "We live in a dynamic civilization," Berkner said, "in which some aspects of technology must always lead the others. Our space program is the greatest spur to technology today." It should be enough for scientists that "in satisfying man's primitive aspirations to conquer the unconquered, we spur him to greater effort."

Berkner went on to dismiss with contempt any suggestion that there might be alternative methods of spending Apollo's billions. "Thinking men" recognized such distraction as "specious." After all, the space program required of the American people only 1 percent of extra effort, and in return it was exercising a "mighty influence" on the progress of education and industry. "The point is," said the old explorer, "that the poverty is far more likely to disappear when men work vigorously under strong motivation." Space provided this motivation, and all Americans, rich and poor, could be proud of the way their program was being managed.

If that was not the opinion of all scientists, or even a majority, it did reassure Capitol Hill that some respectable members of the profession, for whatever reason, believed in the program. Not even Berkner's grand vision, however, could erase the sheer expense of the moon. This was strikingly underlined in a terse, but enduring message which the committee received from Dr. Warren Weaver, mathematician and vice-president of the Alfred P. Sloan Foundation in New York. Weaver had been doing a few elementary sums to compute what else might be purchased with $30,000 million. His conclusions became something of a classic in all discussions of educational and scientific priorities:

> With that sum one could give a 10 percent raise in salary, over a 10-year period, to every teacher in the United States from kindergarten through universities (about $9.8 billion required); could give $10 million each to 200 of the better smaller colleges ($2 billion required); could finance 7-year fellowships (freshman through Ph.D.) at $4000 per person per year for 50,000 new scientists and engineers ($1.4 billion required); could contribute $200 million each toward the creation of 10 new medical schools ($2 billion required); could build and largely endow faculties for all 53 of the nations which have been added to the United Nations since its original founding ($13.2 billion required); could create three more permanent Rockefeller Foundations ($1.5 billion required); and one would still have left $100 million for a program of informing the public about science.

Encouraged, perhaps, by the scientists, politicians too began to open their mouths. The day after their testimony was over, former President Eisenhower was roused from political limbo to scourge his old antagonists. "To spend $40,000 million to reach the moon," he declared, "is just nuts." Republican Senators, whose doctrinal patriotism had hitherto been the master of their equally doctrinal economic conservatism, now discovered a number of cogent arguments against Project Apollo. It involved, they argued in a joint policy document, too much money for too little return in the field of national security. As they also noted, "It is felt by many scientists, among them most of the American Nobel prize-winners, that there are other areas of science as important to the future of the United States as a crash program of lunar exploration."

Even more decisively, Clarence Cannon, the venerable chairman of the House Appropriations Committee and arbiter of the federal budget, intervened to state his surprising conviction that "the project must eventually be abandoned." Two years earlier, when such an opinion from such a man might well have impeded the moon decision, the utterance of it would have been unthinkable. Even now it foreshadowed the first serious obstruction of NASA's accelerating progress. The agency's budget was out by $600 million, and far more legislators than usual were prepared to be seen voting against the hasty attempt on the moon. In 1961, no Senators and only three Congressmen had voiced any doubt about it. In 1962, the House had unanimously approved a space budget of $3700 million, and only four Senators could be found to support an attempt to cut it by 5 percent. But by 1963 the picture had become blurred. A cut in the NASA budget was staved off in the House by the narrow margin of 192 votes to 145; in the Senate it failed for want of only 7 votes.

One of the earliest critics was Senator William Proxmire, an independent-minded Democrat from Wisconsin, a state with very little of the pork-barrel. Proxmire's first concern, like that of the scientists, was about the prodigious demands the space program made on highly trained manpower. He saw scientists being sucked out of defense research and university education, a process which would "cripple our long-run space program, our ability to continue to surpass the Soviet Union in the future."

But Proxmire also spelled out the argument which, on any matter other than one supposedly relating to national security, would have shocked the country into agreement. Like Dr. Ramo, he saw a profound economic shift being wrought by space. In its urgency to beat the Russians, the country was adopting un-American methods which might be seen to defeat the very object of the program—to prove the strength of capitalism. Proxmire pointed out that space spending had nothing to do with private enterprise: "In relation to its rapidly growing volume, the space program is probably the most centralized government spending program in the United States. It concentrates in the hands of a single agency full authority over an important sector of the American economy. . . . The economic situation created by the space program could well be described as corporate socialism."

Proxmire was joined by Senator Joseph Clark, Senator William Fulbright and others, who developed the familiar dialectic of mistaken priorities. At the same time, from a different wing came argument that space should become an admitted and overt military arena.

In many ways this was the most heretical, yet cogent, point of all. Given the many years during which NASA had struggled for control of a civilian and peaceful space program, to suggest that the military should actually have won those interminable battles of long ago seemed the grossest bad taste. But the point had uncomfortable validity. If the central case for going to the moon rested on the greater security it would bring the United States through increased prestige and eventual supremacy in the cold war, was there not good reason for saying that more direct methods to the same end should be exploited if they were available? Military control and a military objective would bring more tangible security against the Soviet threat than a moon landing could ever provide.

It was distinctively a Republican argument. As the Republican Senator's policy document observed, "To allow the Soviet Union to dominate the atmosphere 100 miles above the earth's surface while we seek to put a man on the moon could be, in the opinion of many, a fatal error." A fiery Congressman from New Hampshire, Louis Wyman, put the point more graphically: "Let us continue to try to be first in space. But let us be first in space at the right place and at the right time. The right place, right now, is not 250,000 miles out in the year 1970 with a civilian in a pressure-suit on the moon. The right place, right now, is a man in a navigable armed maneuverable inner-space vehicle with a capacity for interception and destruction of enemy objects in space."

Nor was Senator Barry Goldwater, warming up for his 1964 presidential campaign, to be left out of this apocalyptic vision. "By choice of official policy so far," he told a group of air force officers in Alabama, "we are choosing to relegate the military function of space to a secondary position. . . . We are moonstruck. . . . But while our eyes are fixed upon the moon, we could lose the earth or be buried in it."

There was, however, a question still more corrosive of the case for treating the moon landing as a major priority. It was so elementary that for a long time no one in Washington had even considered it. It related to the very existence of the space race.

In May 1961, when the moon decision was made, the race was accepted as an unquestioned fact. It was assumed, on sound evidence, that the Russians were making a large effort in space which America could not ignore. It was also believed that the ultimate Soviet objective was a moon landing by men. This is what inspired the nation to treat the Apollo program as a vehicle of the national destiny which could not be allowed to fail. Politicians had been struck dumb by the thought; scientists had been attracted to space by the labful, partly in the belief that they were contributing to their country's survival as a power of the first rank.

But on this matter, the summer and autumn of 1963 yielded disturbing evidence of doubt. Was the race still a race? Did the Russians still regard it as such? Worse, did the most important Americans? If the answer to these questions was no, then clearly much of the basis on which Apollo had got under way, and virtually the entire premise of the speed at which the program was being conducted, was in jeopardy.

The alarm was started by none other than the President himself. The men who had launched Apollo as a bid "to win the battle that is now going on around the world between freedom and tyranny" now offered, much to the bewilderment of space officials and propagandists, to clasp the tyrant to his bosom. The race, it seemed, was to be called off.

The date was September 1963, and the circumstances reveal, as did the Bay of Pigs and all the other events of that decisive spring in 1961, the links which connect space inextricably with the political realities of the earthly world. The President delivered an address to the United Nations in which he made an unqualified call for co-operation instead of competition between America and the Soviet Union. "Surely," he said, "we should explore whether the scientists and astronauts of our two countries—indeed, of all the world—cannot work together in the conquest of space, sending some day in this decade to the moon not the representatives of a single nation but the representatives of all our countries."

In his account of the Kennedy years, Arthur Schlesinger, Jr., one of the President's personal advisers, describes the tortuous origins of this proposal. The President's main concern at the time was not with space but with the nuclear Test Ban Treaty which had recently been negotiated. The treaty was threatened with dilution in the Senate, a development which might well provide Moscow with an excuse to withdraw from it. Kennedy was therefore casting about for some way of proving to the Soviet Union and the world that American intentions remained sincere. And just as in 1961 nothing had seemed as potent a symbol of international competition as space, now nothing seemed a more impressive medium of international co-operation.

When the White House began to examine the idea of joint ventures in space, it found that the bureaucracies beneath it had interpreted the prevailing theology—the doctrine of the race—with positively jesuitical rigor. It emerged, for example, that some time ago NASA itself had contemplated a study of the theoretical possibilities of a joint moonshot. But fearing to proceed without political clearance, the agency had searched for higher authority. It had asked the State Department to send it a letter formally requesting such a study to be made. However, the State Department, too, had baulked at the responsibility. It had declined to send the letter "lest it in turn be held accountable for so subversive an inquiry." Schlesinger writes that he himself thereupon wrote the idea into a draft of the UN speech, and the President had quickly approved.

When representatives from the State Department, NASA and the Pentagon saw that the White House had changed its mind, none of them raised an objection. Nonetheless, to men attracted by the easily intelligible concept of the race, the President's speech was confusing. Congressional sponsors of space, like Albert Thomas, wrote letters to the White House asking for clarification. Critics seized upon the proposal as a method of reducing costs, or alternatively as an argument for reducing speed. Either way, the President's seemingly impenetrable motives invited study of something still more incalculable—the true status of the Soviet space effort.

When Apollo began, and the moon entered the American catechism of belief, nobody could say with certainty where it stood in Russian priorities. It was simply assumed to be the probable objective of the era inaugurated by Yuri Gagarin. But this had never been announced. Unlike the Americans, Moscow did not then, or later, lay its intentions before the world. In attempting to make up for this, the seers inside the American space agency could consult only three sources of evidence: the visible achievements of the Soviet program, the unreliable statements of Soviet leaders, and their own preconceptions.

Amid such uncertainty it was inevitably the third of these sources that colored most official prophecies. The official expectation was that the Russians intended a moon landing, and until the evidence proved otherwise that would remain the premise of Apollo.

The onus of proof was one which critics of the space program never succeeded in discharging. A constant theme of NASA's evaluations of the matter was that America had to expect the worst. Time and again before Congress, James Webb responded to questions as he did in 1963: "They have pursued a steady, driving pace, doing one thing above all, bulldoggedly continuing until they do what they started out to do, and then moving on to the next one." The implication was that they were trying for the moon, although no one knew how soon. The analogy, unspoken but manifestly applicable, was with a war situation: you may not know that the enemy has a bomb which he might drop, but in case he does you must have more bombs than he. In space and war, unlike human welfare, there is no margin for a gambler's error.

Some features of the Soviet program were already apparent by 1963. It was strongly propagandist, as witness the mocking jubilation which accompanied the flights of Sputnik, the first space satellite, and Gagarin, the first man. Its early progress had been impressively swift, with a good number of firsts to its credit besides those, the two most spectacular: the first animals in space, the first recovery of live specimens from space, the first photographs of the moon's hidden side, the first crash landing of an object on the moon.

The Russians were also clearly imbued with the kind of romantic aspirations which would surely, one day, drive them to the moon. The heirs of Konstantin Tsiolkovsky drew on a longer tradition of space rocketry than any other nation possessed. Gagarin's flight had been preceded by the kind of simple, emotion-charged ceremony which would be hard to imagine at Cape Kennedy. As he approached his rocket, he was greeted by a party of official well-wishers whom he addressed in terms never yet employed by an American astronaut: "Dear friends, intimate and unknown, fellow citizens, people of all countries and all continents. All I have done or lived for has been done and lived for this moment. . . . To be the first in outer space, to meet nature face to face in this unusual single-handed encounter— could I possibly have dreamed of more?" Of the moon itself the same heated dreams had often been expressed in Russian literature and propaganda.

A third characteristic of the Soviet effort was its caution and economy. Manned flights had been spectacular and comparatively lengthy, but sparing in number. Gagarin's flight had been followed by only one more straightforward orbital flight. After that there had been two groups of simultaneous flights, in which two Vostock spacecraft had approached on each occasion within three miles of each other, seemingly in preparation for space rendezvous. The last of these, in June 1963, had incorporated another element of some propaganda value, the first flight in space by a woman, Valentina Tereshkova. The program was clearly less prolific than Mercury, not to mention the long series of two-man Gemini flights being planned as the next American step toward the moon; but it did not necessarily signify any less urgency.

Russian statements were no more conclusive than the Russian program. But the obvious advantage of a policy of silence, interspersed with the occasional Delphic pronouncement, is that it induces the other side to believe what it wishes to believe. There was no doubt what NASA wished to believe . . . indeed had to believe if it was to sustain the urgency of its work. It was convinced that Moscow was pouring as many resources into the Soviet moon program as it was itself receiving from Washington.

In the summer of 1963, however, new light seemed to be shed on the Soviet conundrum which, to the critics, also illuminated their own case against the hectic speed of Apollo. Sir Bernard Lovell, the British astronomer, whose co-operation in tracking their probes the Russians had often requested, did what no American space policy-maker had been able to do: he visited all the major optical and radio observatories in Russia, and spent many hours talking about the future of space exploration to the president of the Soviet Academy of Science, Mstislav Keldysh, and many other academicians. On his return he made a statement which seemed to surprise even him. He said he had found no conviction in the Soviet Union that it was scientifically or otherwise desirable to place a man on the moon. "A few weeks ago," he admitted, "I was under the firm impression that the landing of a human being on the moon was the centerpiece of the Russian space program. But this is not the case."

Evidently the Academy was constantly debating the problems of getting a man to the moon, but Soviet scientists had identified three "insuperable" difficulties. These Lovell outlined, as he had been intended to, in a letter to Hugh Dryden, NASA's deputy administrator. First, the Russians could see no immediate way of protecting cosmonauts from the lethal effects of solar radiation. Secondly, no "economically practical" method could be found of putting enough material on the moon for useful manned work there, with the guarantee of a safe return. Third, the Academy was convinced that the scientific problems answerable by lunar exploration could be solved more cheaply and quickly by unmanned probes.

Sir Bernard concluded by reporting something which, had it been true, might have given more substance to President Kennedy's apparently eccentric overture at the United Nations. He said that Keldysh and the Russians believed the idea of manned journeys to the moon could be revived later if these problems were solved: but that "the appropriate procedure would be to formulate the task on an international basis."

The Lovell disclosures were quickly exploited by the Washington sceptics. For they seemed to be evidence that the Apollo program, with its massive costs and alarming speed, was being conducted on a wholly false premise. And indeed, in some respects, Sir Bernard's news eventually proved to have been a moderately plausible prophecy. Instead of the moon, he said, the Russian's main objective appeared to be the assembly of a large platform in earth orbit on which would be placed instruments which men would operate for several days, perhaps by rota-visits from earth. And now, at the end of the decade, if a long-term objective can be ascribed to the Russians this would appear to be it. Prophecy was no simpler than it was in the early 1960s, but certainly there are more signs from Moscow of a long-stay manned space station than a manned lunar landing.

In 1963, however, Lovell's exegesis of his Russian trip turned out to be little less Aesopian than the statements of the Russians themselves. His suggestion that the Russians were interested in cooperation on the way to the moon was gleefully scotched by NASA officials, who claimed that the real purpose of the Russian statement was to achieve international support for the evidently negative Soviet attitude to manned lunar flight in the foreseeable future. Lovell was also rebuked by Keldysh who said, according to Radio Prague, that he "obviously came to his conclusion by himself as we had never said this."

No response was heard, either, to Kennedy's own curious attempt to divert the course of Project Apollo. It achieved, if anything, only its ulterior purpose: despite the Senate, the Test Ban Treaty was successfully brought to signature. When Lovell himself next visited the United States, he duly swallowed his words. He had, he said, been misquoted. Any impression he might have given that the Soviet Union had abandoned its own lunar plans was "completely erroneous." He added, "I have every reason to believe the Russians are trying to get to the moon every bit as fast as the Americans are."

Certainly, no Soviet spokesman, even those most candid about the problems, ever denied that his country was planning for moon flight. When the Vostock flights were described at international conferences attended by Soviet scientists, it was invariably in the context of future interplanetary travel. Nikita Khrushchev himself probably spoke the truth in October 1963 when he said that, for them, it was a matter of time, perhaps a long time. "At the present time we do not plan flights of cosmonauts to the moon. . . . We do not wish to compete in sending people to the moon without thorough preparation. . . . For us it is good enough on earth."

The most obvious reason for Khrushchev's caution at that time was not so much the radiation problem on the moon as uncertainty about launching a payload large enough to include the equipment for returning to earth. He had also said that "demooning," not "mooning," was the real difficulty. Even as he spoke, his engineers were preparing for another space "first," the launch of the first vehicle capable of substantial maneuverability. The successful performance of this, Polyet 1, showed that space rendezvous, the key to the lunar journey, was entirely feasible. But that meant little if a rocket of required size did not exist; and in rocket development it was now becoming steadily clearer to American space officials, as they nursed their own gigantic Saturn V along the production line, that the Russians were lagging behind.

Rocketry, more than any other single factor, provided American space officials throughout the later 1960s with the confidence that they would win the space race, but also—just as important—with the argument for continuing as if the race was a constant reality. For four years, Dr. Dryden told Congress in 1962, the space agency had regularly been told that a new Russian booster was about to be produced, but it had not appeared: "We have been waiting for the other shoe to drop." In 1963, according to Brainerd Holmes, the only evidence of a potential Soviet moon journey lay in the possibility of their launching the necessary hardware in several stages into earth-orbital rendezvous. The stages, with present rockets, would be many—"10 or 15 or even 20," according to Holmes—and he did not believe that the Russians had demonstrated anything like the proficiency in space operation required to make so many fault-free rendezvous.

In 1964, there was still no new rocket in evidence, and Webb allowed himself some cautious optimism. "I think they have receded a good deal from their belligerency in space," he told Congress, "because of the very activity of our program, the power of the Saturn V rocket. They can see the beginning of the end of their own supremacy in large vehicles, I believe, but I am not absolutely sure." Far from being a reason to slacken off, Webb argued that this was the moment to nullify the challenge: "I see no reason for stopping something that is successful, that is giving us the technology and at the same time is showing them that perhaps they cannot catch us." The minatory note was sounded more harshly by Dryden, who returned to his old metaphor: "We may maintain the lead for one week, one month, one year or many years. All we can say is that the other shoe hasn't dropped yet—but that doesn't say it won't drop tomorrow."

In fact, another year passed before a new Soviet rocket appeared, and then it was far smaller than the developing Saturn V. It pushed into orbit the greatest payload to date, weighing twenty-six thousand pounds, but that was less than one-tenth the size of Saturn's capability. The feasibility of earth-orbital rendezvous was brought closer for the Russians; such argument as American space officials needed to sustain the urgency of their program was reinforced. But by that time, the middle of 1965, the argument in any case needed no strengthening from any source. It was now perfectly clear that even if some verifiably solemn oath were extracted from the Russians disclaiming any designs on the moon, few Americans would care. Washington and Houston would continue to run the space race exactly according to the timetable set down by President Kennedy.

There was only one circumstance which might have brought Apollo to a halt. Neither what was heard from the critics, nor what could be pieced together of Soviet progress, were ever likely to weaken the space agency's resolve. Congress might have to be placated, and the Russians carefully watched. There might even be some reduction, as there was in 1963, in what NASA regarded as optimum funding— although this was likely to fall heavily on every other item of space work before it fell on Apollo. Something much bigger would be needed to persuade the White House and the space statesmen in Congress that Apollo must stop.

The situation which some people, including the President, envisaged as bringing this about was one which even now most witnesses are extremely unwilling to discuss. It was, quite simply, the possibility of war: not necessarily a world conflagration which would consume the space program along with everything else, but a war or even a major crisis which might require that space installations and space technology be swiftly converted to military use. At no time was this openly acknowledged. If it had been, the idealism felt by many of the thousands of workers in the space program would surely have taken a fatal bruising. That is why it is impossible today to find any person of authority in Washington to admit it publicly. Nevertheless, more than one senior official close to the program will state privately that at least until the autumn of 1963, when a kind of international détente became visible in the wake of the Test Ban Treaty negotiations, the value of the space program and its rockets as a direct military arm was fully understood. With new crises in Berlin or Cuba, the launch sites at Cape Kennedy could have been directed to the military space program; Wernher von Braun might once again have had to go to war.

Happily, that did not happen. And short of its happening, America would not delay, still less halt, her journey to the moon. Once the Apollo decision had been made, the national goal acquired a self-propelling impetus. In this sense it was intrinsically immune from whatever capital the critics could make out of Russian ambiguities. The desire to beat the Russians may have impelled Kennedy to make his commitment in the first place. But once it was made, the promise to reach the moon "within the decade" became, irrespective of the Russians, the test of American technology. It was on that promise that American prestige was riding. It was that promise, solemnly, dramatically and publicly made, which no self-respecting nation could easily surrender.

This, equally, was why the sceptics never had a chance of influencing events in space. The debate tentatively begun in 1963 awakened more Americans to some of the real and pressing issues which Apollo created. But it did not more than momentarily inconvenience the program's managers. By then, vested interests in the moon had taken deep root. It was never remotely possible that they would be shifted by mere argument. Only with the momentous disaster of the Apollo fire early in 1967 would criticism acquire undeniable potency.

Even as the critics were finding their voices, therefore, NASA was preparing the program which would bridge the gap between Mercury and Apollo and, incidentally, mark the moment when the United States at last assumed undeniable leadership in the race. Since October 1957, when Sputnik 1 was launched, the Russians had led the way. For a long time the American performance had been palpably inferior. But with the brilliant series of ten flights by the two-man Gemini spacecraft, beginning in March 1965, the Americans achieved a commanding and probably irreversible supremacy.

Gemini was an immense leap from Mercury. The minimal piloting which Glenn and Cooper had done in Mercury orbit would have to be transformed, if men were to reach the moon, into a major capacity. The brief duration of Mercury—the longest flight was a day—had to be stretched into time of a different order: a minimum of eight days. Could the men and the machines stand up to it? Gemini, not without some alarms, showed that they could.

Five days before the flight of Gemini 3, the first manned craft, a reminder came in from the East. The Russians, with excellent timing, sent up the first man to climb out of his craft and walk, or rather swim, in space. The Americans had plans for that as well, and to counter the Soviet ploy these were advanced from late in the series to the second flight. But swimming in space, or extravehicular activity as it was known, was not in truth a major priority for a moon flight. The most significant accomplishment imperative to a moon flight was that the spacecraft itself should be capable of maneuver, and ultimately of docking with another vehicle. Rendezvous was not a futile trick, as it sometimes seemed to the watching world, but an achievement of absolutely critical importance to the moon journey.

There were several delays before rendezvous was achieved. Gemini 4 was meant to close with the second stage of its own launching-rocket, but the rocket remained just out of reach. Gemini 5, in which Gordon Cooper and Charles Conrad became temporarily the holders of the space endurance record with an eight-day flight, developed trouble in its fuel-cell battery. But Gemini 6 and 7, commanded by two of the more celebrated astronautic names, Wally Schirra and Frank Borman, achieved the momentous breakthrough in December 1965. This almost ended in disaster before it began, when Schirra's rocket, at the moment of blast-off to join Gemini 7 in space, suddenly shut down; and later it was found that a workman had carelessly left a plastic dust cover on an essential power line. But eventually it got off the ground, and a perfect meeting was achieved. Borman, with his companion, James Lovell, stayed in space for no fewer than fourteen days, almost long enough for two journeys to the moon and back.

Apart from rendezvous and long-duration flight, Gemini proved other techniques of great importance to the moon journey. The space walks, even though they were performed at over seventeen thousand miles per hour, were curiously similar to the first lumbering footsteps which would be taken on the lunar surface: both featured men protected from the rigors of space solely by their suits. Again, it was during Gemini that the techniques of controlled re-entry into earth's atmosphere were learned and perfected, as were the arduous operational procedures at the launch site and on the worldwide network of tracking stations. Incidental to the moon landing, but riveting to the world, were the photographs of earth taken by Gemini astronauts. They were the most compulsive visual means yet available to earthly creatures of beginning to imagine what it might mean to go into space: to see lands and seas, deserts and forests and gulfs and continents in more detail than any map could show.

Gemini was in all important respects the perfect precursor of Apollo. It created a bedrock of experience and hardened skill which did a great deal to diminish the fears and perils of traveling as far as the moon. The series had been flown, moreover, in eighteen months during which not a single Soviet cosmonaut left the ground.

Now it was time for America, on her own, to start the last assault.

Apollo itself, the third and final act of the drama, was about to begin. Nothing so far had gone badly wrong. The mistakes were all of the kind which space men could learn much from; and considering the complexity of the operation they had been astonishingly few. Could the record last? Was it to be expected that a program run at such hectic speed toward such a very new frontier would avoid a calamity? Most of the moon planners knew by this time that America would reach her objective, probably on time: but only if NASA's favorite slogan, "zero-defects," continued to apply.

10.

Death by Negligence

To climb into a Mercury capsule and lie back in the couch while the hatch is closed above you is a thoroughly unnerving experience. The molded couch encloses you like a coffin, toecaps restrain your feet, the wall of the spacecraft and the instrument panel are within inches of your face. The nightmarish sense of immobility makes the confinement almost unbearable. That anyone should be hurled into space in such a contraption, orbit the earth and survive the fiery heat of re-entry seems incredible. The capsule seems as inadequate for the task it accomplished as the pioneering craft often cited as the most suggestive predecessor of the spaceship, Christopher Columbus's *Santa Maria*.

Gemini is almost as unpleasant. The couches are more like airline seats and do not enfold you in quite such a paralyzing embrace; there is an almost aesthetic pleasure to be derived from the beautifully neat and accessible arrangement of the controls. But the craft is still as cramped as Mercury. In fact there is even less room to stretch your legs. How anyone managed to struggle into a clumsy spacesuit in such cramped conditions is impossible to imagine.

Compared with its claustrophobic predecessors, the interior of Apollo is palatial. In the center a man can stand comfortably upright. Beneath the three couches, suspended from struts well above the floor, there is room for two men to lie full length. There are five windows. There is not the same feeling as in Gemini of having everything at your fingertips, but in a way this, too, is liberating; it is necessary to have everything within easy reach of the couch only if you are unable to leave it.

Apollo may be spacious by spacecraft standards, yet the habitable volume is still only equivalent to the inside of a big estate-car. In this confined space three men have to work, cook, eat, sleep, wash and excrete for a week or more. They work where the job requires them to, cook by adding hot or cold water to dehydrated food in plastic bags, eat and drink by squeezing the contents of these bags into their mouths, sleep on their couches or under them, tied down to prevent them from floating about the cabin, wash with damp cloths and tissues, urinate into a flexible hose with the help of tight-fitting rubber sleeves like condoms, and defecate into plastic bags which they stick to their buttocks.

And except by comparison with Mercury or Gemini, the interior of Apollo seems oppressively cramped even to visit, let alone to live in. From one of the couches, with the countless switches, dials, indicators, lights, displays and plotters of the great control panel arching over you, it is easy to imagine you are in the control room or some huge power-station which has contracted and is about to crush you, like the sinister chamber in Edgar Alan Poe's *The Pit and the Pendulum*.

Through this panel the astronauts exercise their main function, supervising one of the most complicated mechanisms ever created by man. It is a full-time job. Only for quite brief periods, notably during the docking maneuvers, are they pilots in the conventional sense. Apollo's prime pilot is a cubic foot of electronics located near the feet of the astronauts' couches: the spacecraft's computer. No instrument occupies more of their attention than the display keyboard, a panel rather less than a foot square with nineteen white keys and a series of windows in which luminous numbers appear and disappear. Through it the astronauts and computer communicate.

Most of the vital maneuvers of the flight are controlled by this computer. The astronauts simply push buttons allowing it to get on with the job and then lie back to watch lights and dials as the computer aligns the spacecraft, fires the engine and shuts it down again at the right moment to throw Apollo into or out of orbit round the moon.

Much of the basic data the computer needs to do its job is locked away in its memory before liftoff, but throughout the flight it is continuously fed with the latest information of the spacecraft's position and course. Some of this comes from the ground, from the worldwide network of tracking stations and the formidable computer installation at the Manned Spacecraft Center. Some comes from the inertial measuring unit on board, a metal football containing gyroscopes and accelerometer which register the spacecraft's every movement. And some comes from the many navigational sightings on stars and landmarks made by the astronauts with the space sextant.

Apollo's computer, together with the rest of its navigational system, is one of the items which set it apart from its predecessors. With its help the astronauts can determine their position and speed and solve the complex problems in celestial dynamics needed to get them safely back from the moon to earth without any help from Mission Control. Normally the calculations are made on the ground, the spacecraft's own computer merely providing a check. But the capacity is there if it should ever be needed.

Apart from the computer and its ancillaries the ancestry of most of the equipment competing with the astronauts for space inside the spacecraft is readily traceable through Gemini to Mercury. The air-conditioning system, the communications equipment, the power supply, the landing parachutes, the small rocket motors for controlling the spacecraft's attitude are bigger and more sophisticated in Apollo, but they do the same job.

There is, however, one vital difference. In an emergency, Mercury or Gemini could be brought back to earth in half an hour at most. Apollo, on the other hand, travels three or four days away from safety. Its two million functional components, more than a thousand times the number in a typical motor car, must therefore achieve unique standards of reliability. Every means known to modern technology for improving reliability has gone into the design, manufacture and testing of Apollo, including "redundancy" on an unprecedented scale. Virtually every major component has a back-up, in some cases more than one, which takes over automatically in the event of a failure. The twelve small rocket motors, for example, are arranged in two sets of six either of which is capable of the vital task of controlling the spacecraft's attitude during re-entry.

From the outside the Apollo crew compartment, the command mod-

[29] "Angry alligator": the Agena rendezvous target for Gemini 9 which refused to open its jaws wide enough for docking.

[30] Riding the moon trail: Richard Gordon astride Gemini 11.

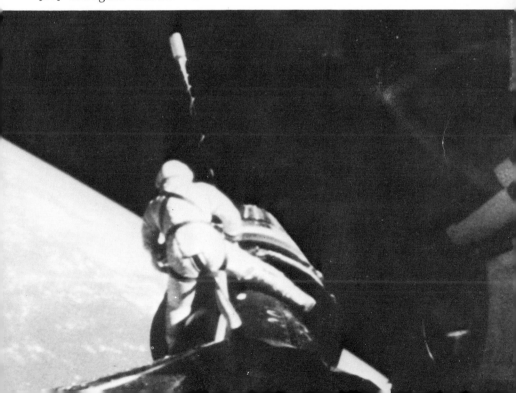

[31] Before... Grissom, White and Chaffee training in a spacecraft simulator a week before the fire in which all three lost their lives.

[32]   And after...the interior of spacecraft O12 after the bodies had been removed.

[33] A blot on the escutcheon:
Melted plastic on the outside of the burnt-out spacecraft O12.

[34] There were Russian victims too. The ashes of Vladimir Komarov, killed when the parachute of his Soyuz spacecraft failed to open, are placed in the Kremlin wall, April 26, 1967.

[35] George E. Mueller; Holmes's successor as manned spaceflight chief: "To resolve that this nation, under God, will lead the way to the planets."

[36] George Low, redeemer of the spacecraft after the fire: "The success of the mission may well depend on the actions of the pilot."

[37] Senator Robert Kerr, keeper of the purse: "Myself first, the state of Oklahoma second, and the people of the United States third."

[38] Fred Black, distributor of the funds: "an *aura* of influence."

[39] Frank Borman, commander of Apollo 8:
"In the beginning God created the heaven and the earth."

[40]   "And the earth was without form, and void;
and the darkness was upon the face of the deep."

[41] Moon journey, first leg: Saturn V leaves the Vehicle Assembly Building at the start of its 3½ mile journey to the launch pad.

ule, is a cone, eleven feet high, with a slightly convex base thirteen feet across. It emerges from the factory covered with a gleaming silvery film. After recovery it looks as though a gigantic blow lamp has been played over its base, charring it to the consistency of burnt toast, with fire-blackened streaks radiating outward and up the sides—the result of re-entering the atmosphere at 25,000 miles an hour, when the temperature touches 5000° F.

The Apollo astronauts are protected, as were those in Mercury and Gemini, in two ways: by the spacecraft's shape and by the nature of its surface. The realization that blunt shapes pick up less heat than streamlined ones during re-entry, together with the discovery of "ablative" materials which char and melt away in such a way that the heat hardly penetrates the surface, were breakthroughs originally achieved in development of intercontinental ballistic missiles. Thus, the rocket technology needed to reach space is not the only debt the moon program owes to the early missile programs: the means of return to earth is equally important.

So it is not by chance that the Apollo command module, the only part of the spacecraft which returns to earth, is cone-shaped and re-enters the atmosphere blunt end first. But where Mercury and Gemini had ablative heatshields covering only their bases Apollo's covers it entirely—nearly a ton and a half of metal honeycomb filled with a mixture of fibers and resins, in places almost three inches thick.

A bigger difference between the appearance of Apollo and its predecessors is that the crew compartment is only one part of the spacecraft. It sits on top of the service module, a squat, cylindrical engine and supply section, and is linked to it as intimately as a helpless patient to a heart-lung machine. This engine, whose disproportionately large nozzle projects from the base of the casing, enables Apollo to maneuver as Mercury and Gemini could never do, to move into orbit round the moon and then to return to earth.

The service module is primarily a propulsion unit, but other bulky pieces of equipment and supplies not required during the final stages of the flight are also placed there: the fuel cells which produce electricity from hydrogen and oxygen; the attitude control motors used during most of the flight; the main reserves of oxygen; the radiator panels where the cooling fluid from the command module's air-conditioning system lets out its heat into space; and the big long-distance communications antenna. Once explosive charges have severed the ties between the command and service modules and driven a guillotine through the wires and plumbing which made them a single space-craft, the command module is capable of sustaining the lives of the astronauts for only a few hours.

The big engine in the service module is one of the most vital components of the spacecraft. If when the spacecraft is in orbit round the moon it fails to fire to put the spacecraft back on course for earth, the astronauts will be stranded forever. It is too heavy to duplicate. It cannot be allowed to fail.

It was designed from the start with reliability as the overriding consideration. It uses a fuel (a mixture of hydrazine and unsymmetrical dimethyl hydrazine) and an oxidizer (nitrogen tetroxide) which ignite on contact, an inherently more reliable arrangement than more conventional combinations such as kerosene and liquid oxygen which have to be ignited by a spark or some kind of explosive device.

Instead of pumps, gas under high pressure is used to drive the propellants into the engine, again eliminating a possible source of mechanical failure. The thrust chamber is cooled not by the normal method of circulating the incoming propellants through its walls, a method vulnerable to mechanical damage, but by coating it with a heat-resistant, ablative material similar to that which protects the command module during re-entry.

And although the whole engine cannot be duplicated, save for the basic structure virtually every component in it can be. There are two high-pressure gas containers to drive the propellants into the engine, either capable of doing the job. Every important valve controlling the flow of the propellants and the mechanism which actuates it is duplicated, some of them quadruplicated. Nowhere in the spacecraft has the concept of reliability through redundancy been more thoroughly exploited.

In the middle of December 1966, this supremely complex object, the most sophisticated and beautiful creation of the space age, was officially shown to the world. Reporters were summoned to Houston to inspect it and to be prepared for the long-awaited flight of the manned Apollo scheduled for early the following year. It was a moment of ebullient self-confidence in the space program. A few weeks earlier the last of the Gemini flights had brought the series to

a triumphant conclusion. Now it seemed that Apollo was to take over
the baton with Olympic smoothness and carry the space race into the
final lap.

No one believed that all difficulties were over; clearly they were
not. The feeling was rather that of an army which after a long battle
against an unyielding enemy suddenly senses that the resistance is
weakening. The occasion was epitomized by a couple of lines of bad
verse dreamed up by Joseph Shea, the man who had played a critical
part in choosing lunar-orbital rendezvous as the method of traveling
and was now the manager of the spacecraft program:

> The NASAs were nestled all snug in their beds
> Convinced that we finally had beaten the Reds.

Among those present were the crew chosen for the first flight: Gus
Grissom, one of the Original Seven; Ed White, the first American
spacewalker; and Roger Chaffee, a novice astronaut. They shared the
mood of heady lightheartedness. When a reporter asked how they
would feel about taking off their spacesuits in view of television
cameras, which would be on board an American spacecraft for the
first time, Grissom replied, "Very bashful."

Of course the meeting had its more serious aspect. Shea described
some of the difficulties experienced during Apollo's five years of
development. At least twenty thousand failures of all kinds had been
logged, he said, more than two hundred of them in the environmental
control system. But for this troublesome item, which had to be removed
and returned to the factory for modifications in October and removed
again in December because of leaks, Apollo might have flown in 1966.

Shea compared the building of Apollo with what had gone before.
"Apollo," he said, "has a requirement for hardware maturity that is significantly higher than the similar requirements we had in Gemini.
It is kind of like watching children grow up. We are going through
that maturing process on Apollo now. My feeling is we are somewhere
in the middle of adolescence."

But even as Shea uttered this euphoric analysis, the moment of
its betrayal was at hand. Unsuspected by him, or by Grissom, White
or Chaffee, the spacecraft in which they were to inaugurate the Apollo
moon program had reached its own maturity with a deadly hidden
flaw. Its number was SC 012, and it was now at Cape Kennedy await-

ing the time when it would be mated with its rocket and dispatched into orbit. But within six weeks the first $100 million moonship would be a burned-out tangle of human corpses and mechanical entrails, and the joyous versifying of December would seem like singular hubris. From a tidal crest of expectation, NASA would be plunged into the bitterest crisis of its brief and eventful life. Nothing was to shed a more vivid light on the problems of managing a race to the moon than the life of Apollo spacecraft 012.

The spacecraft arrived at Cape Kennedy on August 26, 1966. Before leaving the North American plant at Downey, its thousands of parts and scores of subsystems had been checked and rechecked, but a formidable amount of testing remained to be done. As soon as the precious craft reached the Cape, more trials began, some of them in simulated space conditions, in an altitude chamber. The flight crew, Grissom, White and Chaffee, as well as the back-up crew took part. Alongside them, NASA's engineers probed ceaselessly for the weaknesses which no moonship could afford to have. They had learned much from unmanned Apollo flights but, not unnaturally, the manned craft yielded several new defects. Spacecraft 012 was, after all, the most complicated vehicle ever built. It surprised no one that a number of things had to be put right.

On January 6, with the preliminary tests complete, the spacecraft was hoisted to the top of its Saturn IB rocket on Launch Complex 34 and the last climactic weeks of prelaunch checks began. One test, with men aboard, was scheduled for January 27. It was to be a rehearsal of the countdown, "to demonstrate all space vehicle systems and operational procedures in as near a flight configuration as is practical." At the personal request of the crew the test was to end with an emergency escape from the spacecraft, to prove that both they and the escape mechanisms were prepared for any crisis during the launch itself, when the rocket would be fueled and the emergency total.

Grissom, White and Chaffee entered the spacecraft at 1 P.M. on January 27. Grissom at once noticed an odd smell and there was a delay while this was investigated, so the hatches were not clamped down until 2:42 P.M. Spacecraft 012 had three hatches: one sealing the inner, pressurized skin of the spacecraft, a second the outer skin; the third was the protective cover for the early ascent through the atmosphere, designed to be jettisoned along with the launch escape tower. On January 27, the outer hatch was not fully closed because of distortion in the cover produced by several extra bundles of wires needed for the test.

Soon afterward the test controllers started to purge the cabin with oxygen to replace the air. As usual the oxygen was at a pressure of 16.7 pounds per square inch (psi), slightly higher than the atmospheric pressure of 14.7 psi, to check for leaks in the spacecraft. One effect of the excess pressure inside the cabin was to seal shut the inner hatch, which opened inward. It was designed like this deliberately, to minimize leaks of precious oxygen in space.

The simulated countdown proceeded at a leisurely pace, delayed by a defective microphone, which could not be switched off, inside the spacecraft. By 6:20 P.M. it had reached T-minus-10 minutes and was held there pending a solution of the microphone problem. The next ten minutes were occupied with routine checking.

Then, a few seconds after 6:31, came the first intimation that something terrible had happened. Over the intercom, probably from Grissom came a distorted exclamation of, "Hey!" or "Fire!" It was followed almost immediately by another voice, probably Chaffee's, saying, "We've got a fire in the cockpit." For seven long seconds there was silence, then one of the astronauts, possibly Chaffee, said something like, "We've got a bad fire. Let's get out. We're burning up," though the voice was so garbled that according to another interpretation it said, "Fighting a bad fire. Let's get out. Open 'er up." Most people who have heard the tapes agree, however, that the transmission ended with a scream of pain.

On the service structure which stood astride the rocket, the leader of the pad team, Donald O. Babbitt of North American, was standing close beside the spacecraft. On hearing the first report of the fire he ordered nearby technicians, "Get them out of there." But before he could even turn to his communications box to report, he felt a sudden blast of pressure and heat as the spacecraft burst and flames and smoke poured out, instantly setting fire to combustibles outside it.

As Babbitt said later, "My next thoughts were to get out of there as quickly as I could." With three of his technicians he dashed across the walkway to the umbilical tower, through which connections are maintained with the rocket right up to the moment of launch.

Within seconds, however, they had recovered and retraced their steps to the White Room immediately adjacent to the spacecraft. They began struggling to remove the hatches in deadly danger from the rockets in the launch escape tower which might have been ignited. Smoke reduced visibility to a few inches. A few gas-masks and fire-extinguishers were situated near by, but these were completely inadequate, and the Babbitt team had to make periodic dashes for air. It took them, in the end, about four minutes to get the three hatches open.

By then it was already too late. As the smoke slowly cleared and they peered into the smoldering craft, they could see White lying just below the hatch, Grissom on the floor with his feet on his couch, Chaffee still in his place. Firemen had arrived in the meantime and they struggled to get White out, but so intense was the heat that it had welded his suit to the nylon covering of his couch. When doctors arrived they confirmed what everyone already knew: that the three astronauts were beyond any hope of resuscitation.

Medical evidence later established that the men had died from asphyxiation by poisonous gases, particularly carbon monoxide, drawn into the air-conditioning system of their spacesuits when the suits burned through. A fragment of Grissom's suit found outside the spacecraft showed that this must have occurred just before the spacecraft ruptured. The astronauts had lost consciousness in half a minute or less.

Charred and gutted though it was, the interior of the spacecraft permitted investigators to piece together a detailed history of the inferno. It started, the inquiry found, to the left of and below the left-hand couch, Grissom's. Almost certainly it was caused by an arc (spark) from defective electrical equipment or from wiring with damaged insulation. There had been, so the data on the test revealed, a sudden voltage fluctuation inside the spacecraft about nine seconds before Grissom's first cry. This could well have been produced by a momentary arc. The precise site of the arc could not be identified since it was in one of the most badly damaged sections of the spacecraft. But a point where some wiring passed under a compartment door came under strong suspicion. The clearance was very small and the edge of the door might well have damaged the insulation.

The fire had lasted little more than half a minute, but three distinct phases could be identified.

During the first phase the fire grew rapidly but remained fairly localized on the left-hand side of the spacecraft. It fed particularly on the Raschel-knit nylon netting used to prevent small objects disappearing into chinks and corners, and on the nylon Velcro used to secure small objects during weightlessness. (Velcro is a kind of adhesive fabric; two pieces, one bearing a multitude of tiny hooks, the other a fuzzy pile, stick to each other with a burr-like action and can be torn apart again.) Within seconds of the first report a sheet of flames evidently covered the left-hand side, spreading out across the ceiling. Brands of burning molten nylon from the netting were beginning to spread the fire.

As the fire grew in intensity, the temperature and pressure inside the spacecraft rose rapidly, and about fifteen seconds after the first report the capsule burst, with the wall coming away from the floor on the right-hand side, opposite the center of the fire. The second, most violent stage then began. The sudden release of pressure drew the flames right across the interior, over and under the couches. Automatic television cameras outside, focused on the hatch window to monitor the emergency escape practice at the end of the test, showed movements inside the spacecraft which could have been White reaching up in a final effort to open the hatch; then the flames swept across the window.

Six seconds of this holocaust was enough to consume all the oxygen inside the spacecraft, and the fire, now smoldering, entered its final stage. Carbon monoxide and other poisonous gases swiftly rendered the atmosphere in the cabin lethal. Only near the air-conditioning unit, where pipes supplying oxygen and inflammable coolant were fractured, did the fire continue to burn fiercely.

The first reaction to the disaster was naked shock. Nothing in NASA's record of triumphant journeys and safe returns had prepared the public for a calamity of this magnitude. Very soon the shock began to give place to agonized doubt. Everyone knew that spaceflight was a dangerous business, but here were three men who had died on the ground during a routine test. If the accident had happened during a live launch, with the spacecraft poised on a pyre of highly combustible fuel, it might have been easier to comprehend. But the circumstances had been so mundane that they seemed to be without peril. What could have been going on behind NASA's façade of technological perfection? Congressmen, Senators and newspapers, many of whom had for years observed the space agency's activities with star-struck acquiescence, were now driven to ask themselves some very troubling questions.

Within hours of the fire, NASA had established a Review Board charged with discovering how it had happened and how its causes could be eliminated from future craft. The Board's work was conducted behind closed doors, but as its findings began to leak out, suspicion gradually hardened into conviction: the fire began to look less like an act of God or the devil, and more like the kind of culpable human error no one was accustomed to expect from the space agency.

The Board's work was completed in two months, and its published report of the fateful thirty seconds seemed to be a miracle of forensic investigation. Its complexity, its minute attention to detail, its lengthy recommendations for action, all these satisfied many people that justice had been done and, more important, that the manned space program could be expected to move ahead with speed and safety toward the moon. But the Board did not reassure everyone. How could it? To any faintly inquiring mind, its report showed with the utmost clarity that the accident ought never to have happened. Its conclusion, essentially, was this: that both the design and construction of the spacecraft, and the conditions in which the test on January 27 had taken place, were in many particulars an invitation to disaster; a disaster, moreover, which could have been averted if a few quite simple precautions had been taken.

There was a prodigious list of errors. Thus, spacecraft 012 had contained more than seventy pounds of inflammable materials which had been tested as fire hazards in the most perfunctory manner, if at all. Its hatch took ninety seconds to open in ideal conditions; the build-up of pressure inevitably caused by a fire in a sealed space made escape impossible before the spacecraft burst. Because the test had not been identified as "hazardous," there were neither people nor equipment on hand to deal with the emergency. The Board also determined that there were basic deficiencies in design, workmanship and quality control—deficiencies which would certainly have imperiled

men in space if not on the ground. The environmental control
system, for example, had had a long history of failures, and leakage
of the inflammable coolant had been a chronic unresolved problem.
The electronic wiring had been badly designed and installed. The
complete spacecraft had not been vibration-tested. There were no
design features for fire protection.

All this was painstakingly set out by the Board, and yet its report
seemed curiously incomplete. It dealt with all the proximate causes,
as well as it could, but with none of the remoter ones. After a disaster
of these proportions, it might have been expected to penetrate below
the mechanical defects and allocate some responsibility for them. It
might have felt impelled to examine the underlying condition of
NASA and its prime contractor which had permitted the carelessness
to which the fire testified to occur. But the Apollo Review Board
carefully skirted such difficult territory, hurrying through such portions of it as were unavoidable with never a glance to either side.
It approached the tragedy as though the fire had revealed a neatly
definable technical problem in a piece of hardware.

The main reason for this narrow approach soon became clear.
When James Webb was testifying on the fire to the House Space
Committee, he said, "Our object was to get ready to fly again." After
due expressions of grief for the dead astronauts, the future was
NASA's only concern. Similarly with the Review Board. Its report
dug below the physical facts only deep enough to ensure that no comparable accident occurred again. It was designed to show how the men
had died but not, at bottom, why.

In the context of a race to the moon this objective was not entirely
without justification. Recrimination would be an indulgence, likely
only to arouse public hostility to the space program as a whole and
retard the space agency's efforts. It would have exposed many deep-
seated questions. What if the fire proved to be a symptom of some
more profound malaise? Were there deficiencies in NASA's vaunted
senior management? Was the goal of a moon landing by 1970 compelling the agency to take unwarrantable risks? Might the defects
revealed by the fire reappear in some other form, perhaps leading to
more deaths? Such questions were never officially asked. Instead,
NASA adopted the classic bureaucratic reflex of confining the Board's
terms of reference within the strictest limits. Its job was simply to

ensure that there were no more fires. As the chairman, Dr. Floyd L. Thompson, said, "We did not consider ourselves a board of management experts."

One key to the caution which reveals itself on every page of the Board's report is that it was written by government employees. Thompson himself was director of the space agency's Langley Research Center, and no fewer than six of the eight Board members were NASA officials. They had an intimate knowledge of the problems of spaceflight and the complexities of spacecraft construction, and as such they were admirably qualified for an investigation designed to get NASA "ready to fly again." But they were not so obviously the men to conduct a thorough investigation into the heart of the space agency's management.

Nor, as soon emerged, were the elected representatives of the taxpayer any better equipped for the task. Both Houses of Congress held their own hearings on the accident. They, too, conscientiously plowed through the baffling details about cabin atmosphere and electric arcs. They demanded prolonged testimony both from Webb and his associates and from the executives of North American Aviation. Very occasionally the odd Senator crossed into regions scrupulously avoided by the Review Board, but he rarely pressed home the awkward questions. To read through the congressional hearings, which occupy thousands of pages of text and appendices, reminds one of a fight between an unarmed matador and a bull of uncertain temper. Again and again the bull charges at the red rag of technological fact deftly wielded by the engineers and administrators, only to find it as elusive as air. From time to time he gets the matador on the run, but never for long. The fight ends with the bull exhausted by his ineffectual exertions, and the matador with his reputation tarnished but his flesh unscathed.

The congressional record, therefore, is only marginally useful in the discovery of the truth. It exposed a few well-guarded secrets, but these were not directly connected with the fire. Many of the legislators, imbued as heavily as NASA with the spirit of the race, were reluctant to inspect the omens too closely. Those who chose a more adventurous course were easily rebuffed. The House of Representatives, in fact, was so uncertain of the proper role to play that it never published any report of its conclusions. It is left, therefore, to our independent investigation to attempt a more complete account.

According to the Review Board, six conditions contributed to the disaster. These were: (1) A sealed cabin, pressurized with oxygen. (2) A cabin full of combustible materials. (3) Vulnerable electric wiring. (4) Vulnerable plumbing carrying a combustible and corrosive coolant. (5) Inadequate provisions for escape. (6) Inadequate provisions for rescue or medical assistance. Of these the first three are by far the most important, for they caused the fire, and any account must focus on them.

From the medical point of view, the best atmosphere for a spacecraft would be the most natural one: air, which consists of 20 percent oxygen and 80 percent nitrogen, at atmospheric pressure, 14.7 psi. From the engineering point of view the best is the simplest: oxygen at the minimum pressure needed to sustain life. The use of a single gas means that no equipment is needed to control its composition; the lower the pressure the smaller the leakage rate and the smaller the demands on the spacecraft structure which contains it.

Inevitably a spacecraft atmosphere is a compromise, one of the innumerable trade-offs between competing demands which have to be made in any engineering design. The original Apollo specification was for a 50:50 mixture of oxygen and nitrogen at a total pressure of 7 psi, but in August 1962, NASA decided to change to pure oxygen at 5 psi. This was a perfectly reasonable decision. It produced a valuable saving in weight and eliminated a potential source of failure, the equipment for controlling the composition of the mixture. Some medical fears about the use of pure oxygen were expressed at the time, but they have proved to be groundless.

But having chosen pure oxygen, the spacecraft designers cannot be excused for having treated the risk of fire so lightly. The fire risk of pure oxygen atmospheres had been known for years. Oxygen is not inflammable, but it supports combustion, and the difference between the way things burn in air and in oxygen is well known to any schoolboy who has thrust a glowing taper into oxygen and seen it suddenly flare up. Materials which in air are slightly inflammable or even noninflammable burn readily in oxygen. A case has been recorded of an asbestos blanket bursting into flames when it was used in an attempt to extinguish an oxygen fire.

Knowledge of the fire hazards of oxygen is not merely theoretical. There is a long, well-documented history of fires in oxygen chambers, many of them involving personal injury and even loss of life. Two are particularly notable since they occurred, significantly enough, during NASA's own test program designed to demonstrate that the 5 psi oxygen atmosphere chosen for Apollo was medically safe.

The first was on September 9, 1962, at the U.S. Air Force School of Aerospace Medicine in Texas. The fire started when an electrical fault set alight a display panel which soon filled the chamber with toxic fumes. The two pilots taking part in the test were wearing pressure suits at the time, but one of them was asleep and for some reason he opened his visor when he woke up. The fumes got into the suit-circuits and both men passed out. Fortunately they were rescued before they were seriously burned, and both recovered.

The second fire broke out during a similar test at the U.S. Navy Air Crew Equipment Laboratory in Philadelphia, on November 17, 1962. Three subjects and a flight surgeon were in the chamber at the time, all wearing pajamas. While one of them was changing a light bulb, a short circuit occurred and the socket caught fire. The man tried to smother it with a cotton towel but that, too, caught fire, burning so vigorously that it set fire to his clothes. The fire spread to the clothes of the others as they tried to put it out and all four were burned, two seriously.

As warnings of the danger of fire in the Apollo spacecraft, they could not have been better timed. The cabin atmosphere had been changed to pure oxygen only a few months before, and the spacecraft was still in its early design stage. But they were dismissed as having no real significance as far as spacecraft were concerned.

NASA could not make the same claim about a report it commissioned and published on spacecraft cabin atmospheres by Dr. Emanuel M. Roth of the Lovelace Foundation. Part 2 deals with fire and blast hazards, and in it Roth announces his acute awareness of the dangers of oxygen. He emphasizes the precautions which are indispensable if it is to be made reasonably safe: eliminating hazardous equipment or isolating it in special storage compartments; getting rid of all combustibles except those which are absolutely essential, and fireproofing, sealing or separating these with pretested firebreaks; adequate fire discipline; and pretesting to locate potential hot spots. Published in 1964, this urgent catalogue of essentials has a hideously prophetic ring to anyone familiar with the literature of the Apollo fire. It sounds very like the list of modifications made to the Apollo spacecraft after the accident, modifications allegedly made in the light of new knowledge gained from the fire.

Of course, the fire risk was not ignored completely in the design of Apollo. The underlying approach was described by Seamans in a memo to Webb as controlling "the known risk of fire—on the pad or in orbit—by isolating and rendering safe all possible ignition sources."

The same approach had been used in Mercury and Gemini, and NASA's confidence in it was justified to the Senate Space Committee by Dr. George Mueller, the director of manned space flight, in remarkable words: "The fire in the Apollo spacecraft cabin occurred under conditions and using procedures which had been verified by seven years of manned spacecraft operational experience. [These had] demonstrated that the possibility of a fire in the spacecraft cabin was remote." Even before the fire it would have been a strange argument, equivalent to saying that it was not worth bothering to insure one's house because it had stood for twenty years without getting burned down. After the fire it sounded even more absurd: the Review Board Report made it perfectly clear that seven years of experience in no way demonstrated that fire risks were remote.

In practice two procedures were thought adequate to eliminate sources of ignition: careful insulation of all wiring and electrical components, and screening of materials to weed out those which could be ignited easily. This screening was based on a specification developed by North American, and approved by NASA, in the early days of Apollo. It ruled out for the interior of the command module materials which could be ignited by a spark at a temperature of 400° F. in an atmosphere of pure oxygen at 16.7 psi. It said nothing at all about the total bulk of inflammable materials, their location inside the spacecraft, or the permissible rate at which they should burn.

On January 27, 1967, the inadequacy of these precautions was cruelly laid bare. The salient question posed by NASA's central response to the fire is whether the agency could reasonably have been expected to discern their inadequacy before it was proved in death.

The main thrust of NASA's testimony throughout the congressional hearings was to the effect that the fire had revealed facts which not only were not, but could not, be foreseen by any reasonable man. The evidence, both actual and experimental, suggests that this view was at best a delusion, at worst a deception.

Shortly after the fire, a similar fire was induced in the mocked-up interior of a spacecraft in order to discover the course it had taken. It was an obvious experiment for the investigators to conduct. But equally, it should have been an obvious test to have made *before* any men were invited to risk their lives in such a combustible bundle as the all-oxygen Apollo. If the fire risk had been estimated correctly, the experiment would have been elementary. It would immediately have alerted the spacecraft's designers to the speed and fury with which a fire would feed on the materials placed in it, and it would have forced them to reconsider the adequacy of their policy of "isolating and rendering safe all possible ignition sources." Had there been serious concern about fire risk, it is inconceivable that such an experiment would not have been conducted long before spacecraft 012 was complete. Had there been an experiment, there would in all probability have been no fatal fire—the danger points would have been seen and removed.

But in spite of the Roth report, and in spite of the oxygen-chamber fires which had occurred during NASA's own tests, the concern for fire was minimal. The approach to the problem, in fact, was not experimental, as one might expect in a program reaching beyond the frontiers of past human experience. It was, essentially, intuitive.

Experiments would not even have been necessary to expose the fire risk on the ground, which in many ways is greater than in space. Dispassionate analysis would have been enough. After the hatches of an Apollo spacecraft are sealed, the pressure inside remains, until after the launch, at 16.7 psi; and materials burn still more readily in 16.7 psi oxygen than in the 5 psi to which it is reduced in space. Once in space, moreover, the astronauts can depressurize the spacecraft, a certain way of extinguishing a fire. On the ground this is impossible because of the atmospheric pressure outside.

This additional risk of fire on the pad was predicted in so many words in 1964. The *Journal of Spacecraft and Rockets,* published by the American Institute of Aeronautics and Astronautics and doubtless having some readership in Houston, carried an article by Dr. F. J. Hendel, an employee of North American, which said of oxygen, "It presents a fire hazard, which is especially great on the launching pad, when the cabin is purged with oxygen at 14.7 psi." The significance of this warning lies not so much in the fact that it was overlooked (the spacecraft designers could hardly be expected to incorporate every outside suggestion) as in its proof that the risks on the pad could be anticipated by any reasonably well-qualified person who bothered to think about the fire hazard.

Had the dangers on the pad been recognized, the lives of the three astronauts might have been saved by some quite elementary precautions, such as having properly equipped rescue teams standing by. And the hatch would not, of course, have been designed so that it sealed itself immovably in the event of a fire. A quick-release, outward-opening hatch was already on the drawing board at the time of the accident—not as a fire precaution; it was designed to make space-walking easier.

True alertness to the hazards would also have precluded another unhappy circumstance. On January 27, 1967, spacecraft 012 was still littered with launch-pad junk. Almost eleven of the seventy-five pounds of combustible materials there were never intended for flight. Polyurethane pads weighing over two pounds were on the floor to cushion the hatch when it was removed during the emergency-escape practice; there were even seven pounds of paper and half a pound of cotton tags marked "Remove before flight." These had not the remotest pretention to fire resistance.

In fact, the whole policy of "isolating and rendering safe all possible ignition sources" was evidence of the intuitive, rather than the empirical, approach. The Apollo spacecraft contains some fifteen miles of wiring and tens of thousands of electrical and electronic components. Even given perfect workmanship it would have been rash to assume that there would be no arcs or hot spots capable of starting a fire. And, as investigation revealed, the workmanship was far from perfect.

Bad workmanship in the wiring was particularly serious. Among other examples of carelessness, the Board found wiring routed through narrow channels with many right-angle bends, where pressure from the corners could have damaged the insulation; wires pressed tightly up against panels; and floor wiring not protected from damage by technicians working in the spacecraft or the astronauts themselves. Some of the wires which survived the fire were found to be "mashed," presumably for this reason.

Of course, the Apollo designers did not rely entirely on a foolproof electrical system. The specification also included restrictions on materials. The inadequacy of these has already been outlined, but one of the defects of the testing procedure is especially notable: the 400° F maximum temperature used in the tests. A North American report on "Fire Detection and Extinguishment in Spacecraft" dated April 22, 1965, underlines how surprisingly low this was. The report states, "Causes of local high temperatures are varied. Electronic equipment may generate temperatures up to 800° F. Electric motors develop frictional energy resulting in high temperatures if the accumulating heat is not dissipated. Local temperatures created by the already mentioned electrical arcing can be very high."

Even this lax specification was applied very loosely. According to a North American statement to the House committee, it was waived when small quantities were involved, when only small areas were exposed, when there was no ignition source nearby, or when the material was protected from an ignition source. As a result of such waivers, over three hundred items used in the spacecraft did not meet even this specification. They included the couch padding, to which astronaut White's body was welded by the heat: this, it emerged, could be ignited by a spark at 250°.

But the most glaring omission in the specification was that it said nothing whatever about the location or total quantities of inflammable materials. Blandly assuming that a fire could never start in the spacecraft, the designers did nothing to prevent one from spreading. Roth's warnings about the need to get rid of all combustibles except those absolutely essential and to seal or separate the rest with properly tested firebreaks were ignored.

So it was that as the design and construction of the spacecraft progressed, more and more inflammable materials found their way into it. In particular there were the nylon-netting debris-trap and the nylon-Velcro, which between them lined most of the spacecraft's interior and spread the fire so catastrophically; there were also the couch pads and large quantities of polyurethane foam. This last was apparently incorrectly tested. In the North American lists of materials which had passed the flammability test, it was listed as acceptable, but its true fire point turned out to be only just over 300°.

Perhaps the most revealing comment of all on the policy of viewing the elimination of ignition sources as the paramount method of avoiding a fire came from NASA itself, when Dr. Mueller told the Senate Committee, "The fact is now clear that we will not be able to eliminate completely ignition sources in the cabin. We will continue to take every precaution to minimize possible ignition sources, but we cannot expect perfection." Naturally this was after the fire, which proved that perfection had not been achieved. Only now was Mueller saying, after tests and analyses which could equally well have been carried out before the fire, that perfection was unattainable.

"There was," Mueller sadly confessed, "a basic flaw in our engineering judgment." He went on to draw an analogy with the Martin 202 aircraft, whose wings failed through metal fatigue in spite of "very careful design and very careful testing." But the analogy is a dubious one. Metal fatigue at the time was a comparatively new and little-understood problem. It is still not fully understood. There was no lack of understanding about fire. NASA and North American knew what needed to be done in general terms a few days after the disaster.

The right method, they now realized, was rigidly to control the use of inflammable materials in the spacecraft. Before the fire the designers had put themselves, quite unnecessarily, in the position of the operators of an oil refinery who are obliged to rely on ignition control as their sole method of fire prevention; an oil refinery cannot avoid dealing in inflammable petroleum. But as the measures taken after the fire proved, the bulk of the inflammable materials could have been eliminated from spacecraft 012. By keeping combustible materials down to the absolute minimum, and isolating those that were essential, the spacecraft could have been designed to "fail safe" from the start, so that if there did turn out to be ignition sources in spite of all efforts to eliminate them they would not lead inevitably to disaster.

As Mueller acknowledged, "the selection and location of materials" was the "central problem." It is also the area where the Review Board's hesitation to plumb all the facts is particularly evident.

Materials, in fact, emerge as the crucial instance of avoidable and deadly negligence. The Board did a characteristically thorough job of recording what was in spacecraft 012 at the time of the fire, assessing inflammability and recommending what needed to be done. But it had virtually nothing to say about the history of the various materials specifications. In particular, it omitted to take any account of the fact that, for at least six months before the fire, NASA and North American had been in dispute over the fire risk of materials in the spacecraft, with the agency belatedly trying to impose more stringent standards on the manufacturer. This point would unquestionably have been seized on by the congressional investigators as fundamental had it emerged clearly from the report of the Review Board; but in three thousand pages it gets a mere two paragraphs, buried deeply in an appendix. The documents on which they are based are locked away in the Board's archives, which can be inspected only by permission of the chairman.

It is now possible, however, to disclose an essential piece of evidence about materials which was put neither to Congress nor to the Review Board. Brief extracts appeared in the *Sunday Times* in July 1969. The evidence consists of part of a transcript of a Customer Acceptance Readiness Review meeting, held at the North American plant at Downey in August 1966. The meeting was the last between NASA and North American officials before spacecraft 012 was shipped to the Cape.

The meeting took place after a "walk-through" inspection of the spacecraft by representatives of both parties. The transcript reveals that NASA officials are seriously concerned about the fire hazards they have seen. It begins with a statement from an engineer named William M. Bland from the Manned Spacecraft Center. "I know we are still trying to figure out a way to manage the materials that go in," Bland says, ". . . and a way to control them. I would like to observe that we do not have a system for the selecting of materials yet. I know that North American has one by contract but it is not necessarily up to date. I would like to observe that we have some materials in spacecraft 012 which, when we considered spacecraft 008 safety, we did have removed. [008 was used for manned tests on the ground at Houston. It was not intended to fly.] These are made of nylon and Velcro. Piece by piece and individually they are not too bad, but in certain places there are large amounts measured in feet and probably in pounds where these chafing straps are gathered. I consider them hazardous. . . ."

Dale D. Myers, North American's Apollo Program manager, is evidently unimpressed. He replies, "Regarding the Velcro chafing guards, our position is that our criteria are satisfactory. . . . There are other materials that could be used but we do not see the necessity of changing these particular ones."

But Bland continues to urge his point. He suggests that large quantities of materials like Velcro be kept away from electrical wiring, "the only source of fire on board." In response to more prevarication by representatives of North American he goes on: "The only thing I can say is that when you have a broken conductor ignited it burns like mad and sputters all over, as tests have shown. . . . We have some rather strong thoughts in NASA as you are aware. I think we must bring this to resolution and not let it drift on. On SC 008 we did remove these large quantities of nylon-Velcro chafe guards—these were the ones on the floor of the spacecraft. I might say they are very heavy as well as very inflammable. On SC 008 it was relatively simple; these things get replaced by a pad on the floor that the crew slept on. In the case of a flight spacecraft, I think it would be a little more difficult, but I imagine a fiberglass cover to protect these same wire bundles could easily be made. Fiberglass being much more preferred than a nylon-Velcro cover."

The company's chief Apollo engineer, George Jeffs, replies crushingly to this appeal, "I guess it's a matter of how far you go—you can go a long way relative to taking all kinds of things out of the spacecraft. I guess the point is, can we pinpoint those things which are really of rational concern, and what is taken to remove and replace them, and then go ahead and make the decision as to what we are going to do."

Bland agrees with this: "I think we can, and I think we have picked by reasonable criteria the items we can remove. We understand that almost all nonmetallics will burn, Velcro being one of the worst, but if you have it in a reasonable position, and in reasonable quantities, you can get by with it." But Bland goes on to outline the large scope of the problem: "To say that possible removal would be from two places only would be like saying remove everything. I think we have one place on the bottom of the floor which is the largest. We have asked people to see if there are any other areas of concentration."

202   JOURNEY TO TRANQUILITY

Then the senior NASA man present, Joseph Shea, chief of the spacecraft program, intervenes to terminate the discussion. In doing so he admits that some of the NASA criteria have been inadequate, but urges that the obviously crucial danger points should be rectified without delay. "It seems to me," he says, "that there are materials in the spacecraft which are flammable and that we probably did not have as good control of spacecraft materials as we would have liked through the run of the program. I think we are trying to take a rational position, which says that the real concern is to get these flammable materials in a position where they cannot be ignited. The only place where we can see these getting ignited, since we are not going to carry matches on board, is the possibility of a wire breaking and some kind of shorting. . . . I think we should stop bitching at each other and go clear the thing up. . . . It's like we're standing on a matter of principle instead of fixing something that is relatively easily fixed."

The discussion ends on a bitterly macabre note. Astronaut Gus Grissom, the commander of 012 and a man with possibly more "rational concern" than anyone present, says, "You will 'kill' this before it leaves here. You are not going to fool around with wire bundles after we test it down at the Cape."

Unhappily, something very like fooling around did go on at the Cape. The offending chafing guards were in fact removed; but they were replaced, in the casual atmosphere then attending spacecraft ground tests, by a further nineteen pounds of inflammable materials, including five thousand square inches of new Velcro, installed after 012 arrived in Florida. It is one of the many tragic ironies of the disaster that another walk-through inspection of spacecraft 012, which would probably have led to the removal of many combustibles, was scheduled for January 29, two days after the fire.

The background to the Downey meeting was as follows. During 1966 the Manned Spacecraft Center introduced a new specification for spacecraft materials, refining the one already in force. In general terms it said that materials which in a standard test burned at more than half an inch per second should not be used within twelve inches of wiring and electrical equipment.

This specification had several shortcomings. Like North American's, it said nothing about total quantities of inflammable materials, and it was devised specifically with fires in space in mind. Thus the tests were carried out in 5 psi oxygen instead of the more dangerous 16.7 psi used on the ground, and they involved measuring the rate at which the samples burned *downward*. This was intended to simulate burning rates in weightlessness, where, because there is no convection, fires spread slowly and tend to smother themselves in their own by-products. Fires on the ground, of course, burn far faster upward than they do downward; for them the specification gave a quite unreal picture.

Nevertheless, the new specification was an important improvement, for the first time introducing limitations on the rate at which materials burned and on their locations.

Since the precise point at which the fire started could never be identified with certainty, it is impossible to say whether strict enforcement of the NASA specification would have prevented the disaster. But if one of the most suspected points of origin was indeed the place where the fire started, then noncompliance may very well have been crucial. This point was low down in the forward left-hand corner of the spacecraft, where some wiring passed close under an aluminum panel, protected by a nylon chafing guard. Three-eighths of an inch from the end of the nylon strip, and only one-eighth of an inch from the adhesive material which extended beyond the end of the strip, were the tell-tale signs of an electrical arc. Tests after the fire showed that tension in the wire could make the edge of the panel penetrate the insulation on the wire and produce an arc, that the arc could set the nylon strip alight, which would lead in turn to nearby Velcro and nylon netting. If the nylon strip burned faster than half an inch a second then, according to the latest NASA specification, it was not permitted to be in that position. Had it not been there, a fire could not have started at that point.

In the middle of 1966, NASA started to put pressure on North American to add the new specification to its own. The company was in no hurry to do so. Discussions dragged on for months and as late as January 10, 1967, NASA refused to accept a letter from North American setting out its position. Agreement was reached soon afterward, but the NASA specification was not formally incorporated into North American's until January 27, the very day of the fire, and even then it was not contractually imposed.

Where they deal with these specifications at all, the congressional hearings demonstrate only their extraordinary confusion at the time of the fire. Thus the report of the Panel on Materials, an appendix to the Review Board report, says of the difference the NASA specification would have made to spacecraft 012: "The two most significant differences were the restrictions given to the application of Velcro and the Uralane [a form of polyurethane foam] in the NASA criteria. Such restrictions would have prevented the installation of these materials any closer than twelve inches to electrical leads. This would have made a significant difference in the amount of both of these materials installed in the spacecraft at the time of the accident."

However, only a few days after the report was published the following exchange took place between Mueller and Representative Vander Jagt, a member of the House Space Committee.

Dr. Mueller, ". . . 012 and all spacecraft exceeded the NASA standards."

Mr. Vander Jagt, "Is the Review Board's statement that NASA's standards were not applied to the contractor correct?"

Dr. Mueller, "That is not correct. The NASA standards were applied to the contractor; the contract had not been changed to include those standards as a contractual item."

Then in a written answer to a question submitted by Representative Emilio Daddario on the same day, Mueller said, "Inspection of spacecraft 012 subsequent to the fire revealed that Velcro had been used in contact with wire bundles in some cases. This was in violation of the NASA criteria, the general terms of the top contractual specification, and of technical direction resulting from the 'walk-through' inspection at the spacecraft's acceptance review."

In another written answer, North American listed two violations of the NASA specification merely in the region where the fire started. In one case wiring harness was in direct contact with polyurethane insulation in the environmental control unit. In another, Velcro was within six inches of wire harnesses in the same area. Some of this was Velcro installed at Cape Kennedy at the request of the astronauts and authorized by a body called the Spacecraft Change Implementation Board which, although a NASA body, was not using the NASA specification.

Nowhere does the Review Board's reluctance to grasp the management nettle emerge more clearly than its handling of this central issue of materials. What with the Manned Spacecraft Center and North American's rival specifications, the ambiguous status of the former, materials removed at Downey at NASA's request because of the fire risk being put back at Cape Kennedy under the auspices of another NASA body working to an entirely different set of rules, the situation was evidently chaotic. Here was a manifest collapse of management, not technology, yet all the Review Board had to say in its final report was a single sentence: subsection (e) of Finding No. 11 which says "discrepancies existed between North American and NASA specifications regarding inclusion and positioning of inflammable materials."

These evasions of key issues passed virtually unnoticed, or at any rate unquestioned, by Congress. Members of both committees expressed a keen interest in the differences between the two specifications, but not in why NASA's had taken so long to implement. And Mueller's astonishing statement that "it is clear that the control of flammable materials was under a single appointed control, so I am not aware of . . . a lack of co-ordination" was hardly contested.

Nor were the baffled legislators any more successful in exposing many of the space agency's other evasions. Two examples will suffice.

In response to questions from Mr. James Gehrig, staff director of the Senate committee, concerning differences in burning-rates in 5 and 16.7 psi oxygen, NASA produced a graph illustrating the differences for three materials. These were Nomex, used in the outer layer of the spacesuits, neoprene-coated nylon, used in the liferaft, and Velcro hook fabric. In the worst case the increase is an undramatic 30 percent or so and the failure to perform tests at the higher pressure did not seem too serious an omission.

But the graph would have looked very different had Raschel-knit netting, which spread the fire more effectively than any other material, or polyurethane foam, another major fuel, been included. Their rate of burning more than doubles with the increase of oxygen pressure.

Second, the question naturally arose of whether there were less inflammable materials which could have been used in place of those involved in the fire, and if so why had they not been used before the fire. It was answered in several ways, but NASA's general line was that suitable substitutes had only recently become available as a result of sudden research discoveries.

The following written answer is typical: "The functions performed by the materials in question were necessary. The materials which are now considered as substitutes were not available at the time of design release or start of fabrication in the form necessary. In fact it remains to be determined how successfully some of the candidate replacements can be used." It then goes on to cite in some detail a new glass fiber suitable for spacesuits.

Now flameproof spacesuits and oxygen supplies might conceivably have saved the lives of Grissom, White and Chaffee. But it has never been suggested that their suits formed anything but a minor contribution to the fire, which began to burn well after the fire had started. The major fuels were the Raschel net, Velcro and polyurethane foam.

In view of this, it is not uninteresting to note the materials eventually used as substitutes for these three. The Raschel net, probably the most combustible material of all, was replaced with aluminum panels, the polyurethane foam with molded glass fibers—hardly exotic new materials. As for the Velcro, the original nylon-based material was replaced by one made from various fire-resistant fibers, developed promptly by the Velcro Corporation at its own expense as soon as the need became evident. It could have been developed just as quickly before the fire, had anyone thought to request it.

Very little of this extraordinary story was really fathomed by Congress. In a haze of technological confusion and muddled patriotism, the legislators failed to fasten on to the most damaging implications of the fire. Their most significant discovery, in fact, had no direct connection with the events of January 27, 1967. On the other hand, it perhaps did something to explain part of the reason why, ultimately, that disaster had ever been allowed to happen.

Congress, or rather one Congressman, a sceptical New Yorker named William Fitts Ryan, disclosed that, little more than a year before the tragedy, NASA had become profoundly concerned by the general performance of its main contractor. In the autumn of 1965 it had dispatched a top-level inspection team to the Space Division of North American in California to try to establish what was going wrong. The team spent two weeks at the plant, under the leadership of General Samuel Phillips, Apollo Program director. What Congressman Ryan obtained not long after the fire was a copy of the Phillips Report on the sad condition of North American Aviation.

It proved to be a shattering document, possibly one of the most devastating indictments of any industrial corporation ever to appear in print. It was addressed privately to the North American chairman and it had all the riveting candor of a secret memorandum—in vivid contrast to most of NASA's public statements.

The team had gone to Downey, the report said, because there had been "continual failure by North American to achieve the progress required to support the objective of the Apollo program." As the program had progressed, NASA had been forced to accept over a long period "slippages in key milestone accomplishments, degradation in hardware performance and increasing costs."

Neither Apollo nor stage two of the Saturn rocket, which North American was also building, was spared. On the Saturn S-II, Phillips discovered:

> Key performance milestones in testing, as well as end-item hardware deliveries, have slipped continuously in spite of deletions of both hardware and test content. The fact that the delivery of the common bulkhead test article was rescheduled five times, for a total slippage of more than a year, the All Systems firing rescheduled five times for a total slippage of more than a year, and S-II-1 and S-II-2 flight stage deliveries rescheduled several times for a slippage of more than a year, are indicative of NASA's inability to stay within planned schedules. . . . The S-II cost picture has been essentially a series of cost escalations with a bow wave of peak costs advancing steadily throughout the program life. . . . NASA's estimate of the total 10-stage program has more than tripled.

The spacecraft showed scarcely better progress:

> The propulsion spacecraft, the systems integration spacecraft and the spacecraft for the first development flight have each slipped more than six months. In addition, the first manned and the key environmental ground spacecraft have each slipped more than a year. . . . North American is forecasting that the total cost of the reduced spacecraft program will be greater than the cost of the previously planned program. . . . The final estimate does not represent either in tasks to be done or in resources re-

quired the legitimate program requirements as judged by the program manager, but represents total work and dollars required to support a certain level of effort within the Space Division of North American. Frankly stated, we firmly believe that the Space Division is overmanned and that the S-II and C.S.M. [command and service module] programs can be done, and done better, with fewer people.

Listing a massive series of technical faults in the hardware, the Phillips Report found "a continued inability to meet internal objectives." Remarkably, "effective planning and control from a program standpoint does not exist." Moreover, "the principles and procedures for configuration management as agreed between North American and NASA are not being adhered to by the engineering organizations. . . . The condition of the hardware shipped from the factory, with thousands of hours of work to complete, is unsatisfactory to NASA. . . . North American quality is not up to NASA required standards."

In a covering letter to the North American President, Lee Atwood, dated December 16, 1965, Phillips made it perfectly clear that his report was more than routine nit-picking. "I am definitely not satisfied with the progress and outlook of either program," he wrote. "Even with due consideration of hopeful signs, I could not find a substantive basis for confidence in future performance."

For months later, the team returned to Downey and concluded, so NASA said later, that the company had dramatically improved its performance in the light of the agency's recommendations. It had been put under intense pressure to establish a firmer grip and speed up its production; it lived under the unspoken threat of the Apollo contract even being removed from its hands. This was not without relevance to the fire: the urgency which the company felt suggests one plausible reason why it was reluctant to adopt any new specification on materials which might have involved yet further delay.

Naturally, neither this nor any other implication of the Phillips Report attracted the interest of the fire Review Board. The Board found that "deficiencies in command module design, workmanship and quality control" were creating "an unnecessarily hazardous condition." Other of its findings bore a similarly close resemblance to the language of Phillips. But of the Phillips Report itself, which the Board was able to inspect, not a single mention appeared. The Review Board's report gave no indication that North American had been seen to be ailing many months before the fire.

But for Mr. Ryan's intervention, it is possible that no one would have heard of the Phillips Report to this day. For a long time, both NASA and North American denied that it existed. "I know of no unusual Phillips Report," Dr. Mueller told the Senate space committee on February 27, when rumors of it leaked out. When James Webb was asked for a copy he first offered to make one available to the Comptroller-General, then confused it with a completely different document, and finally said, "Let us look it up."

On April 11, the Report's existence was still being denied. This time it was North American's man, Lee Atwood, to whom Phillips' covering letter had been addressed, who blandly responded to Congressman Ryan, "The Phillips Report to whom?"

"Has not that been discussed with you?" asked Ryan.

"I have heard it mentioned, but General Phillips has not given us a copy of any report," replied Atwood, who was on oath at the time.

But by degrees the truth emerged. First, despite its explicit title, the Report was acknowledged as a "set of notes." Later, Phillips gave a copy of it to the Senate. After denying that it existed, NASA now termed it "an extraordinary effort." Lee Atwood, with the cat out of the bag now, unblushingly said that he had tried "very, very hard" to comply with its recommendations. He had, he said, "put a tremendous amount of emphasis" on it.

It was understandable that North American should have attempted to keep the report at the back of its files; less that NASA should have done so. NASA, after all, was a government agency which might have been expected to have somewhat different standards from a commercial corporation. Moreover, the agency emerged not discreditably from the report. It had been making a commendable effort to improve its contractor's standards and, among other things, reduce fire hazards.

But the intimacy with which NASA stood behind North American tells a lot about the principles on which the machinery for reaching the moon was built. These were partly spelled out by Robert Seamans, speaking to the Senate committee: "For a relationship to be effective between government and contractor there must be mutual

confidence and if on every occasion there is a minor or a major review this is going to be exposed in all its detail, it will soon erode the
confidence that is so necessary."

The relationship could be described rather more explicitly. NASA
was in the position of a father guarding the reputation of his family
from the misdeeds of a wayward son. A public airing of the deficiencies
of North American would have rebounded on to NASA itself and the
entire space program. "Perfection is the goal," North American had
said. "Zero-defects" was the policy of the space agency. To some extent the organizations were indistinguishable from each other, with the
staff of each working on the other's ground. If one failed, they both
suffered; if there were mistakes, it was in the interest of both to establish not that the other was to blame but that neither were. This policy reached a zenith with the investigation of the fire: *people* were
not responsible, machinery had merely failed to work properly.

No conspiratorial collusion is needed to put this policy into effect.
Like the components of the military-industrial complex, the NASA-
industrial complex has a natural community of interest. As far as
documents such as the Phillips Report are concerned, that interest is
perfectly clear: to keep the matter strictly between themselves.

Congress was a willing abettor of this policy. Hearings on the 1967
NASA budget had passed without any mention of the condition of
the firm which would gather in the largest single portion of it. With a
few bold exceptions, Congressmen behaved with similar decorum after
the fire. "I have asked about the Phillips Report," said Representative
Olin E. Teague, chairman of the Manned Spaceflight Subcommittee
in the House, when the question of its existence was raised. "It is my
understanding this is nothing more than a group of notes. . . . There
really is no Phillips Report." And when one of his colleagues asked
why Joseph Shea, clearly a key witness and the only senior NASA official to leave the program after the fire, was not being called to testify,
Teague replied, "It is the prerogative of the chairman to call witnesses.
If the gentleman doesn't get the information he wants from the
witnesses that are before us today, I don't think he can get them anywhere in the world." NASA did not want Shea on the stand beside its
more senior officials, and Congress never insisted that he should attend.

Perhaps the frankest insight into congressional attitudes toward

NASA, even in the wake of disaster, was offered by a senior member of the staff of the Senate Committee. When questioned recently about the Phillips Report, his only concern was to express amazement at the clumsy manner in which NASA had allowed its existence to leak out. "If only they had come to us privately," he said, "and told us this thing existed, we could have made sure that it was handled quietly, in a way which would not have caused public alarm at the way the program was being run."

In the end, NASA's prevarication over the Phillips Report somewhat spoiled the success achieved by its smooth handling of the consequences of the fire. Many committee members were notably sympathetic in their questioning of NASA officials after the fire, though less so with representatives of North American. They were particularly hard on an unfortunate fellow who offered the not unreasonable suggestion that Grissom might accidentally have kicked a wire and damaged its insulation. The very notion of astronautic negligence was greeted as though Grissom had been charged with lighting a cigarette inside the spacecraft.

But one thing Congress never likes is that it should be made publicly evident that it has been taken for a ride. Some previously sympathetic members became suspicious and aggressive when the Phillips Report emerged: angry with NASA for having told them nothing about the crisis at the time, furious when Webb first pleaded ignorance of the Report and then refused to hand it over. As Senator Walter Mondale said in an addendum to the Senate Committee's own pallid report, belatedly published a year after the accident:

> NASA's performance—the evasiveness, the lack of candor, the patronizing attitude exhibited toward Congress, the refusal to respond fully and forthrightly to legitimate congressional inquiries, and the solicitous concern for corporate sensitivities at a time of national tragedy—can only produce a loss of congressional and public confidence in NASA programs. And neither NASA nor the nation can afford such a loss.

For all the weaknesses of the congressional response, there is no doubt that the fire, coupled with the Phillips Report's revelations, did damage confidence in the space agency's operations. In the long term this had a considerable impact on the future of the whole space program. With the Vietnam war at its height and the domestic crises of the nation at last being borne in on the federal government, NASA needed every scrap of credit it could find if it was to sustain its call on public money. The Phillips Report, especially, spoiled the picture. Even though most legislators preferred not to exploit to any great extent, they could not avoid taking note of the defects it exposed in the NASA-industry team. Coupled with the agency's patent lack of integrity, this had its effect on funding and on Congress's reluctance to initiate the space program of the seventies.

More immediately, the events of early 1967 revealed for the first time just how perilous the space business was. Until then, few people had sensed the true complexities. Thanks to the confusion planted by NASA in the public mind between perfection as a goal and perfection as a fact, hardly anyone had understood that truly awesome obstacles stood between earth and the moon. Some of these were now more clearly seen. They provided a measure of how much remained to be done, after six months of numbed inertia on the launch pads, if man was to reach his destination on time.

11.

The Machines Which Must Not Fail

For North American Aviation the bitterest result of the fire was a personal matter conducted far from the committee rooms of Congress. Harrison "Stormy" Storms, the man who was afraid he might forget something, was replaced in his job at the top of the company's Space Division. He had warned his men against giving the world any excuse for throwing "dirt in our face." To this end he had instituted programs for improving their motivation, with resonant names such as PRIDE—Personal Responsibility in Daily Effort. But North American had bungled and Storms had to go.

The sting, however, was delivered by the men who replaced him. Two new managers arrived: William B. Bergen and Bastian "Buzz" Hello, respectively the president and launch-operations director of Martin-Marietta—the very company which North American had beaten to the Apollo contract. Even as Bergen and Hello were putting the first pieces together at North American, Congress was being told that one reason why Martin's had not got the contract in the first place was because North American's own managers possessed "by far the greatest technical competence" to deal with "the very great engineering complexities." It was surely the unkindest cut of all.

The task facing Bergen was prodigious. After the fire, Congress cut the NASA budget request by almost half a million dollars. Although this fell as a much heavier blow on future plans than on Apollo itself, the prospect of a moon landing before 1970 had substantially receded. Clearly some dramatic success was needed if North American and NASA were to face the world once more with confidence.

But where was it to come from? Bergen says now, "We had to help people hold up their heads again." It could not but be a slow process. Work had begun at Downey and Houston on such basic measures as replacing inflammable materials and installing a quick-opening hatch. NASA had appointed George Low, the original moon zealot, to master-mind the spacecraft program following Joseph Shea's removal to Washington. But the complete redesign of the spacecraft according to the Review Board's specifications would clearly be a long slog. Dr. Mueller, in an upbeat moment, had spoken of a manned Apollo flight by the spring of 1968, only a year late. This sounded optimistic at the time; and so it proved to be, by more than six months.

Project Apollo, however, was not merely a spacecraft. In Florida, on Launch Complex 39 at Cape Kennedy, the moonport's Vehicle Assembly Building, then billed as the largest building ever erected, towered squarely over the flat scrubland. And in the largest building, the greatest rocket ever conceived was already being put together. Wernher von Braun's Saturn V was affected only marginally by the aftermath of the fire. As the date of the first manned flight of the space-craft slipped remorselessly further back through 1968, the big rocket became the focus of all hopes for the renaissance of Project Apollo.

It was an appropriate symbol. The spacecraft, for all its novelty, was an anonymous structure, so remote from common experience that it was hard to come to grips with. But everyone could understand a rocket; and Saturn V was manifestly on the scale of the moon enter-prise itself. Even on the ground it seemed to soar, like the spire of a medieval cathedral. It stood 363 feet from its base to the tip of the es-cape tower, which would drag the spacecraft clear if the launcher showed signs of blowing up. Saturn V had cost almost $5000 million to develop, and each finished example cost nearly $200 million to produce. When it flew, it would at last give the United States the ir-refutable lead in rocket power which the nation had craved for ten long years since Sputnik 1. It was also a truly national creation: 20,000 contractors and subcontractors, in just about every State of the Union, had helped to build its 900,000 components.

The first stage, which at 138 feet long and 33 feet in diameter could be conveyed on earth only by water, had arrived at the Cape by barge from Huntsville, the home of The Team whose dearest child it was. The parts were made by Boeing, and after the first two Saturns had passed the German's inspection, the makers took charge of assembly as well.

To visit the Boeing plant outside New Orleans is to be carried momentarily into the past as well as the future. Half-finished boosters lie about like the skeletons of dinosaurs. They rest under a roof of ordinary height, with men inside them, beside them and on top of them. In the factory they seem more overwhelmingly huge than on the launch pad, where everything is larger than life. Even on their sides they are as high as houses; a tall man could stand in the gaping, bell-shaped mouth of one of the five engines without being able to reach the top.

As you tramp from place to place seeing metal machined, welded, washed, assembled into tanks, and tanks assembled into rockets, your mind is wearied by the never-ending flow of astounding statistics: tanks big enough to hold three removal vans side by side . . . 200,000 gallons of kerosene . . . nearly a third of a million gallons of liquid oxygen . . . a pump of 55,000 horsepower, as much as the main engines of two supertankers, to drive the fuel into the engines . . . consumed at 15 tons a second . . . all gone in two and a half minutes . . . a million and a half pounds of thrust from each engine . . . 180 million horsepower.

Yet apart from its size there was nothing revolutionary about the first stage of the Saturn V. It was born of the same rugged tradition as earlier rockets and missiles designed by von Braun's men: Saturn 1, Jupiter, Redstone, the V-2. It even used many of their parts, chosen for their well-tried reliability. It was just immensely bigger.

No part of the stage was more conservatively designed than the engine, called the F-1. This was a gargantuan version of the engine that powered the Saturn 1, itself an organic growth from engines developed for missiles in the 1950s. The engine which eventually became the F-1 had originally been proposed to a bemused Defense Department by Rocketdyne in 1955, but it did not get support commensurate with its size until a new-born NASA decided to back it and to design the moon-winning rockets round it.

In spite of its conventional design, the F-1 had a full share of the rocket engineer's most enduring problem: combustion instabilities, the sudden wild fluctuation in pressure inside the engine which can blow it apart in a fraction of a second. The answer usually lies in the design of the injector, the perforated plate through which the propellants are sprayed into the combustion chamber. But injector design was, and remains, something of a black art, with hunch and trial and error playing a major part. Although the F-1 was first tested early in 1961, Rocketdyne was still struggling with the design of the injector at the beginning of 1963. The engine's tendency to blow itself up was not eliminated until experts from industry, universities and NASA centers all over the country had been called in to advise, and technicians had sweated for weeks turning their ideas into hardware and testing it on the stands.

But by the time the first Saturn V reached the launch pad the F-1 engine had a record of more than fifty hours of testing and 2,500 separate firings behind it; the instability problem seemed to have been well and truly licked. Again and again the engine had survived drastic "bombing" tests, in which explosive charges were detonated inside it while it was running, to see if they would trigger off instabilities. If an F-1 engine failed during the coming unmanned flight of Apollo 4, the first by Saturn V, it would surely not be because of combustion instabilities.

The second stage, too, had arrived at Cape Kennedy by barge, after a journey of several thousand miles via the Panama Canal, from Seal Beach, California. On the way it had stopped off for a test firing on the stands of the Mississippi Test Facility, built by NASA in the swampy country near the mouth of the great river to save the ears of the long-suffering citizens of Huntsville.

The second stage was late in arriving. It, too, was a product of North American Aviation, and the Phillips team had found in late 1965 that it was already more than a year behind schedule. Its troubles had continued in the following year, when a complete stage was lost in an explosion during a test and cracks were discovered in the liquid hydrogen tank.

Technically, however, stage two of Saturn V was a lot more adventurous than stage one. It was on a similar scale, 33 feet in diameter and 81 feet long, but it was propelled by five J-2 engines fueled with liquid hydrogen instead of the conventional kerosene. Liquid hydrogen is much more efficient, but since it boils at −423° F and leaks out of apparently leakproof containers, it is also far more difficult to handle.

One of the trickiest problems in the development of the second stage was the bulkhead which divides what is, in effect, a single tank into two, one portion containing liquid hydrogen, the other liquid oxygen. The temperature difference across the bulkhead is 126°, and a tiny leakage of heat from the liquid oxygen to the even colder liquid hydrogen could produce an explosion. There would be no such danger if the two propellants were in completely separate tanks, but that would make the stage 10 feet longer and almost 4 tons heavier.

The third stage had reached Florida from the McDonnell-Douglas plant in Los Angeles in a bulbous air freighter called the Super Guppy. The Apollo 4 flight was not to be its debut in space, since it had already done service as the upper stage of the souped-up version of the Saturn I. However, during the Apollo 4 mission it would be called on to do something it had never done before: restart in orbit, just as it would later need to do to push the complete Apollo spacecraft out of orbit round the earth and put it on course for the moon. The maneuver sounds simple but was in fact very complicated. First the engine had to be purged of all traces of the previous firing by having helium blown through it, next it had to be cooled by liquid oxygen and hydrogen, and then small solid-propellant rockets had to be fired to force the floating, weightless fuel to the bottom of the tank.

One final section completed the Saturn V. On top of the third stage, immediately beneath the spacecraft, was an instrument-lined ring only three feet high, the brain that would control the millions of pounds of thrust below. In this was a pair of computers which between them, every couple of seconds, would consult instruments telling them in turn where the rocket had got to, compare this with the flight plan already planted in their memories, calculate how much the engines need to swivel to put it back on course, and send the necessary instruction. Here, too, the signals from the thousands of instruments measuring temperatures, pressures, rates of flow, positions of valves, accelerations in every stage of the rocket would be collected for relaying to the ground. In future manned missions the instrument unit would have an additional role: warning the astronauts of impending trouble in their launcher.

During the first half of 1967, while the fire-blackened interior of spacecraft 012 was being gutted and NASA was trying to pretend the Phillips Report did not exist, the three stages and the instrument unit of the first Saturn V were stacked with a dummy lunar module and real command and service modules on top of one another at Cape Kennedy. Human acolytes of the computers, to which the job of checking out the rocket had been almost entirely entrusted, swarmed over it, obediently following the instructions of their electronic gods. And by the end of August the vehicle was finally ready to be moved to the launch pad.

No previous NASA rocket had ever been assembled and checked out for flight anywhere but on the pad. Often the great machines stood there for months, exposed to the corrosive salt-laden air and, in the season, passing hurricanes. Saturn V and the Apollo spacecraft, with literally millions of functioning parts, needed, NASA had decided, something better. The result was Launch Complex 39, as fertile a source of mind-bending statistics as the rocket itself. At the complex, everything is bigger and heavier than anything else in the world: the Vehicle Assembly Building where four Saturn V's can be assembled simultaneously is so vast that only the air-conditioning prevents clouds from forming in it. The mobile launcher on which the rocket is assembled, carried to the pad and launched, is a two-deck steel platform, covering half an acre, with a tower 400 feet high and a hole in the middle 45 feet wide to receive the blazing exhaust of the five engines. The crawler, which picks up the 5000-ton load of launcher, tower and rocket, carries them bodily three and a half miles to the pad without allowing the rocket to move more than a fraction of a degree out of vertical and sets them down within two inches of the appointed spot.

Now, seven months after the fire, the moonport was almost ready to dispatch its first ship. This would not go to the moon, and it would not carry men, but the voyage would be ambitious all the same. More than the new superrocket was on trial. A new approach to flight testing, forced on NASA by budget cuts and the pressing deadline for the moon, was being employed for the first time.

The earlier, much smaller, Saturn I had been brought into service cautiously, step by step. The first stage was launched successfully four times with a dummy second stage filled with water before a live second stage was added. In the interests of speed, Saturn V was being tested for the first time with all three stages live, not to mention a spacecraft on top.

Nor was this all. Although it had taken fifty or sixty flights to work up the old Atlas rocket to a pitch of reliability where it could be trusted with a man, NASA was planning to "man-rate" the Saturn V after only three flights. Before long the figure had been cut to two. Once it had been thirteen. Shortages of time and money were the main reasons why the proving-flights had been so drastically eliminated, but the rocketeers, increasingly confident of their wares, had been delighted to accommodate the accountants.

Rockets and spacecraft had not only got bigger since the first unmanned Mercury-Atlas exploded less than a minute after leaving the launch pad; they had also become many times more reliable. The history of the three unmanned lunar explorer programs is a good illustration of how dramatically the picture changed in the first ten years of spaceflight. Beginning in 1961, the first six out of nine Rangers all failed. Beginning in 1966, five out of seven of the far more complicated Surveyor soft-landers were successful. During roughly the same period there was not a single failure in five Lunar Orbiters. Von Braun's Saturn I had had an even more remarkable record. Since the first flight of the lower stage in October 1961, it had been fired thirteen times without a single failure, a good omen for its giant descendant.

The increasing reliability of the hardware was not only due to growing experience. It was the result of a wholly new engineering approach. During the late fifties, missiles like Atlas were developed with desperate urgency to bridge the missile gap. The overriding priority was to get something deployed. Numbers could compensate for unreliability. For military purposes, two missiles with a 50 percent chance of success were almost as good as one with a 100 percent chance of success, and if they could be made available sooner they were better. The wrinkles could be ironed out later.

Such an attitude was hardly appropriate to a rocket like Saturn V, designed solely for manned flight. Besides, machines costing almost $200 million a time could not be ignited like fireworks just to see whether some engineer with a hangover had made a mistake. Instead NASA resorted to a ground-testing program of fanatical thoroughness for components, systems and complete stages. By the time Apollo 4

was ready to go, engines required to operate in space for minutes
had accumulated days of successful firings on test stands. The whole
rocket and the spacecraft had been put together at Huntsville and
shaken bodily to see how it might behave in flight. The performance
during tests over several years of virtually every component had been
documented and was instantly available for analysis in the event of a
failure.

So confident was NASA of the efficiency of its ground-testing program (and so pressing the shortage of time and money) that an important trial of the spacecraft was made part of the Apollo 4 mission
as well. After the third stage of the Saturn V and the spacecraft had
gone into orbit 115 miles above the earth the third stage was to be re-
started to push the spacecraft into an orbit reaching 10,700 miles out
from the earth. The spacecraft's own engine would further stretch
this, to 11,400 miles, and then, as it swung back toward earth, the engine would fire a second time to drive it into the atmosphere at 25,-
000 miles an hour, the speed of a spacecraft returning from the moon.

So as the launch of Apollo 4 approached, it became for the space
agency, the nation and, indeed, the world, as much a symbol of American prestige as the launching of Vanguard ten years earlier. Vanguard
had blown up on the pad. With the fire not long past, NASA could
not afford a similar debacle. If the first Saturn V exploded or crashed
ignominiously into the sea it would at the very least mean the certain
abandonment of the national goal. An American would not land on the
moon by 1970.

At first the auguries were not good. A rehearsal of the countdown
started on September 22. It was meant to last three and a half days,
but it dragged on for more than three weeks. Gauges, wiring, the spacecraft's fuel-cell power supply, computers, all went wrong in turn.
Twice, half a million gallons of kerosene and liquid oxygen in the
first stage had to be unloaded. Once the countdown got to within
seventeen seconds of the end before it had to be stopped.

However, when the live countdown began late in the night of November 6, it went without a hitch. At 7 A.M. on November 9, a little
less than six years after it was conceived, the rocket that was to take
America to the moon lifted off. Its noise shook the palpably prespace-
age grandstand three and a half miles away and almost buried Walter
Cronkite of the Columbia Broadcasting System in the rubble of his

own commentary trailer. A little more than eight and a half hours later, the crew of the *U.S.S. Bennington* in the Pacific heard a double sonic boom and watched the spacecraft drifting down on its parachutes. Not long afterward it was on the deck, charred but intact. Every stage of the flight had gone perfectly.

At one stroke, sick Apollo had made a startling recovery. In October, James Webb was predicting the worst: "It's increasingly doubtful that an American—or Russian—will be on the moon in this decade. Certainly in our program we've slowed down." A month or so later, after the flight of Saturn V, his prophecy was very different: "It is important that we realize that this flight put us well on the way to the achievement of the lunar mission."

Above all, the fire could be forgotten. Webb had become so obsessed by the damage the fire was doing to the morale of space workers that he had earlier forbidden the very mention of the dreaded monosyllable in the corridors of the space agency. Now it could begin to be genuinely erased from memory.

Further improvement in NASA's fortunes was registered early in 1968 with the debut in space of the final element in the Apollo package: the lunar module.

With its spidery legs, bulging windows and projecting antennae, the lunar module had an engaging resemblance to the bug-eyed monsters of science fiction. Nor was it mere chance which made it so different from the smooth geometrical cone and cylinder of the command and service modules. Both these would be exposed to the buffeting of the atmosphere at the beginning of the flight, and had to be streamlined to withstand it. The command module also had to re-enter the atmosphere, a moment when any unshielded protuberances would be burned away. The lunar module, on the other hand, was a true spacecraft, built to operate in space without the compromises imposed by earth's penumbra. Not until Apollo was unambiguously in space, already on its way to the moon, would the bug emerge from the protection of its chrysalis in the final stage of the launcher.

In spite of its fragile appearance, the lunar module's chronic problem was always its weight. It was not requisitioned until the choice of lunar-orbital rendezvous demanded it. This was almost a year after the rest of the spacecraft was planned. The lunar module therefore had to be built within the limit of what was left over of Saturn V's weight-lifting capability. It was like a boxer who tries to develop a heavyweight's muscle while remaining in the flyweight class.

The weight limit originally set for the bug was ten tons. It proved to be quite inadequate, and the increased power forecast for the Saturn V soon allowed it to be raised to over fourteen tons. Even this seemed too little. The bug's designers at Grumman Aircraft cut the large, heavy windows to two small downward-facing triangles, and threw out the astronauts' seats in favor of a kind of parachute harness to restrain them in a standing position. But despite these and other eliminations, the designers found by early 1965 that the lunar module was creeping inevitably over the fourteen-ton limit.

That year a new verb entered the space vocabulary: the verb to "swip." Naturally it was another acronym, from Super Weight Improvement Program. Swipping meant scrutinizing every rib, panel, valve and switch in the module, looking for ways of saving weight. Teams went out to the subcontractors to breathe on them as they too sought to lose a few precious pounds, ounces or even fractions of an ounce. Grumman was willing to spend tens of thousands of dollars to save a pound of weight. Typical of the swipping measures was the removal in places of two of the twenty-five layers of aluminized plastic film used for thermal insulation on the spacecraft; this material is thinner and lighter than tissue paper.

Gradually the weight problem was brought under control, but the bug became a very flimsy structure indeed, about as comfortable for the occupants as a bone-shaking vintage motorcar. According to astronaut Tom Stafford, the commander of the first crew to fly the bug near the moon, whenever one of the small thruster rockets fired "it sounded as if somebody had put a washtub over your head and was banging on it with drumsticks."

With the Apollo 5 flight on January 22, 1968, this flimsy structure was exposed to space for the first time, unmanned, in orbit round the earth. The first lunar module lacked life support, radars and much communications equipment, but this did not preclude tests of its two most critical components: the engines—one in the descent stage, used for the landing, the other in the ascent stage, in which one day two astronauts would take off from the moon using the descent stage as a launch platform.

Of all the parts of the lunar module these were the ones whose failure was most likely to bring catastrophe. If the ascent-stage engine failed to start, the astronauts would be stranded on the moon; if it failed on the way up, they would crash back to the surface. The descent-stage engine was not quite so critical, since the ascent stage would provide a means of escape in some kinds of emergency. But other crises could easily be fatal. Failure of any kind, moreover, would inevitably mean an unsuccessful mission.

In short, the two main engines of the lunar module had to be infallible. Yet in January 1968 the ascent engine in particular was proving to be only too prone to error. This was in spite of a design incorporating every measure for improving reliability known to the rocket engineers. Many of these were shared by the descent engine, and the equally vital engine in the service module: propellants which ignite on contact; pressurized gas instead of a pump to force the propellants into the engine; uncooled combustion chambers with protective, ablative linings.

There the resemblance between the motors ended. For the descent engine incorporated a feature shared by no other rocket engine of any size ever built in the United States: it was throttlable, so that the astronauts could control their descent and hover just above the moon's surface while choosing a landing site.

This was not an easy requirement to satisfy. A rocket engine cannot be throttled like a car engine, simply by controlling the amount of fuel going into it. If the propellants are allowed to dribble in they will not mix properly and will leave the engine before they are burned, which cannot be allowed to happen when every ounce of fuel counts. The first solution, proposed by Rocketdyne, was to bubble helium gas (which will not burn) into the fuel stream to dilute it while keeping up the pressure. But quite soon Rocketdyne ran into difficulties, and in July 1963 Grumman awarded a back-up contract to TRW (Thompson-Ramo-Wooldridge Systems), which ultimately found a new answer.

For the company it was a considerable breakthrough. As latecomers into the rocket-engine field, they needed to come up with a new idea, and they found it in the work of a Jet Propulsion Laboratory scientist called Glenn Elverum. He was experimenting with a new type of fuel injector in which the propellants were sprayed into the center of the combustion chamber instead of through hundreds of tiny holes in a plate on top of it. This promised to avoid the problem which, according to one expert, takes up 70 percent of the cost of developing a new rocket engine—combustion instabilities like those which plagued the F-1. TRW hired Elverum and backed the development of a small throttlable version which attracted the interest of Grumman and NASA.

In principle the injector is simple enough. The propellants are sprayed out through holes in the base of a cylinder projecting into the combustion chamber, so arranged that jets of fuel and oxidizer intersect. To throttle the engine a sleeve moves up and down on the cylinder, reducing the size of holes through which the propellants emerge. Thus, although the total flow is reduced, the jets still move at high speed and the propellants mix and burn efficiently.

The principle of the engine was straightforward, but months of laborious experiments, calculations and sheer trial and error were needed to turn it into even the beginning of an engine that could lower men to the moon. Finding the best shape, size and angle of the tiny holes from which the propellants emerged so that they would mix efficiently at all throttle settings drove the engineers involved half crazy with frustration. The holes had to be machined to an accuracy of a thousandth of an inch, and spaced with an accuracy of one ten-thousandth of an inch. "It was one hell of a learning process," said Arnold I. Hoffmann, TRW's project manager for the engine at the time of the moon landing.

At one stage the team almost despaired of finding a suitable material for the tip of the cylinder from which the propellants emerged. It was in the hottest part of the combustion chamber and there were few materials which could stand up to the temperatures. They tried steel; steel plated with copper, chromium, teflon, nickel; steel with copper plugs in it to improve the thermal conductivity. Finally they hit on an exotic metal named columbium, which worked perfectly. Columbium was also used for the skirt, the long bell-shaped extension to the nozzle, which had to be strong enough to take some of the engine's thrust yet flimsy enough to collapse if it hit a rock standing higher than the surrounding surface when the lunar module landed.

Yet another difficulty was posed by the protective lining in the combustion chamber. It tended to erode much too fast, until TRW thought of separately spraying some of the fuel down the walls. But in spite of all these problems the engine triumphantly vindicated the designer's original claim that it would not go unstable. In the whole history of its development it never once did so, even in thirty bombing tests.

The ascent engine, developed by Bell Aerosystems, had a very different history. This was even more vital to safety, but by the end of 1967, it had recorded instabilities in 173 bomb tests out of 667—a grim record for the engine on which the astronauts' ability to get off the moon would absolutely and irreplaceably depend. In the middle of 1967, NASA placed a back-up contract for an alternative injector with Rocketdyne. This gave better grounds for confidence and was incorporated into the engine of all lunar modules after number three.

In the meantime the first trial module had been launched into earth orbit on top of a Saturn 1-B in January 1968, and had continued the successful pattern re-established by Apollo 4. The descent engine was fired three times, the (unmodified) ascent engine twice, and the only hitch was a premature shut-down of the descent engine on its first firing. However, the error was traced to a programing error in the spacecraft's computer and was nothing to do with the engine itself. The flight was so successful that NASA decided to skip a second planned test of the unmanned lunar module. Yet another flight had been cut from the program, a few more precious weeks saved.

Now memories of the fire were almost vanishing, overshadowed by the latest successes. On January 30, after months of delay, the Senate Space Committee finally published its report on the tragedy. Although it spoke of NASA's "over-confidence and complacency" it was hardly an incisive document, and in this it reflected the uncertain shadow-boxing of the hearings. It did not even mention the Phillips Report. The critics of NASA had had their day. They could still yap at its heels, but they no longer looked capable of barring the way to the moon.

Yet in April, when the Saturn V made its second flight, designated Apollo 6, it looked for a time as though they might have another chance. The first stage apparently performed without fault, but soon after the second-stage engines ignited, the flight controllers at their consoles saw the thrust of engine number two falling off. Then it cut out completely, to be followed by engine number three. When its turn came, the single engine in the third stage ignited perfectly, but a few hours later, for no obvious reason, it failed to restart in orbit.

Then after the flight, when the engineers began analyzing the recorded data, they found that the first stage had not performed as immaculately as they had thought. In the readings from pressure gauges and accelerometers they found sinister signs of another notorious affliction of big rockets; it was called pogo—alternate stretching and contracting along the rocket's length like a pogo stick. The Saturn V was flexing and unflexing five times a second with a force well over twice the maximum allowed for in the design. It was enough to put the points where the lunar module was attached at risk and would also have made it very difficult for any astronauts on board to read their instruments. In a more extreme form, it could actually have destroyed the rocket.

There was still another problem. At a height of about thirty miles, instruments in the region of the lunar module recorded what appeared to be an impact on the rocket, and the pressure inside its compartment fell sharply. A film taken from a high-flying aircraft equipped with a radar-directed camera actually showed a piece of the rocket breaking away.

So within a day or two of the flight, the builders of the Saturn V knew that they still had several major problems to contend with. The questions these raised were profoundly disturbing. Had the perfect first flight been a fluke? Did the Saturn V design include serious defects? Was the great moon rocket in for a run of troubles which would push the landing irrevocably beyond the 1970 deadline?

Even in retrospect it is staggering to find that within three weeks of the crippled flight of Apollo 6, Webb, Mueller and Phillips were nevertheless informing the Senate Space Committee that they planned to put men on the next flight of Saturn V. The thirteen unmanned test flights of a few years before had been cut to two; one of these had now been a partial failure. Was it recklessness or a sensible decision based on a sober assessment of the odds which prompted the agency's confident promise?

By a kind of technological alchemy, NASA now proceeded to transmute the troubles of Apollo 6 into the pure gold of confidence-building success. The space agency had attempted something of the sort after the disaster of fifteen months before, with its talk of new knowledge gained from the fire. Those efforts were singularly unconvincing. Now they were to be completely successful, and completely valid. It could not be denied that deficiencies existed in the Saturn V, but they were either half foreseen and prepared for, or else of a kind that not even the most prescient engineer could have anticipated. They were tackled with supreme skill and energy, in what General Phillips, with complete justice, called "one of the most aggressive, thorough and determined engineering test and analysis programs I have ever seen." Confidence in the builders of the Saturn V, and therefore in the rocket itself, far from being eroded, was actually increased.

The engine failures in the second and third stages were diagnosed and cured by engineering detective work of consummate brilliance. Since the story illuminates the sheer technical virtuosity of the space engineers and the total mastery they had gained over their monstrous creations, so different from ten years before when they were as unpredictable as half-tamed lions, it is worth telling at least part of it in some detail.

Testing a rocket is very different from testing, say, an airplane. An airplane can be taxied about on the ground before it is flown, and then when it takes to the air, coaxed gradually up to full performance. The process may take a year or more. A rocket, too, can be tested, tethered, on the ground, but there can be no gradual approach to full performance in the air. It is all or nothing. And the rocket cannot be recovered for inspection if something goes wrong. Its remains will probably be at the bottom of the sea.

For virtually every scrap of information about how a rocket behaves in flight, engineers depend on the readings, radioed back to ground, of instruments spread through every part of it, monitoring temperatures, pressures, rates of flow, strains, accelerations, the positions of valves and switches. All readings are recorded in the control center; the most important ones are also displayed on the controllers' consoles, so that they can see situations developing. In this way the flight controllers of Apollo 6 knew instantly when two of the second-stage engines cut out and when the third-stage engine had failed to restart.

The investigation into why they had failed started at Cape Kennedy within hours of the launch, while the spacecraft was still in orbit, with a meeting of engineers from NASA and the principal contractors.

Their immediate task was to scan some fifty miles of recording tape, searching for any kind of abnormality in the instrument readings, however small, that might be relevant.

It took them only twenty-four hours to discover a series of anomalies which put them on the right track. The list, with timings as from the moment when the engines of the stage in question started up, went like this:

In the second stage:

70 *seconds*: Instruments in the engine compartment begin to detect chilling. The flow of fuel to No. 2 engine increases.

110 *seconds*: The thrust of No. 2 engine starts to fall off gradually, dropping sharply at 169 seconds. At this time also the load on the mechanism which swivels the engine to steer the rocket increases suddenly, as though the engine has begun to push sideways as well as forward.

263 *seconds*: No. 2 engine's thrust falls sharply again and there is a sudden rise in temperature in the engine compartment. Almost immediately afterward an automatic device for shutting the engine down if its thrust falls below a certain value cuts it off completely. One second later engine No. 3 in the second stage turns itself off too.

In the third stage:

68 *seconds*: Temperature starts to fall in the engine compartment.

107 *seconds*: The thrust of the single J-2 engine starts to fall off. Rate of fall-off increases at 115 seconds.

119 *seconds*: Heating in the engine area.

170 *seconds*: The engine cuts off in accordance with the flight plan, but will not restart again several hours later.

One odd aspect of the behavior of the second stage was soon cleared up: the abrupt shutdown of the apparently quite normal No. 3 engine a second after the shutdown of No. 2 engine. The information radioed back to the ground showed that a valve controlling the flow of liquid oxygen to No. 3 had closed at the moment when the equivalent valve in No. 2 engine should have done so as part of its shutdown sequence. Clearly there had been a wiring error, and the signal to close the valve had gone to the wrong engine. To clinch the matter the records showed that the wiring in question had been modified a few months before and not properly tested afterward.

With this problem solved, the investigators were free to concentrate on No. 2 engine and on the third stage with its single engine. There was a compelling similarity between the sequence of events in the two stages. In both cases there was the same chilling, starting about seventy seconds after engine ignition, the same fall-off in thrust starting about forty seconds later and the same sudden heating later still. It could hardly be coincidence. The conclusion that the same thing had happened in both stages seemed inescapable. But what was it?

The first vital clue was the chilling of the engine compartments. The J-2 engine burns liquid hydrogen at $-423°$ F and liquid oxygen at $-297°$ F. A leak of either would lead to cooling, but since the temperature had fallen as low as $-400°$ in places, oxygen was ruled out. It had to be liquid hydrogen that was escaping.

The pattern of cooling in the second stage also provided irresistible evidence of a propellant leak. The five engines are arranged like the spots on a dice, with No. 5 in the middle. The cooled area spread out from No. 2 engine toward the middle of the compartment, enveloping No. 5, with tongues extending beyond it on either side. The temperature around the engine directly opposite No. 2, behind the central engine, was normal. This was exactly the pattern to be expected if liquid hydrogen were spraying out of No. 2 engine toward the center of the compartment, with the central engine screening the one beyond.

The next step was to discover where the hydrogen was coming from. The cooling pattern was the chief clue; the size of the leak and layout of the engine helped. The investigators' suspicions began to focus on a stainless-steel pipe about as thick as a man's finger which wound its way from the middle of the engine up to the top. In it were three flexible bellows sections to allow a little movement, one of them exactly where the leak seemed to be.

The pipe carried liquid hydrogen to the engine's starting device, a chamber about an inch in diameter in a block of copper in the middle of the injector plate at the top of the engine. Another pipe carried liquid oxygen to the chamber, where the propellants could be ignited by a pair of spark plugs, making a blazing torch to light the main stream of propellants sprayed through the hole in the injector plate.

Now, with the likely source of the leak identified, the investigating team could explain what had probably happened.

In the second stage: first a break in the pipe leading to the starter, spraying liquid hydrogen into the engine compartment; the reduced flow of hydrogen into the starter changing the composition of the mixture burning in it from 1:1 to something much richer in oxygen, the sort of mixture used in a cutting torch; the cutting flame eating its way through the starter and into the engine's vitals, finally breaking right through the casing and releasing blazing gases into the engine compartment before the engine shut itself down. In the third stage: something very similar. Only one anomaly was unexplained: the sudden sideways thrust of the disintegrating second-stage engine.

Hypothesis alone was not enough. The investigators could not have complete confidence in their theories until what had happened in space had been reproduced on the ground. Within a week of the flight, Rocketdyne had started work at their Santa Susanna test site in California, trying to simulate the events of Apollo 6 by deliberately inducing leaks in different parts of the engine. Only the suspect pipe leading to the starter seemed to fit the bill. Before a month was out both Rocketdyne and the NASA designers at Huntsville were ready to reproduce the breakdown of No. 2 engine exactly.

Computers programed to simulate the behavior of the engine saved weeks on the test stands. With their help, the investigators were able to estimate accurately the sizes of the leaks needed to produce the observed changes in the engines' thrusts. In the case of the second-stage engine, it was one pound a second for sixty seconds, then increasing abruptly to eleven pounds a second. In the case of the third stage, it was half a pound a second increasing slowly, and culminating in a complete break in the pipe in a little over a minute.

When the time came for the critical trials, the computers proved their worth. The test simulating the failure of the No. 2 engine in the second stage had to be stopped prematurely because of a bad fire; but even so the starter was almost completely burned away and the main injector was damaged. Inevitably a major structural failure would have followed soon afterward.

(One of the tests at Huntsville also explained the remaining mystery of the second stage's behavior, its sideways thrust. Halfway through the test a fragment of the disintegrating starter flew out and punc-

[42] Apollo 9: David Scott, standing in the hatch of the command module, snapped by Russell Schweickart from the porch of the docked lunar module.

[43] The lunar module: the weird contraption which would finally land men on the moon.

[44] Steak, scrambled eggs, and last advice over breakfast for the crew of Apollo 11 from their handler, Deke Slayton. In the background, William Anders, a member of the backup crew.

[45] The launch of Apollo 11. Momentarily, no sceptics.

[46] "The loudest, bigges, most sensitive balancir, in the w

HERE MEN FROM THE PLANET EARTH
FIRST SET FOOT UPON THE MOON
JULY 1969, A. D.
WE CAME IN PEACE FOR ALL MANKIND

NEIL A. ARMSTRONG
ASTRONAUT

MICHAEL COLLINS
ASTRONAUT

EDWIN E. ALDRIN, JR.
ASTRONAUT

RICHARD NIXON
PRESIDENT UNITED STATES OF AMERICA

[47] On the lunar module, international rhetoric.

[48] On the moon, national pride.

[49] Footprints that will last half a million years.

[50] Two relics for the scientists: the moon experiments are deployed.

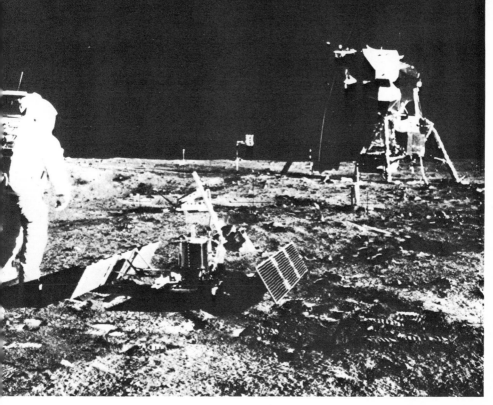

[51]   Tranquility Base. In the foreground the moonquake detector with
       laser reflector behind. At left of Eagle the flag and the television camera.

[52]   The shadow of the engine which could not be allowed to fail.

[53] From the sublime: Eagle approaching Columbia...

[54] ...to the Mobile Quarantine Facility: "A date with your wives."

tured the wall of the engine's bell-shaped thrust chamber, starting a serious leak of the liquid hydrogen circulating inside. It was just as though a subsidiary engine had started up, working at right angles to the main one.)

The simulation of the third-stage failure explained why the engine did not shut itself down like the one in the second stage. As soon as the pipe leading to the starter was completely broken (as the computer suggested it had broken in flight) hot gases from the combustion chamber blazed back through it and enveloped the stand, but the engine continued to run until it was deliberately shut down at the same point as it had been in flight. The starter was too heavily eroded to work a second time, but the engine was not as badly damaged as the one in the second-stage simulation, because with no hydrogen at all reaching the starter through the broken pipe there was not the same cutting-torch mixture inside it.

So before a month was out, the investigators knew exactly what had happened to Apollo 6. They knew how to prevent it from happening again: all they had to do was strengthen the liquid hydrogen pipe leading to the starter so that it could not break. But knowing *what* had happened was not enough. They could not wind up the inquiry until they knew *why* it had happened as well. Unexplained failures could not be allowed in the Saturn V. The pipes in question could be strengthened, but unless the cause of their failure was fully understood this was no guarantee that there would not be failures from the same unknown cause elsewhere.

Now the inquiry moved into the second and more difficult phase. Before it was completed, it had drawn in more than 350 people, three-quarters of them from the makers of the J-2 engine, Rocketdyne.

Before Apollo 6, ten other J-2 engines had flown, six of them in the first Saturn V of all. Nothing comparable to the failures during Apollo 6 had happened to any of them. The only difference between Apollo 6 and the previous flights was that the power of the engine and therefore the rate of flow of hydrogen through the pipe to the starter, had been increased slightly. When the engineers at Rocketdyne retested the pipe at the new flow-rate they found that it did tend to set up vibrations in the bellows section which had failed in flight. But the vibrations were not bad enough to cause a breakage, even in runs lasting far longer than the engine ran in flight.

The pogo oscillations of the launcher also looked like a possible source of trouble. Had they given the pipe such a shaking that it was seriously weakened? This approach too proved fruitless. The pipe showed no signs of leaking when it was vibrated far more violently than in flight. Vibration tests of the whole engine were equally unhelpful.

All this testing occupied several weeks and left the investigators none the wiser. As a last resort they decided to test the effects of both vibration and the increased flow through the pipe together. For safety reasons they set up the rig using ordinary gaseous nitrogen at room temperature instead of liquid hydrogen in the pipe, of course at an equivalent rate of flow. And by pure chance, so often the decisive factor in engineering discoveries, this substitution gave them the hint they needed.

While one of the engineers conducting the test was still adjusting the flow of nitrogen through the pipe, before the vibrator had even been switched on, it suddenly failed at the suspect bellows section. Another test pipe was put in and that failed too, and so did several more, one of them in as little as two seconds. A careful examination of the broken bellows showed that they had failed because of metal fatigue, the result of vibrations induced merely by the flow of gas.

But why did the bellows break with nitrogen at ordinary temperatures and not with liquid hydrogen? The pipe had, after all, been filled with liquid hydrogen during the flight. At last one of the Rocketdyne engineers hit on the answer: the flight engine was operating in space; the tests on the ground were conducted in the atmosphere, where with the pipe at a temperature of around −400° F ice and even liquid air would form on it, affecting its vibration characteristics—just as a coating of ice would change the note of a tuning fork.

Hurriedly they set up the final test: pumping liquid hydrogen through the pipe *in a vacuum chamber* where no ice or liquid air could form on it. Five times the experiment was repeated, at flow rates similar to those in flight. Each time the pipe failed at the suspected bellows, once in only twenty seconds, never in more than ninety-nine. The long investigation was over. The pipe could be replaced by one without bellows with complete confidence that it would not fail again. Every other comparable bellows in the Saturn V was quickly checked to make sure that they were not vulnerable too.

The J-2 inquiry was one of the cleverest pieces of technological trouble-shooting in the history of the space program, but it also illustrated the terrifyingly narrow margin between success and failure, or even disaster, in all space engineering. If there had been men in the Apollo 6 spacecraft they would have come to no harm, but if there were some equally unpredictable, equally subtle defect in the lunar-module ascent engine, for example, it would be a very different story. Unlike the fire danger, there are some hazards of spaceflight which are truly unpredictable.

Inquiries into the other Apollo 6 failures proceeded in parallel with the J-2 investigation. The pieces that broke off the rocket turned out to be only a patch of its outer skin which was not properly stuck down. Better inspection was the prescribed remedy. The pogo was more difficult to deal with and involved over seven hundred engineers from NASA and the contractors, but pogo was a familiar problem which had cropped up before, and engineering sleuthing played only a minor part in the inquiry.

While the third Saturn V, scheduled to fly with men on board for the first time before the end of the year, was being modified in the light of the experience from Apollo 6, the spacecraft side of the program was once again approaching the stage it had reached at the time of the fire: the final preparation for launching.

In the eighteen months since the disaster the Apollo spacecraft had been completely redesigned. Virtually all the 1412 nonmetallic materials found in it had been either deleted, replaced, redesigned or proved not to be a fire risk. It had been given an outward-opening, unified hatch which the astronauts could open from inside in three seconds, the ground crew from outside in ten. It had been vibration tested and rewired; the vulnerable soldered joints in the environmental control system cooling circuit had been armored. Even these sweeping changes had not made it completely safe with a 16.7 psi oxygen atmosphere. After a series of flammability tests with spacecraft mockups, NASA decided, more than a year after the fire, to go over to a two-gas atmosphere for the launch only.

North American, which incurred most of the odium from the fire, had been overhauled too. William Bergen, the new chief of the Space Division, set in hand a more comprehensive redesign that most people would have thought possible in the time available. "At the time of the fire, spacecraft 101, destined to be used for the first manned flight, Apollo 7, was finished and ready for delivery," he recalls. "It had to be taken back into the shop and have the guts ripped out—a lot more difficult than starting from scratch." For two or three months Bergen stayed at work night and day, sleeping in a little room next to his office.

One of his innovations was to appoint a supremo for each new spacecraft, with full responsibility for seeing it right through the production process. To supervise 101 he brought in yet another man from Martin-Marietta, his former employers, named John Healey.

When Healey arrived at Downey, spacecraft 101 had just been stripped down and now had to be put together again. Confidence was the problem: "Each guy was questioning himself," Healey said recently. Bergen gave him a free hand. "I could literally command all the resources of the company. Bergen wrote out a charter in very strong language." Healey did not fail to take advantage of it. "Once early on I wanted something done," he remembers. "I said to the guy I'd be back at four for it. He said, 'I'll check with my management.' I said, 'I am your management.'"

Healey, a fearsomely tough customer, worked sixteen hours a day, often seven days a week, for ten months on spacecraft 101. He drove the men under him as hard. "As soon as you get all warm and understanding with a man you start to level him off," he says. "If you don't like it, you say it stinks. Most guys you have to hit twice. With good guys once is enough."

Twice a week he met the crew that would fly his precious craft on the first manned flight: Wally Schirra, Donn Eisele and Walter Cunningham. "The toughest problem was freezing the design," Healey remembers. Qualification testing was going on at the same time as design and construction, and unless the design was fixed, testing could not proceed. "You've got to discipline the engineer who's always got changes. At one time there were three hundred people working on spacecraft 101 trying desperately to keep up with two thousand who were still working on the design."

In the spring spacecraft 101 was delivered to the Cape. It was October before it was ready to fly, on top of a Saturn 1-B, all that was needed for earth orbit. But the Apollo 7 mission proved virtually perfect, enlivened by Wally Schirra's engaging display of bloody-minded-ness over the television, marred only by the astronauts all getting colds, and some minor electrical problems. The engine in the service module on which the astronauts' lives would depend on a moon flight per-formed flawlessly in eight separate firings.

Back on the ground, another event, which, had it occurred eighteen months earlier would have shaken NASA like a major earthquake, passed off almost as smoothly as the flight of Apollo 7. Early in Oc-tober Jim Webb, the space agency's boss since the premoon days, astonished everyone by resigning with effect from October 7, his sixty-second birthday.

He left in circumstances very different from the devious moves that first installed him in the job. "I have felt for some time," he told the Senate Space Committee, "that at some proper time I should retire from full-time federal service. During the past year I have devoted a great deal of my time, working with senior NASA officials, to the task of ensuring that the strongest possible organization was emerging. Last month I reported to the President on a number of matters and pointed out that NASA has, with the recent induction of a number of ex-perienced executives, the strongest and most capable organization it had had in its ten-year history. I told him that it was fully capable of functioning at peak efficiency without me." But he stayed on as a consultant, directing his attention, as he said later, in a characteristi-cally freewheeling metaphor, "toward helping younger men who are in the playing field, while I am on the coach's bench, as they proceed to work out their own participation in the tumultuous events of these times."

Dr. Thomas O. Paine, Webb's deputy since the beginning of the year, became acting administrator. An engineer with a background in industry, he was a much paler figure than the fast-talking, aggressive Webb, closer perhaps to the engineers who made up the bulk of the organization under him, less familiar with the ways of Washington than the astute politician he succeeded.

The change at the top did nothing to slacken the pace. Now, with the success of Apollo 7, NASA was in full cry. The redesigned Apollo spacecraft had been proved in manned flight; the Saturn V was man-rated, and its first manned flight was planned for before the end of the year. This was intended to be the first trial in earth orbit of the complete Apollo spacecraft, including the lunar module. But internal electrical interference in the lunar module, which affected the communications equipment, was proving difficult to eliminate. Even before Apollo 7, NASA had begun to toy with the heady possibility of leaving the bug out of the next mission and sending Apollo 8's command and service modules on a Christmas flight round the moon.

The success of Apollo 7 clinched the matter, and on November 12, Paine confirmed the already widespread rumors. "After careful and thorough examination of all the systems and risks involved," he said, "we have concluded that we are now ready to fly the most advanced mission for our Apollo 8 launch in December, the orbit round the moon."

As far as the newly man-rated Saturn V was concerned, the ultimate destination of the flight made no difference, but a trip round the moon would make untested demands on the spacecraft. If anything went wrong with the life-support system it might take as long as three days to get the astronauts back to earth, compared with a quarter of an hour or so from earth orbit. And if the engine in the service module failed in lunar orbit, the astronauts would be beyond hope of rescue. But the risks had to be accepted sometime. A voyage to the moon was what the spacecraft was designed for.

In spite of the carefully documented case for the moonflight which NASA presented in November, the decision gave a powerful impression of haste. Shortly before, it was announced that the Russians had recovered two unmanned spacecraft after flights round the moon. Conceivably, despite the unimpressive Soviet performance of recent years, these could be precursors of a manned expedition. Was the decision to send Apollo 8 round the moon a pre-emptive strike against this possibility? With the Saturn V man-rated after only two flights, and the spacecraft dispatched to the moon after only one manned flight, there were certainly grounds for suspicion. For all NASA's thorough ground-testing, neither piece of hardware could be said to be thoroughly proven in space.

Critics could certainly be heard. In the *New Republic*, for example, Dr. Ralph E. Lapp, a well-known scientific commentator, said in an interview, "We are pushing our luck, gambling that everything will work perfectly. NASA experts will assure you that they have thought through the risks and have planned for them. Well, they didn't in Apollo 204 [the vehicle involved in the fire]."

But soon after dawn on December 21, at the time to the second laid down months before, Apollo 8 lifted off the pad at Cape Kennedy and put Frank Borman, Jim Lovell and William Anders on course for the moon.

On Christmas Eve they went into orbit round it, and Lovell sent back the first eyewitness report of a view previously seen only by the robot lenses of unmanned probes: "The moon is essentially gray, no color. Looks like plaster of paris or sort of grayish beach sand. . . . The craters are all rounded off. There's quite a few of 'em. Some of them are newer. Many of them look like—especially the round ones— look like they were hit by meteorites or projectiles of some sort. Langrenus is quite a huge crater. It's got a central cone to it. The walls of the crater are terraced, about six or seven different terraces on the way down." On Christmas Day, Borman, Lovell and Anders were on their way back, heading for a splashdown within a few miles of the waiting aircraft carrier.

Suddenly it was all starting to come true. In spite of the flood of handouts celebrating seven years of steady progress toward the moon, in spite of Gemini and rendezvous, in spite of unmanned spacecraft skimming only a few miles above the moon's surface, in spite of the Saturn V and Apollo, the moon landing still seemed unreal, faintly suspect even, like a glossy brochure put out by a company in difficulties. Then almost overnight America and the world woke up to find that men were actually on their way to the moon, that the landing might be only months away. Apollo 8 had an impact unequaled since the first American orbital flight of John Glenn.

Similarly it was far more than just another flight to those inside the space program. Apollo 8 notched up first after first at every stage of its flight: the first manned spacecraft to escape from the earth's gravitational influence; the first to re-enter the earth's atmosphere at the lunar return speed of 25,000 miles an hour; the first to venture into deep space, several days from safety; above all, the first to go into orbit round the moon. The tension in mission control at Houston as Apollo 8 disappeared behind the moon for the first time was electric, more intense than ever before or since until the moments of the Apollo 11 landing seven months later.

Now Project Apollo was in the final straight. In February, the complete spacecraft, including the lunar module, flew for the first time with men on board, in orbit round the earth. On the fourth day of the flight yet another vital piece of Apollo hardware was exposed for the first time to space. A novice astronaut, Russell Schweickart, donned the portable life-support system, which would soon sustain the first lunar explorers when they ventured outside their spacecraft to walk on the moon, and climbed through the hatch of the lunar module onto the small platform outside. Unlike the Gemini space walkers, who were always connected to the spacecraft by oxygen hoses, Schweickart was completely independent, the 84-pound pack on his back supplying oxygen, removing carbon dioxide and moisture, and pumping cooling water through a network of fine tubes built into the inner layers of his suit.

The climax of Apollo 9 came the following day, with the rehearsal of the crucial rendezvous between the lunar module and the mother ship which had caused such bitter heartsearching when the mode was chosen seven years before. The commander, James McDivitt, and Schweickart moved off in the lunar module to a distance of fifty miles from David Scott in the command module before guiding themselves back and aligning their fragile craft for docking.

Scott, lying on his couch in the command module, had a small triangular window not much bigger than his hand about a foot in front of his nose. He worked his controls delicately to position the sights in front of the window on a T-shaped target on the lunar module. Then he started to close in, keeping his speed down to about one foot a second. The probe on the nose of the command module, which resembles a short stick with three small catches on the end, found the conical recess of the drogue on the lunar module and the catches snapped into place in the hole at its bottom. Then Scott gently retracted the probe until twelve main latches engaged, locking the craft together with a firm, gastight seal.

One more flight remained before the landing, the most frustrating any astronaut was ever asked to fly. In May, Apollo 10 commander Tom Stafford and Eugene Cernan in the lunar module they had named Snoopy swooped down to within 50,000 feet of the moon while John Young orbited overhead in the command module. They struggled with defective cameras as they skimmed low over site No.

2 in the Sea of Tranquility, already selected as the most suitable for the first landing. A short burn of the descent engine would have taken them down—but this was the final rehearsal, not the first performance.

Tantalizing though their flights were, so close to the moon yet so far from a place in history, Apollo 8 and Apollo 10 caught a compelling glimpse of the lunar perspective on the universe. Now it was possible to see not merely the earth from a great distance or the moon from a short one, but to see both at once in a new dimension. Over the horizon of the moon, the earth was as small as a pebble suspended in the blackness. The picture somehow seemed to complete the work begun by Copernicus four centuries before, when he banished the earth from the center of the universe and allotted it its proper, insignificant place as a satellite of the sun.

Of course, as we could also see, the earth remained the more inviting place to be, with the blue of its oceans, the green and brown of the land, the ever-changing white overlay of the clouds. By comparison the moon was barren, dry and impossibly stark. The closer it was approached, the more apparent this became. Besides testing the durability of the moon men and their machines, Apollos 8 and 10 were the final phase of an investigation which had continued for centuries. The study had been directed to a question which was every bit as absorbing to the men of Apollo as ever it was to Galileo. Precisely what manner of place was it to which so many people had contributed such vast resources in fulfillment of the American destiny?

12.
The Target
Approaches

Many questions had to be answered before men landed on the moon, but none was more elusive than the most basic question of all. Much could already be predicted with confidence in 1961, when President Kennedy unleashed American technology for the assault. It was certain that the rockets could be built, certain that a craft could be devised to carry and preserve the men on their journey through the void. Important details of the hardware remained to be decided and proved. But formidable as these problems were, they were not beyond the power of time and money to solve. The equations were known; the techniques of space travel existed; man could unquestionably be sent to the vicinity of the moon. What was not known was whether or not the moon was capable of being landed on. It seems ridiculously elementary, but it is a fact. America was committed to landing on the moon, and returning, before any astronomer was able to promise with conviction that a landing craft could land intact or that the men would not be swallowed up.

It was the one problem which no amount of time and money could eliminate. Both commodities could be spent on verifying the existence of hazards, and the degree to which these might imperil the astronauts. But they could not change the surface of the moon, which might well have manifested so many inhospitable dangers as to make Kennedy's assertion that men would land there a demand carrying intolerable and unjustifiable risks.

Such theories as did exist about the moon's surface were far from comforting. With earth-based telescopes unable to see anything on the moon much smaller than half-a-mile across, speculation was as prominent as observation in the science of selenology, as the study of the moon is known in the patois. Among the hazards foreseen by selenologists, a notoriously freewheeling bunch, were fields of boulders which would send the spacecraft toppling over as it landed; hardened lava flows full of fissures waiting to trap its legs; a temptingly smooth but treacherous surface which could turn out to be only a thin crust concealing deep clefts below, like the snow bridges which form over crevasses in a glacier. Most forbidding of all was the possibility that the spacecraft would disappear without trace into a soft, deep sea of dust.

Admittedly, in 1961 means were at hand which promised to bring the centuries of speculation to an abrupt and satisfactory conclusion. NASA planned to launch two groups of unmanned satellites with the specific object of settling the debate about the moon's surface. The Ranger program, scheduled for 1961, was designed to send back close-up television pictures from satellites approaching the moon and finally crashing into its surface. Surveyor was to follow in 1964. By making a controlled landing on the moon and transmitting pictures of its surroundings, Surveyor was designed to establish once and for all that the moon was a suitable place to land on.

But neither Ranger nor Surveyor did quite what was expected of them. Apart from the fact that both programs were seriously delayed, neither resolved the passionate dialectic of the selenologists. As a result of the technical delays and failures, the manufacturers of the lunar module were at work for three years before being given any satisfactory idea of the substance on which the craft would have to land. Ranger and Surveyor did eventually provide that crucial advance toward the manned landing. But among scientists, they served only to intensify the debate which has lasted for centuries. What is the moon's history? Has it an interior like earth's? What forces shaped the craters which pock its surface? What are the maria, the Seas of Tranquility, Storms and the rest, the great dark plains which can be seen from earth even with the naked eye?

No clear answers have yet been given to these questions. The rooms full of computer tapes and pictures on which the data collected by Ranger and Surveyor are recorded have produced no final agreement among astronomers. Each selenologist has found in the evidence support for his own favorite theory. The controversies continue as before, even after the return to earth of the first precious samples of the moon's crust.

Eventually, of course, the answers are sure to become clearer if governments are willing to continue to finance physical exploration of the moon's surface. But whether it takes one year, ten years or a hundred, that will be a very small fraction of the time which men have spent guessing, theorizing and fantasizing about what is there: a process which, despite the elementary ignorance which at first cast some doubt on Kennedy's national goal, has nevertheless produced an extraordinarily large body of knowledge.

Scientific interest in the moon can be traced back to the point where recorded history begins to merge into the mythologies of Egypt and Babylon. But the first people to think about cosmology in a way that can reasonably be described as scientific were the Greeks. Cosmologically their ideas were almost pure speculation. Anaxagoras, born in 499 B.C., held that the moon was like the earth and could support life. He had as little evidence for this belief as Anaximander, almost a contemporary, could offer for the statement that the moon was a hole in the dark air, enclosing a ring of fire. However, it was the Greeks who took the first significant steps toward man's understanding of the solar system. They did not only speculate; they showed that the moon must be a sphere, explained its phases and eclipses, and understood that it shone with light reflected from the sun. Remarkably, it was a Greek of the second century B.C., Hipparchus, living at Alexandria, who determined the moon's size to within a few hundred miles, and its distance from earth to within a few thousand.

But the greatest single legacy of the Greek astronomers was Ptolemy's description of the motion of the sun, moon and planets. Although his account put the earth at the center of things, as a geometrical description of the motions that could be observed it was very satisfactory. It stood unchallenged for 1500 years until it was overturned by Copernicus.

During the Middle Ages the theories propounded by Ptolemy existed, somewhat uneasily, alongside those of Aristotle. While the professionals stuck to Ptolemy, the Aristotelian cosmology became an integral part of the Catholic faith. In this, the earth was set in the center of the set of concentric crystal spheres rotated by angels. The moon was carried on the one inner sphere, nearest to earth. Then came Mercury, Venus, the Sun, Mars, Jupiter and Saturn. Beyond the moon's sphere everything was eternal and unchanging. The moon itself was not quite perfect, as the markings on its surface showed. This was the universe destroyed almost inadvertently by Copernicus, Tycho Brahe, Kepler and Galileo.

In 1610, Galileo turned toward the moon a newly invented device called a telescope and saw for the first time the craters, mountains and plains which have now become so familiar. He wrote, "We could perceive that the surface of the Moon is neither smooth nor uniform, nor very accurately spherical, as is assumed by a great many philosophers about the Moon and other celestial bodies, but that it is uneven, rough, replete with cavities and packed with protruding eminences, in no other wise than the earth, which is also characterized by mountains and valleys." The crystal sphere was cracked beyond repairing. The moon's imperfections could be seen and they were mundanely familiar. They were exactly like the earth's.

Hard on Galileo's revelation followed a flood of fantasies about travel to the moon; and this was no coincidence. Galileo had described another world with mountains, valleys, and, it was thought at the time, seas. Why should men not go there and why should the place have not inhabitants of its own?

The astronomer Kepler's allegorical *Somnium* appeared in 1634 and *The Man in the Moon: or a Discourse of a Voyage Thither* by Domingo Gonsales, the pseudonym of Francis Goodwin, Bishop of Hereford, in 1638. Gonsales's journey was made in an "engine" drawn by geese, and he inaugurated a sound astronautical practice by sending up his engine with a lamb on board before trying it himself. John Wilkins' *Discovery of a New World; or, A Discourse tending to prove, that 'tis probable there may be another Habitable World in the Planet* was written in the same year. Wilkins tried to base his fable on fact, and it includes what seems to be the earliest mention of weightlessness. He believed that at a height of about twenty miles the earth's influence would end and bodies would be "devoid of gravity." Far from disconcerting the travelers, this enabled them to do without food on the journey.

In 1686 De Fontenelle carried things a stage further with his *Dis-*

courses on the Plurality of Worlds in which he speculated about life
on the other planets of the solar system, though not the moon, which
he correctly surmised to have too rarefied an atmosphere. David Rus-
sen's *Iter Lunare: or a Voyage to the Moon*, of 1703, was another
landmark. His moon vehicle was shot off a ramp by a huge coiled
spring, an idea implying a very different kind of mind from the au-
thors of the earlier fantasies involving geese-drawn chariots.

While such men were founding a tradition which would lead
through Jules Verne and Tsiolkovsky directly to the German Raketen-
flugplatz, the astronomers were steadily composing a picture of the
moon's observable surface features.

Galileo himself made quite reasonable estimates of the height of
lunar mountains from the shadows they cast, but as a cartographer
he was less successful. Not a single feature in his drawings can be
identified with a known feature on the moon's surface. Others did better. The maps in Giovanni Riccioli's *Amagestum novum* of 1651 were
accurate enough for many of his names to have survived. It was Riccioli
who invented for the huge, smooth maria (they were thought to be
seas at the time) such romantic but enduring names as Mare Imbrium,
the Sea of Rains, and Oceanus Procellarum, the Ocean of Storms.

Observations grew steadily more accurate as the power of telescopes
increased and as experience was gained in mapping the lunar landscape; this last is a peculiarly hazardous business since the light is constantly changing, and a feature which throws a long shadow at dawn
may become completely invisible when the sun is directly overhead.
By the middle of the nineteenth century, all the main types of feature
visible by the most sophisticated telescope more than one hundred
years later were already identified.

The map and description of the moon published by the German
astronomers Wilhelm Beer and Johann Maedler in 1834–36 show
it all. Most conspicuous are the maria, some circular and surrounded
by walls of mountains, others irregular. The biggest, the Oceanus
Procellarum, covers an area larger than the Mediterranean. Most of
the great mountain ranges are grouped round the maria, though there
are isolated peaks scattered all over the surface.

But the moon is most marked by craters. Ranging in size from giants
like Clavius, 146 miles across, down to the limits of telescopic visibility
they cover the surface of both seas and highlands. Galileo compared

them to the eyes in a peacock's tail. Some are walled plains almost as big as the smaller maria, often with the same dark floors. Many have prominent central peaks. A few are surrounded by streaks of lighter material radiating outward like splash marks.

Less easy to see are the rilles, shallow trenches in the surface like those that form in mud as it dries and contracts. Some rilles are straight, others sinuous, with meanders reminiscent of a terrestrial riverbed. Often they merge into chains of small craters.

But as this mapping of the moon proceeded, one of its effects was to destroy the hypothesis of the man who had first put lunar cartography on a dimly scientific basis. Galileo's notion of another world collapsed. The maria might be relatively flat, but they certainly were not oceans, for how could oceans have so many craters in them? The absence of clouds was another indicator that the moon was very different from earth. So was the way stars and planets in the night sky disappeared abruptly behind the moon's disc instead of first appearing blurred. Both facts suggested that no atmosphere like earth's existed up there. If the moon had an atmosphere at all it was exceedingly thin. Without water or atmosphere, the existence of life of any kind seemed highly improbable. Nor was there the slightest geological movement to alter this picture of utter sterility. Observation over two centuries had failed to detect any change whatever.

Lifeless as it appeared to be, however, the moon became during the nineteenth century the subject of increasingly fierce scientific debate. Most of the early lunar astronomers had assumed almost without question that the lunar craters were formed by volcanic action. But in 1802 von Bieberstein made the revolutionary suggestion that they had an entirely different origin: that they were caused by meteoroids (a meteorite is a meteoroid that hits the earth) crashing, over millions of years, into the moon's surface.

This, the most absorbing of all debates about the moon, has not yet been fully resolved. There is general agreement that both mechanisms have been at work, but not about their relative importance. The popularity of the meteoric theory ebbed and flowed during the nineteenth century as authorities such as Franz von Paula Gruithausen in 1823, R. A. Proctor in the 1870s and G. K. Gilbert in the 1890s took it up. But those who favored the meteoroid theory did not really begin to establish an ascendancy over traditional volcanists until after the

Second World War, when the American scientist-industrialist, R. B. Baldwin published a series of influential books. Even now, however, the controversy is marked by that special degree of passion reserved to disputes in which neither side can prove that it is right.

The immediate question raised by the meteoroid theory is why, if the moon is covered with impact craters, is the earth not nearly so widely pockmarked with them. A number of meteoric craters do exist on earth. The most famous one, three-quarters of a mile across, is in Arizona. There is also the twelve-mile-wide Ries Kessel in southern Germany; there are several in Canada and there is the Vredefort Ring in South Africa—although the crater controversy extends even to earth, some volcanists refuse to concede all the terrestrial meteorite claims.

It is only to be expected that there are many fewer craters on earth than on the moon. Earth is very solidly protected by its atmosphere. The buffeting created by the atmosphere causes many meteorites to disintegrate before they reach the surface, reducing their size and force of impact. The famous Tunguska Event in Siberia in 1908 was probably caused by a comet which could have produced massive scars on the moon but which because of the cushioning effect of the atmosphere produced no crater at all on earth, though it leveled trees over hundreds of miles around.

Furthermore the earth does not carry its scars for long. Erosion by wind, rain and frost, not to mention geological upheavals, can in a relatively short time eliminate all traces of terrestrial craters. On the moon, by contrast, the big craters may be thousands of millions of years old.

Old or young, lunar craters are nearly always neat and circular. Meteoroids coming in at a low angle might be expected to produce long gouges in the surface; however, bodies traveling as fast as meteoroids virtually explode as soon as they make contact with a surface and this does tend to produce a neatly circular cavity. The phenomenon can be reproduced on a small scale in the laboratory.

In its modern form, the volcanic explanation of the lunar craters does not stress dramatic eruptions spouting fire and rocks. The terrestrial structures most closely resembling lunar craters are called calderas. They are formed by subsidence after molten rock has poured out or withdrawn from an underground chamber. A plug of solidified lava is often left in the center of the collapsed area. This accounts conveniently for the central peaks found in many lunar craters, but the impact theory inevitably has its own explanation for these too. They are due, it suggests, to a rebound effect at the bottom of the crater, or even to temporary volcanos following large-scale melting at the time of a meteoroid impact.

The volcanic theory seemed to get an unexpected boost in 1958 when the Russian astronomer, N. A. Kozyrev, actually observed what appeared to be an emission of glowing gas from the crater Alphonsus, giving the central peak a reddish tinge. But a release of gas alone can hardly be described as an eruption. The gas may even have been cold and may have glowed only because it was excited by radiation from the sun.

The maria, too, have to be accounted for. The flat, dark surfaces at first seem evidence of gigantic lava flows which have obliterated all earlier features. But equally the impact of a big meteoroid would produce a lot of melting; so even the presence of lava is not conclusive evidence of volcanism. Nor are the shapes of the maria any more helpful. The circular ones might be huge meteoric craters and the Mare Imbrium, eight hundred miles across, could hardly be a caldera. On the other hand, the immense, irregular Oceanus Procellarum has nothing to suggest it was caused by impact.

Just as astronomers have argued about the craters, so they have speculated about the moon's very origin. The great French mathematician Laplace suggested at the end of the eighteenth century that the solar system, including the moon, was formed from a great ball of hot gas which surrounded the sun like an atmosphere and rotated with it. As it cooled, the gas separated into a series of rings which eventually condensed into the planets and their attendant satellites.

Laplace's "nebular hypothesis" did not last long in its original form, but it is an obvious ancestor of modern theories. Most astronomers now believe that the planets formed by the gradual accretion, under their own gravitational attraction, of the particles in a dust cloud surrounding the sun. The sun may even have originated in the same dust cloud as the planets, at the same time. Certainly, there is no need to assume that the earth was once molten in order to explain its now molten core. Heating of an originally cold earth by the radioactive materials it contained is quite adequate to account for that.

But did the moon form where it now is, so extremely close to the earth?

As a planetary satellite the moon is distinctly odd. Its weight is just under one-eightieth of earth's. Between all other planets and their moons there is a much greater disproportion. It is much less dense than the earth as a whole, roughly as dense as the mantle—the layer which extends from the thin surface crust down to the liquid core. Why, if it formed near the earth, does it not have a similar composition? These were among the considerations which, in 1908, persuaded George Darwin, the son of the great biologist, to suggest that the moon had once been part of the earth. In an earlier, more fluid state, he thought, the composite planet might have rotated so fast that it became unstable and split into two parts, with the moon a fragment of the primeval earth.

Darwin had another important argument for this theory. Three hundred years or so before, Kepler had correctly surmised that tides in the seas on earth were due to the attraction of the moon. In fact there are quite easily detectable tides in the rocks of the earth's crust as well, producing movements of several feet. This influence, of course, works in both directions, and was used by the eighteenth-century philosopher Immanuel Kant to explain the well-known fact that the same side of the moon always faces the earth. Kant argued that the friction of the tides raised in the rocks of the moon's surface by the earth's attraction would gradually slow the moon's rotation down until the present state of affairs was reached: a permanent slight blister of the earthward side of the moon. An explanation not so very different is accepted today.

One inevitable physical consequence of this kind of interaction is that the moon moves gradually farther from the earth; therefore, it is argued, there must have been a time when the two were much closer. According to one calculation, 4000 million years ago the moon was only 8000 miles away. Obviously, the difference between 8000 miles away and actually forming part of the earth is very small indeed.

Darwin's theory has many attractions, but by and large it has been abandoned by modern thinkers. A number of powerful mathematical arguments have convinced astronomers that the earth and the moon could not have been formed, alone, from a single body. However, one relevant possibility remains: a split of the protoearth into two bodies of roughly equal size, with the moon as a fragment in between. As the third body in this astrogeological upheaval millions of years ago, Mars, which seems to have some resemblances to earth, fits the part very nicely.

Not that this is now the most widely favored theory. Current astronomical opinion postulates no such dramatic fragmentation. Instead, before the first sample of the lunar crust arrived the moon was generally held to be a totally separate planet in origin. It is roughly the same size as Mercury, and is thought, according to this theory, to have been captured by the earth through some chance conjunction in the development of the solar system. Perhaps the main advantage of this theory is that it explains a very common fact: that if calculations of the moon's orbit are taken far enough back, they show that its distance from earth is not narrowing but increasing.

To the men who were charged with landing on the moon, these rival theories, subjects of great contention among academicians, were of only minor significance. The origins of the moon and of its craters may have been the chief preoccupation of lunar astronomers for more than three hundred years. They might well offer by far the most exciting questions for resolution when the landing had been made and the first lunar samples examined. But in the prelude to the landing they were not relevant problems. If man and his machine were to land safely, it was not craters or seas which mattered, but boulders and dust: not the grand theories but the fine detail. And it was on the details that most of the lunar studies stimulated by Apollo were directed. Only after they had been examined and mastered might the wider questions be once again pushed toward an answer. In reaching down to the smallest detail, the telescope, the conventional tool of the astronomer, was of little use. On one point, however, its evidence was already reassuring. Imaginative pictures of the lunar landscape once showed towering crags and pinnacles far more precipitous than any found on earth. There was some justification for such artists' conceptions, for with weaker gravity and without erosive wind and water the moon could be expected to have a more angular surface than the earth. But close telescopic study then revealed that, by and large, lunar mountains were far less steep than those on earth. Even in the mountainous regions, the average slope has only ten degrees.

Earthbound study by more exotic methods than the optical telescope had disclosed a few more features. Infrared radiation (heat rays) from the moon, for example, could be used to measure its temperature. In 1930, Edison Pettit and Seth B. Nicholson placed an infrared detector at the focus of the Mount Wilson telescope and estimated the moon's temperature directly under the sun to be 275° F, falling to −241° F at night. The figures were new but the extreme range came as no surprise. Without any atmosphere on the moon to absorb some of the power of the sun's rays and to even out day and night temperatures, something of the sort was expected. Surface heat escapes so quickly into space when the moon is in shadow that during an eclipse temperatures can fall 350° F in an hour.

Microwaves, very short radio waves, were also used to take its temperature, but they gave very different answers from the infrared measurement. The explanation is that microwaves come not from the surface itself but from a surface layer of appreciable thickness, and it is the average temperature of this layer that the microwaves measure. The temperature of the moon at a depth of a few feet turned out to be more or less constant at a temperature, according to one estimate, of about −40° F. This was an invaluable clue to the nature of the surface materials, for if the temperature of the surface itself can fall 350° F in an hour while three or four feet down it does not change at all, the materials involved must be extraordinarily poor conductors of heat. Solid rock was ruled out at once. The most likely possibility seemed to be some kind of porous structure containing a great deal of empty space, perhaps something like pumice stone, perhaps dust or a loosely packed granular material. All three hypotheses seemed quite compatible with the idea of a surface continually bombarded and churned up by meteorites of all sizes down to particles smaller than grains of sand.

The way the moon reflected light and radar waves supported the idea of a dust-covered surface. On average only about 7 percent of the light from the sun which reaches the moon is reflected, about what would be expected from a surface covered with a fine dark-colored dust. To the much longer radar waves, on the other hand, the moon's surface acted like a mirror. If a surface is to act as a mirror any irregularities must be small compared with the wavelength of whatever is being reflected. A gently undulating, dust-covered surface therefore seemed the most convincing possibility: it would be rough to light waves, which are very short, but smooth to the much longer radar waves.

Thus in the final phase of lunar observation conducted solely from earth, the notion of a dust-covered moon was very popular. The main disagreement, in fact, concerned not so much the existence of dust as its thickness. The most extreme view was put forward by Professor Thomas Gold of Cornell University in 1955, when he was still at the Royal Greenwich Observatory in England. According to Gold, the dust particles picked up an electric charge from the wind of electrified particles streaming out from the sun. This made them repel each other so that they would flow, slowly but with the remorseless inevitability of liquid, into the lower-lying parts of the moon. The dust in the maria, Gold asserted, might be thousands of feet deep and likely to engulf any object, including a spacecraft. Not many people went so far, but the prospect was a nightmare which the Apollo planners could not avoid taking seriously. It was part of the picture which had to be proved or disproved by closer inspection.

As the inspection began, with the unmanned precursors of Apollo 11, the picture of the moon was roughly as follows: it was a planet with one-quarter of earth's diameter but only one-eighty-first of its weight, formed independently and captured by some astronomical fluke; its surface features had been shaped perhaps by inherent volcanism, perhaps by thousands of millions of meteoric impacts, perhaps by both, with most people inclining to the meteor theory; the surface itself was open and porous to an unknown depth, almost certainly covered by a layer of dust, which one or two astronomers thought might be very fine and deep indeed; the temperature varied from more than the boiling point of water during the two-week lunar day to almost the boiling point of liquid air during the two-week night. Were the Lunas, Rangers, Orbiters and Surveyors which were now sent to investigate to confirm or deny these details? Would they find the moon easier or more difficult to land on than they expected? Or would they, perhaps, find it impossible?

The first phase of the investigation was an entirely Russian affair, forming part of the crescendo from Sputnik 1 to the orbital flight of Yuri Gagarin, when every Soviet space exploit seemed to underline another American weakness. In 1959 the Russians sent up Lunik 1 which passed within only three thousand miles of the moon before becoming the first artificial satellite of the sun. Nine months later Lunik 2 actually hit the moon. Neither spacecraft carried a camera, but between them they showed that the moon had virtually no magnetic field, a point of considerable scientific interest since a field comparable with earth's would have been strong evidence of the moon having a liquid core.

The first two Lunas could be described as feats of rocketry rather than sophisticated spacecraft engineering, an area where the United States was already claiming a lead. Then, on October 4, 1959, the second anniversary of Sputnik 1, the Russians launched Luna 3. Looping round the back of the moon at a distance of some forty thousand miles, it successfully transmitted back to earth pictures of a large part of the previously unknown face. Their quality was not particularly good, but the feat was a remarkable one; it was no longer possible to regard Soviet satellites as crude hunks of ironmongery.

Meanwhile the American lunar investigation program had got off to a disastrous start. In 1958, the first four attempts to send spacecraft to the environs of the moon all failed, the Ranger flights began in 1961 with a seemingly endless series of catastrophes. Not one of the first six missions was successful and not a single picture of any part of the moon was received from any of them. The cost of this humiliating debacle had been $260 million. The row which followed came close to closing down the Jet Propulsion Laboratory where the Rangers were designed and built.

Finally, on July 31, 1964, amid scenes of almost hysterical glee in the Jet Propulsion Laboratory auditorium, Ranger 7 successfully completed its mission. During the final quarter of an hour of its three-day flight, as it plunged toward the Mare Nubium, its six cameras sent back 4316 pictures, the first taken from a height of 1120 miles, the last from only 1735 feet above the surface.

The quality of the pictures was superb. The final photograph taken by one of the high-resolution cameras showed features only a foot or so across. A tiny section of the moon had been brought a thousand times closer than was possible with the largest telescopes on earth. Yet when the euphoria over this unprecedented technical achievement had subsided, those who studied the pictures had to admit that they still could not be sure whether the surface was suitable for a manned landing, still less identify the forces which fashioned its features.

On one point the Ranger pictures were reassuring. Although they showed craters continuing down in size to the limit detectable with the cameras, they also revealed that the Mare Nubium was smoother and flatter than many people had feared. But as to the strength of the surface, few clues were vouchsafed. Clearly, if there were dust, it did not flow like water; if it had done, the small craters would have been filled in. Professor Gold, however, pointed out that deposits thousands of feet thick could have formed during the moon's lifetime even if the dust particles had moved only a minute fraction of an inch a year. He also suggested that the softly rounded rims of older craters, as compared with the sharper outlines of the more recent ones superimposed on them, were produced by a slow accumulation of dust.

The adherents of Professor Gold's theory had another well-prepared defense. Very little was known about how quite commonplace materials would behave in the alien conditions of the moon's surface, in a total vacuum and under constant bombardment by microscopic meteoroids and radiation from the sun. They certainly would not behave as they did on earth. Laboratory experiments with powdered cement, for example, had shown that in a vacuum it tended to build up into fragile "fairy castle" structures, full of voids and cavities. So dust on the moon might well consolidate to form a material rigid enough to preserve the shapes of small craters but sure to collapse even under a small load.

Where Gold saw comforting evidence of dust in the Ranger pictures, others found support for quite different theories. Dr. Gerard P. Kuiper of the University of Arizona, who headed the Ranger scientific team, claimed that the pictures confirmed his view that the maria were lava flows. Nobel Laureate Dr. Harold Urey, another member of the team, could see no evidence of lava. Dr. Eugene M. Shoemaker of the U.S. Geological Survey, the team geologist, thought there might be an upper layer of pulverized material. Though most people who examined the pictures thought the surface would be strong enough for a landing, their total disagreement on other points of interpretation hardly inspired confidence.

From the purely scientific point of view, the most interesting feature of the Ranger 7 pictures was the small craters, which turned out to be far more numerous than expected. Most lunar specialists agreed that the excess must have been due to debris scattered over the surface when the larger primary craters were formed.

Ranger 8 followed Ranger 7 after an interval of nearly seven months, and besides building up the evidence on which a landing would be attempted became something of a turning-point in the fortunes of the volcanic theory of the origin of the craters. In the pictures it sent back it was easy to pick out dimple craters, which seemed to have been formed by material draining out of a crack at the bottom. Their appearance and the way they were strung out along the rilles were such strong evidence of some kind of internal activity on the moon that even the most hardened members of the impact school were forced to acknowledge it.

The ninth and last Ranger, which crashed into the crater Alphonsus on March 24, 1965, was equally encouraging for the volcanologists. It showed more craters along rilles, elongated in the same direction as the rille, and surrounded by halos of dark material almost certainly ejected during eruptions. Obviously craters were produced by some kind of internal mechanism; the halos provided strong evidence for actual volcanos. From estimates of how far particular pieces of debris had traveled, and of how deeply they were buried, the scientists also tried to get a rough figure for the bearing-strength of the surface, but as Dr. Kuiper said when the Ranger program was over, "I would be willing to guess that the hardness would be sufficient to support a landing vehicle . . . but honestly this is not a measure; this is obviously just a guess." The Rangers had brought the moon a thousand times closer than the terrestrial telescope, but it was not close enough. The program to put a man on the moon was four years advanced, yet still no one could promise that he would ever be able to set foot there safely. Less than a year passed, however, before the moon was brought a thousand times closer still.

Again, ironically, it was the Russians who got there first. On February 3, 1966, Luna 9 landed in the Ocean of Storms. A few hours later it was transmitting the first pictures of the moon direct from the surface. The transmissions were picked up at Jodrell Bank, and Sir Bernard Lovell was able to release them well before the Russians, with a warning that they might be on different scales vertically and horizontally—as they were, which the pained Russians pointed out soon afterward. Luna 9 was standing on the surface, not buried beneath it—this, for the Apollo planners, was the supremely important fact about it. For the first time an object had landed intact and been seen not to sink without trace. The probe was a ball weighing about 220 pounds, which bounced and rolled after landing before four petal-like panels opened to expose the camera. Clearly a surface on which a 220-pound ball could bounce and roll was reasonably strong. The Russians reported later that the soil was hard and porous.

The pictures showed a scene of total desolation: rolling landscape which might have been covered with cinders and clinker, here and there a rock throwing a long shadow, in the distance a shallow crater and—more ammunition for the volcanologists—a low ridge which might have been the boundary of an ancient lava flow.

More than two years late because of endless troubles with its launcher, the American Surveyor 1 soft-landed on the moon, four months after Luna 9. True to the pattern that has prevailed throughout the unmanned exploration of the moon—the Russians do it first but the Americans do it better—it returned pictures of much higher quality. Among them, the five successful Surveyors (only two were failures) removed all doubts about whether men could land and walk about on the surface of the moon. In its unregarded way, it was almost as momentous a development as that of the Saturn V itself.

The Surveyors were scaled so that their footpads would exert the same pressure on the surface as those of the future, manned lunar module, and their television cameras were positioned so that they could be brought to bear on the pads. None sunk in more than an inch or two. Surveyor 3 provided an unexpected bonus. One of its engines failed to shut off at touchdown, causing the craft to bounce several times before coming to rest. The consequent marks made possible even more refined estimates of the surface strength.

Later Surveyors were equipped with small mechanical scoops for digging in the soil, picking up lumps of it, squeezing them and dropping them. The soil itself turned out to have the consistency of damp beach sand. It stuck together easily but the lumps broke up when squeezed or dropped. Mixed up in the soil were a number of much harder objects, presumably stones, which did not break up under the same treatment. When the scoop was set to digging a trench a foot or so deep the sides did not cave in.

The Surveyor pictures also provided some valuable clues to the thickness of the layer of rubble which covers the surface of the moon. Many craters were surrounded with jagged stones and boulders, presumably fragments of bedrock thrown out when the crater formed. If such fragments were to be seen round a crater, say, ten feet deep, then bedrock could not be more than ten feet below the surface. The depth of the rubble layer as estimated in this way varied widely from place to place. Close to Surveyor 7, which landed in the southerly highlands near the edge of the great crater Tycho, it was only a few inches. In parts of the maria, on the other hand, it was more than sixty feet. Deep as the rubble seemed to be in some quarters of the moon, it certainly was not dust. The Surveyors were not buried in dust; they finally buried the deep-dust theory.

Scientifically, the Surveyors' greatest achievement was the first analysis of lunar surface material made by the last three spacecraft of the series. By bombarding the surface with alpha particles, a form of nuclear radiation, and picking up the characteristic radiations emitted by the different chemical elements in the lunar soil when excited in this way, this analysis showed that the chemical composition of a mare soil was similar to basalt. Of all rocks, basalt is the most characteristic of volcanism and it can only form from rock in a liquid state. But even this apparently conclusive piece of evidence did not settle the classic argument. Volcanic action was not the only possible source of melting. Meteoric or cometory impacts big enough to have produced the maria would have produced the same phenomenon. Besides, the analysis of the lunar soil showed not that it was the same as terrestrial basalt, only that it resembled basalt. For the Apollo planners, however, Surveyors pictures were almost all they wanted. They showed what man standing on the surface of the moon would see. And they showed that he could indeed stand. Yet somehow they were still too foreign. The utter unfamiliarity of the landscape, the weird lighting, the obvious boundaries between the individual pictures joined together to make panoramas, gave them an air of unreality. They seemed as contrived as pictures of the tracks of nuclear particles in a bubble chamber. It was impossible to imagine a man standing on the edge of one of those craters, even a man in a spacesuit.

A third and final series of exploratory probes, however, was already underway. One picture from this, the Orbiter series, had already rendered the moon a place in which man could be comprehended. This picture, perhaps more than any other, took the moon out of the scientists' textbooks and into the grasp of men. It showed the crater Copernicus, taken obliquely from a height of twenty-nine miles. In the foreground, the near wall of the crater slopes down to the floor, in the middle distance the central peak is in sharp relief. Sixty miles away is the rugged farther wall of the crater. On the horizon, gently rolling hills are silhouetted against the black sky. The picture shows far less detail than many taken previously, and the scale is deceptive, but to the casual eye it might have been shot from an aircraft flying over some mountainous desert on earth. If Surveyor brought the moon a million times closer for the astrogeologist, this picture from Lunar Orbiter 2 did the same, psychologically, for everyone else.

After Ranger and Surveyor had established that the moon was suitable for a landing, the object of the Orbiters was to provide evidence from which to choose a landing site. In the search for detail, this was the last refinement. The craft were highly complex—each carried several cameras, processed the film on board and could change orbit round the moon on command from earth. But they were possibly the most successful of all American unmanned spaceships—the only failure in five attempts was a single camera in Lunar Orbiter 1.

Altogether the Orbiters photographed virtually the entire surface of the moon, showing details down to about one hundred yards across. These pictures now provide almost as detailed a survey of the lunar topography as is available for earth itself. The Orbiters also photographed potential landing sites and areas of particular scientific interest with high-resolution cameras capable of picking up details a hundred times smaller still than those on the general survey.

The Orbiter pictures produced no big surprises, but astronomers will need a generation to analyze them in detail. Some of the most interesting provide unmistakable evidence of change on the moon's surface. One picture shows the tracks of two huge boulders which have rolled a thousand feet or so down a slope, and shows the boulders themselves now resting at the bottom. Countless others reveal the disproportionately small number of small craters in the walls of bigger ones, and other signs of a slow downward movement of material which, over millions of years, has rounded the edges of craters and gradually filled them in. Again, the pictures have focused attention on the sinuous rilles which wind their way across the surface like dried-up riverbeds. Few people now doubt that these were produced by some kind of flow, perhaps of lava, perhaps even of water from the interior which might have run for a short time across the surface before evaporating.

Other apparently volcanic features abound: craters on top of peaks, crater chains, dimple craters, broad low domes like the volcanos of Iceland and steep-sided, flat-topped ones like some old volcanos in Arizona, the remains of obvious lava flows in the maria. Some of these flows can be traced back to wrinklelike ridges which may mark the place where the lava welled up from the interior along a fissure in the crust.

Another result of the Orbiters was to confirm the finding of the Russian Luna 3 and its successor Zond 3 that there are no maria on the far side of the moon. According to the impact school this was due because gravity tended to concentrate major meteorite impacts on the near side; the volcanologists were less ready with an explanation. Less open to dispute was the evidence provided about the thickness of the rubble layer. Careful analysis of the pictures showed that many of the medium-sized craters have a kind of kink in their walls which could mark the level where loose rubble ends and bedrock begins. If so, the rubble layer was anything from ten to fifty feet thick in the maria, a result which agreed closely with the estimates derived from Surveyor.

One of the discoveries most relevant to a manned landing did not come from the pictures at all, but from a careful study of minute irregularities in the orbits of the spacecraft, which turned out to be due to concentrations of mass under the surface. Twelve of these "mascons" have now been identified, all located directly under different dark areas, particularly maria. On the theoretical level, they are a gift to the impact men, who triumphantly insist that they must be the buried remains of gigantic meteorites which, as everyone knows, produced the maria in the first place. For practical spacemen, they introduced yet another complication. Whatever their origin the changes these mascons could effect on the course of a spacecraft in orbit round the moon clearly had to be reckoned with.

When Lunar Orbiter 5 crashed on the moon on January 31, 1968, the American unmanned lunar exploration program was over. What did it achieve? Scientifically the results were perhaps disappointing.

They resolved nothing. The old controversy about the origin of the craters lingered on, although there had been some convergence of opinion and no one could any longer doubt that there was or had been some kind of volcanism on the moon. In so far as there was a consensus, it could be summarized like this: the maria were lava flows from the interior; the big craters were produced by meteoroids, but many, such as Tsiolkovsky, had been invaded by lava from the interior since their formation. Many other craters and features like rilles and domes were of purely internal origin. The moon once had a hot interior and some kind of slow evolution was still going on.

But that consensus, if consensus it was, was an incidental development. Ranger, Surveyor and Lunar Orbiter had not been designed to bring it about. Their primary objective had not been scientific, in the pure sense of the term, but pragmatic. They were steps on man's own path to the moon, sent before him to see whether he could land there and where exactly he would be best advised to try. They had done their work in parallel with all the other operations which were required before he could get there: the building of the rockets, the invention of the spacecraft, the development of rendezvous in space, the refinement of the computers, the selection and training of the uncommon men who were to do the job. Even as the final unmanned craft landed on the moon, the Apollo spaceship which would carry men there and back was on its final proving tests. It would not be long now before the men would land, in the way Surveyor showed them they could, and at the point which Orbiter dictated. To them it would perhaps be of secondary interest whether the moon was made of volcanos or meteorites or even, perhaps, green cheese. To the men who sent them it was, in all but fact, the same fiery hole in the air perceived by Anaximander the Greek: romantic, mysterious, distant and, so they hoped, the bringer of unimaginable glory to the nation which managed to seize it.

13.
The Eagle
Has Landed

If the observed universe were to be mapped from coast to coast on the surface of the United States, not even the most powerful microscope could distinguish the correct location of earth from that of the moon, so immense is the universe and so insignificant the gap between the two of them. Light, whose speed is the best measure of universal distance, takes several thousands of millions of years to reach us from the fringes of the observable universe. It takes 100,000 years to cross the Milky Way. It takes a few hours to cross the solar system. It takes little more than seconds to reach earth from the moon. The actual distance, about 238,000 miles, is less than a billionth of the distance between earth and some of the stars which can be seen from it with the naked eye.

However, for men to get there, would take three days and a degree of perfection in their mechanical skills never before attained. Measured against the universe, the journey would be invisible. But on planet earth it would be the most widely witnessed event in history.

It began, like so many moments of the space age, in an atmosphere of extravagant contrast. The men chosen to go to the moon, astronauts Armstrong, Aldrin and Collins, were brought from their training quarters to offer their last thoughts to the world. They were seen only over closed circuit TV, to guard them against the smallest infection, but as they sat there in colored beach shirts they looked like stage Americans discussing the ball game. Neil Armstrong, commander of

Apollo 11, fielded most of the questions, sounding painfully shy, and stuttering over his mild pronouncements.

All his life, Armstrong has lived for flying. On his Gemini 8 flight, he took a fragment of the Wright brothers' plane with him; he goes gliding for relaxation. He has also been in many tight situations—over Korea, in the X-15 rocket plane and in the lunar landing simulator. Professionally he is the ultimate in calm. And he was even more dedicated than most astronauts to being the first man on the moon.

The second man on the moon, Edwin Aldrin, is one of the brainiest and most athletic of the space pilots, with a research degree from MIT. He is also a scout merit-badge counsellor and an elder and trustee of the Webster Presbyterian Church. His official biography says his hobbies are running, scuba diving and high bar exercises. What the document does not say is that he has a bar over his bed so that he can chin-up last thing at night and first thing in the morning.

At the germ-free press conference, Michael Collins seemed by far the most relaxed of the three, quietly humorous, gallantly insisting that he was perfectly happy with his lonely role in the command module. Before Collins joined the space program he had shown none of the single-minded intensity of Armstrong and Aldrin; and it was characteristic that the mustache he grew during the moon flight looked hippie rather than soldierly. Like both his companions he had been in space once before, with John Young in Gemini 10.

Two days later at 6:25 A.M., with the first light in the sky, the three men came out of their robing center, looking at last like astronauts. They walked with a rolling gait in their heavy spacesuits, grinning behind the plastic domes of their helmets. "Like Mickey Mice," said a voice. The crew waved long enough for some of the shoving photographers to get a picture, then stepped into the van which moved off at once with its beacon flashing.

The viewing stands three and a half miles from the launch pad faced into the rising sun, and by 7:30 A.M. the temperature under their tin roofs reached 100 degrees. One of the NASA contractors handed round colored paper sunhats, heightening the sense of carnival. Photographers lined a canal bank facing the rocket, Sunday fishermen shoulder to shoulder, all of them after the same catch.

"T minus one hour, twenty minutes and fifty-five seconds and still counting for Apollo 11 at this time," said mission control, as the white rocket steamed industrially on the flat landscape three and a half miles away. "At this point in the countdown spacecraft commander Neil Armstrong once again appears to be the busiest worker in the space-craft as he is performing a series of alignment checks associated with the guidance system . . . The hydrogen leak problem that we did en-counter earlier has been solved. That is real good news, says Arm-strong . . ."

A million people were reported to be in the area, dousing them-selves with lotions to keep away mosquitoes and sunburn, frying breakfast steaks in a spectacular log-jam of traffic, listening to the countdown on their radios. "Thirty seconds and counting," said the mission commentator. "Astronauts reported, feeling good. T minus twenty-five seconds. Twenty seconds and counting. Fifteen seconds, guidance is inertial. Twelve, eleven, ten, nine. Ignition sequence starts. Six, five, four, three, two, one, zero. All engines running. Lift-off. We have liftoff."

The voice is unalterably monotonous, even weary, and perhaps fervor would have been an intrusion, cheapening an event that in dramatic terms is sensationally self-sufficient. There is no sight or sound on earth to equal the launch of a Saturn V and the experience for those watching at the Cape is immensely personal.

The voyage of Apollo 11 began with a soundless light under the rocket, so brilliant in intensity that it hurt to watch and obscured the first two hundred feet of the launch tower. The light spread out to one side of the pad and the rocket pushed itself slowly off the ground, the loudest, biggest and most sensitive balancing act in the world.

A sound never caught by the television microphones rolled back across the swampy headland, ruffling the jungle and beating down on the long-suffering heads of the alligators in the Cape's wildlife sanctuary. Apollo 11 took off not with a steady roar but with a series of satanic cracks, shocks that rattled the tin roof of the viewing stands and shook the clothing of those who gaped. It moved into the sun's glare, banging louder as it gained height. At 15,000 feet it pierced a thin cloud layer and its shadow broke away and streaked to the north.

In the bedlam of the launch there were, momentarily, no critics of the space program; the Poor People's March to the Cape gates seemed unimportant, the sniping of scientific critics peevish and glib. NASA has always tried to exploit this fleeting suspension of disbelief by packing the VIP stands with Congressmen. This time they went a little further, gracefully persuading Dr. Ralph Abernathy to abandon his Poor People to the local sheriff and sit with former President Lyndon B. Johnson and other honored guests in the VIP enclosure. Little more was heard from him in the train of events that overwhelmed the following week's newspapers.

The moon journey proper started two hours forty-five minutes later. With Apollo in orbit round the earth, the engine in the final stage of the Saturn fired again, pushing it faster and faster out toward the moon. The spacecraft shook loose and turned to extract the lunar module from the rocket's shell.

The crew slipped away from earth like men eloping, the least loquacious of all the Apollo astronauts, their minds dominated by what lay ahead. As the spacecraft moved deeper into space, it revolved slowly to even out the $300°$ difference of temperature which would otherwise develop between its sunlit and shadowed sides.

If reticence is an index of technical brilliance, the safety of Apollo 11 was assured from the start. After four hours of flight Armstrong noted the countries of planet earth as if they were digits on a computer. "Houston," he said, "you might be interested that at my first-hand window right now I can observe the entire continent of North America, Alaska, over the Pole down to the Yucatan Peninsula, Cuba, northern part of South America and then I run out of window."

Oddly enough it was the taciturn Armstrong who had the fastest heartbeat during many of the tensest moments of the voyage. The thuds transmitted from his chest to sheets of paper in Mission Control showed a man quite humanly scared but with his fear rigidly under control. In the minutes after the launch his heart beat 110 times a minute, Collins's 99 times and Aldrin's heart, which feeds a computer brain, beat an almost normal 88.

The crew of Borman's Apollo 8 had been ill in the first hours of their voyage and the information had been dumped secretly to one of the ground receiving stations. The astronauts, with their onboard distrust of all medical men, hate information being released about their heaving stomachs or any quirks of temperament: after Apollo 7, commander Wally Schirra professed to be astonished that anyone outside Mission Control should have heard his outburst over switching on the spacecraft's TV camera.

But both events gave the crews involved a certain charisma; they were, after all, human, with weaknesses that could be recognized on earth, and yet their voyages were successful, warts and all. The words of the crew of Apollo 11 showed no weakness at all, being largely restricted to obscure exchanges like the following between the capsule communicator—an astronaut who speaks to the spacecraft from Mission Control—and Armstrong.

CAPCOM. "Apollo 11, this is Houston. At the time of your cyclic accumulator stroking, we were on low bit rate data and consequently not receiving the OK flow parameter. We expect that what we're seeing is probably nominal, that it's probably what we'd expect from a transducer that's malfunctioning in effect and it's probably going to keep on getting worse like that. Nothing to worry about. We'll monitor things on the ground here. Over."

SPACECRAFT. "Okay. It does look it's gradually degrading to about zilch."

This was a prize example of Apollo's most obvious bequest to the listening world: the murder of the English language. The flights have fathered a whole new language—Astronymish—in which the hazards of space are reduced to initials which petrify the momentous events of which they speak. There are dictionaries of Astronymish, in which the acronyms of space are tortuously unwound. But not even they allowed for zilch.

Jim Lovell livened the voyage a little when he spoke to Aldrin, his old companion aboard Gemini 12. Aldrin discovered the view of earth and Lovell drew from him a description of the sun setting over the eastern Mediterranean and the greenness of the British Isles compared with lands further south.

And later Collins, the chattiest of the three—he was, after all, staying in lunar orbit with a much higher chance of getting home—talked about the domestic life of Apollo 11. "We do have a happy home," Collins said. "There's plenty of room for the three of us and I think we're all willing to find our favorite little corner to sit in.

"Zero G [gravity] is very comfortable but after a while you get to the point where you sort of get tired of rattling around and banging off the ceiling and the floor and the side; so you tend to find a little corner somewhere and put your knees up and that seems more like home."

Back on earth there was increasing preoccupation with Luna 15, an unmanned probe launched toward the moon by the Russians three days before Apollo 11. It had already wrung from George Mueller, NASA's head of manned spaceflight, a rare admission that space was indeed a race; he said he regarded competition as a good thing. But now, in fact, the contest was to produce a rare piece of co-operation.

Luna 15 went into orbit round the moon soon after Apollo 11 set off, posing for NASA a problem which could not be ignored. At 6 A.M. one morning early in the flight, Colonel Frank Borman, NASA's ambassador to Moscow and the White House, placed a call from his bedroom near Houston to Academician Mstislav Keldysh, president of the Academy of Sciences of the U.S.S.R.

A rumor started later that Borman, being a tidy man with money, had reversed the charges, but the purpose of the call was too serious for that. Borman, speaking for Mission Control, asked Keldysh for details of Luna 15's orbit. NASA was surprised, and delighted, to get a reply in the form of a cable in which Keldysh told them that the Russian craft was circling the moon every two hours and thirty seconds in an elliptical orbit ranging from 30 to 110 miles. "I'm very pleased with this Russian response," Borman said later. "I hope it's indicative of a more fruitful type of co-operation in future."

Borman's political star had burned with increasing brilliance since the world tour he made after his Apollo 8 mission round the moon. His official role was manager of a NASA group designing re-usable spacecraft. But his real authority went far beyond the title on his Washington door. In the summer of Apollo 11 he emerged as one of the most influential and capable space lobbyists in the White House— a personal friend of the President, who calls him "Frank."

Borman's call to Moscow reassured the crew that even the million-to-one chance of a collision with Luna 15 did not exist. And on the third day of the flight, with Apollo 11 175,000 miles from earth, they at last found their human tongues for long enough to transmit a ninety-six-minute color television spectacular. It was not only the first color movie from space, it was also the best film taken inside an American spaceship.

It opened with Armstrong in the tunnel that linked the command and lunar modules working to remove the docking gear which obstructed it. "Mike must have done a smooth job in that docking. There isn't a dent or a mark on the probe," he said as he passed it back. Aldrin moved through into the lunar module, where he floated around communicating a sense of curiosity about the effects of weightlessness —chasing a loose washer, floating a pair of sunglasses against a mid-air package. At one point he pretended to push the module's abort button and Mission Control held its lurching heart and said, "We don't recommend that."

Struggling across Eagle's cabin with trailing cables Aldrin said, "The restraint straps are doing a pretty good job of pulling my pants down." "We haven't quite got that before the fifty million TV audience yet," said control.

Little was heard from Armstrong, who moved closer each hour to the title given him by *Pravda*—Czar of the Ship. At one point Collins gently sent up his commander. "The czar's brushing his teeth," he said, taking a call from Houston. "I'm filling in for him." "Roger," said control. "If you don't get in the way of the czar brushing his teeth we'd like you to bring up the primary accumulation quantity a little bit."

Armstrong observed a lofty silence about being the czar, and his mood seemed to affect the rest of the crew. Apollo 11 ducked behind the moon for the first time without a word, an omission that was remarkable only because it was so unquestioningly accepted on earth. The event involved loss of communication between the spaceship and Mission Control but there was scant evidence of the electric strain that had characterized the first disappearance of Borman's Apollo 8.

It is a remarkable reflection of NASA's assiduously cultivated air of self-confidence that its audience has become immune to, if not unaware of, the dangers of maneuvering in space. In December 1968 the suspense of lunar orbiting disrupted the flow of life for those who observed it at home. In the summer of 1969, just six months later, the operation seemed almost commonplace and the uncoupling of the module Eagle from its command ship Columbia—only the second operation of its kind over the moon's surface—had the dramatic impact of a goods train separating in a city marshaling yard.

The danger was there: the smallest technical failure would have monstrous consequences. But the American people, conditioned by the hypnotic casuistry of NASA's public optimism, watched Apollo 11 prepare to land with a blind faith that precluded any thought of disaster. A few days earlier it had been left to Dr. von Braun, a lone voice, to hope that they would have the maturity to accept the worst.

But exactly on schedule, Apollo 11 came back from behind the moon, having fired its engine on the far side to put itself in lunar orbit. Minutes later Armstrong and Aldrin were getting their first view of the landing approach path they would take next day. On their second orbit they switched on their television camera to give earth, too, a glimpse of what it would be like.

To the astronauts, the landmarks on the track were as familiar as the road from Houston to Clear Lake City. Maps and pictures had scored them indelibly in the memory. But now they were seeing the real thing: the triangular Mount Marilyn immediately below the point at which they would fire their engine to start the powered descent; Boot Hill and crater Maskelyne; the features the crew of Apollo 10 had named Sidewinder and Diamondback, "like a couple of snakes down there in the lake bed." But before they reached the tiny oval target in the Sea of Tranquility they had crossed the terminator, and the surface of the moon below them was in darkness.

Behind the moon once more they fired their engine a second time to make their orbit circular, and Armstrong and Aldrin climbed through into the lunar module for some final checks before all three settled down to a meal and a few hours' rest.

On the tenth orbit they were back in the lunar module again, tuning it up and preparing it to become the independent Eagle. Unlike some airlines, which allow no seats to be numbered 13, the planners of the moon journey had shown a proper disdain for superstition, and Eagle broke away from Columbia out of sight of earth during the thirteenth orbit.

The two craft reappeared flying side by side. "The Eagle has wings," reported Armstrong, but this brief excursion into metaphor was soon submerged in a flood of computer data. Collins gave Columbia a tiny burst of power, taking it away from Eagle at two and a half feet per second. They swept across the face of the moon, the distance between them slowly increasing. Not for the last time, control had difficulty in keeping in contact with the module, and used Columbia as an intermediate transmitter.

CAPCOM. Columbia, Houston. We've lost our data with Eagle. Will you please have him select AFT omni. Over.

COLUMBIA. Eagle, this is Columbia. Houston would like you to select AFT omni. Over.

EAGLE. Roger. I got it now. Houston, you reading Eagle now on AFT omni.

CAPCOM. That's affirmative, Eagle. Reading you 5 by.

EAGLE. Roger.

"Eagle has been given a go for descent orbit insertion," said Mission Control as the steadily separating craft vanished again. "That maneuver to occur in 7 minutes 40 seconds."

At the Manned Spacecraft Center the great control complex was filling now with many famous figures from Project Apollo, come to witness the climactic moment of their years of labor. In the control room itself were George Mueller, Sam Phillips, Robert Gilruth, and Deke Slayton, with the Apollo 8 astronauts Jim Lovell and Bill Anders. Behind the glass of the viewing room stood Wernher von Braun and several of his team, Robert Seamans, now secretary of the air force, Thomas Paine, the man to whom Webb had handed over NASA on the eve of triumph, John Glenn and other veteran astronauts.

With Columbia and Eagle 1100 feet apart, Armstrong and Aldrin fired Eagle's engine for half a minute, throwing it into a new orbit that looped down to within 50,000 feet of the moon's surface. But their craft was still in orbit; there was no danger of crashing on the moon, and even if both Eagle's engines had failed Collins in Columbia could still at this moment have descended to rescue its crew.

Columbia edged back first into contact with Houston. "Listen, babe, everything's going just swimmingly. Beautiful," exulted Collins.

CAPCOM. Great. We're standing by for Eagle.

COLUMBIA. Okay, he's coming round.

CAPCOM. Columbia, Houston. We expect to lose your high gain radio antenna some time during the powered descent. Over.

COLUMBIA. Columbia. Roger. You don't much care do you?

CAPCOM. No, sir.

Eagle joined them, already down to a height of only twenty miles, its ugly legs groping stiffly forward, still descending. A stream of mathematical figures, the language of spaceflight at its tensest moments, ran 230,000-mile errands for Mission Control.

Seventeen minutes later, Eagle had reached the low point of its orbit. The spacecraft was traveling feet first, its two triangular windows peering down as the barren surface of the Sea of Fertility rushed past less than ten miles below. If Armstrong and Aldrin had any doubts, it was still not too late to draw back and let Eagle remain safely in orbit. But neither the instruments crowding the tiny cabin nor the consoles back in Mission Control showed any signs of trouble, and Armstrong punched the "proceed" button to allow the computer to fire the descent engine. Flames blasted out of the big engine bell to slow the spacecraft down and send it dropping in a long arc toward the planned landing site three hundred miles to the east. Apollo 11 was past the point any previous flight had reached, plunging into the most dangerous and unpredictable twelve minutes of the mission.

Houston and Eagle exchanged terse, bullet-like packages of technical data as the seconds ticked away. The computer fired the little attitude control rockets clustered at each corner of the spacecraft to roll it gently over on to its back. A blue and white earth a quarter of a million miles away swung in front of the windows in place of the bare surface of the moon. The pace of events was quickening all the time. Pulses from the landing radar reflected from the surface below fed the astronauts with continuous information about their altitude and rate of descent.

"Eagle, Houston," said Mission Control. "You are go. Take it all at four minutes. Roger, you are go—you are to continue powered descent." But a crisis was at hand. The job of processing the flood of data needed to control the spacecraft's descent was getting too much for its computer. At about 33,500 feet above the surface an alarm light flashed on, and the warning number 12 02 appeared on the computer keyboard just by Armstrong's right hand.

During their long training, the astronauts had been through simulations of every alarm in the lunar module the designers had been able to imagine. They had memorized the drill for dealing with the most likely emergencies and scribbled memos about others and attached them to the instrument panel. But the alarms that now lit up during Eagle's descent were not among them. They were completely unfamiliar. The success of the whole mission hung on the judgment, nerve and co-ordination between the men in the spacecraft and those back at Mission Control. Four times during the descent the alarm was repeated. Each time the guidance officer in Houston—Stephen

Bales, an engineer still in his twenties—had to make an instant decision that the alarm was not mortally dangerous, and give Eagle a "go."

For five minutes the astronauts wrestled with their almost critically overloaded computer as their spacecraft gradually tipped over toward an upright position, ready for landing under the control of the automatic guidance system.

MISSION COMMENTATOR. Fido says we're go, altitude 9200 feet.

CAPCOM. 8300. You're looking great.

EAGLE. Good. Roger.

MISSION COMMENTATOR. Descent rate 129 feet per second.

CAPCOM. Eagle. You're looking great. Coming up nine minutes.

MISSION COMMENTATOR. We're now in the approach phase of it, looking good. Altitude 5200 feet.

EAGLE. Manual auto attitude control is good.

CAPCOM. Roger. Copy.

MISSION COMMENTATOR. Altitude 4200.

CAPCOM. Houston. You're go for landing. Over.

EAGLE. Roger, understand. Go for landing. 3000 feet.

Not until Eagle reached this point, 3000 feet from the surface, did Armstrong get the chance to look out of the window and get his bearings. The view was quite different from what he expected. Instead of the smooth landing ground Eagle needed he saw a crater the size of a football field, filled with big boulders and surrounded by rocks. A navigational error had brought Eagle into the final phase of the descent four miles away from the intended landing site, to a place where the ground was so uneven that the craft might easily have tipped over on landing.

The listening millions back on earth got no hint of how close the mission was to an abort, or an even more disastrous failure, from the clipped tones of the astronauts as they maneuvered down the last three thousand feet, the computer still perilously close to seizing up, and periodically flashing alarms.

EAGLE. 12 alarm. 12 01.

CAPCOM. Roger. 12 01 alarm.

EAGLE. We're go. Hang tight. We're go. 2000 feet. 47 degrees.

CAPCOM. Eagle looking great. You're go.

Armstrong, realizing that the automatic guidance system was going to carry Eagle down among the boulders, took over control from the computer. With Aldrin reading off the vital figures from the control panel he was able to give his whole attention to the controls and the terrain below.

EAGLE. 35 degrees [*the angle of approach*]. 35 degrees. 750 feet [*altitude*]. Coming down at 23 [*feet per second*]. 700 feet, 21 down. 33 degrees. 600 feet, down at 19. 540 feet, down at 30. Down at 15. 400 feet down at 9 (garbled).

By moving the attitude control handle in his right hand Armstrong could tilt the spacecraft in any direction. Using the thrust control handle in his left hand he could travel horizontally. The computer still had control over the rate of descent.

EAGLE. 8 forward. 350, down at 4. 330, 3½ down. We're pegged on horizontal velocity. 300 feet, down 3½. 47 forward (garbled). Down 1 a minute. 1½ down. 70. Got the shadow out there. 50, down at 2½. 19 forward. Altitude-velocity lights. 3½ down, 220 feet. 13 forward. 11 forward, coming down nicely. 200 feet, 4½ down. 5½ down. 160, 6½ down, 5½ down, 9 forward. 5 percent. Quantity light. [*A warning that the fuel was almost exhausted*].

Several times as Eagle skimmed westward from the football field crater, Armstrong had seen possible landing sites, only to reject them on coming closer. Back in Houston, Mission Control knew how desperately close Eagle was to the mandatory abort line, where with his landing fuel tanks virtually empty Armstrong would have had to fire the ascent engine to hurl the spacecraft back into orbit without landing. The lunar module, almost untried, with the weight of fuel allowed for contingencies pared to a minimum, was the weakest link of the chain forged to lift men to the moon. It almost broke at that moment.

EAGLE. 75 feet, things looking good. Down a half. 6 forward.

CAPCOM. 60 seconds.

EAGLE. Lights on. Down 2½. Forward. Forward. Good. 40 feet, down 2½. Picking up some dust.

Eagle's exhaust blasting the soil of the moon was throwing out dust on either side, making it difficult to judge the spacecraft's speed over the ground.

EAGLE. 30 feet, 2½ down. Faint shadow. 4 forward. 4 forward, drifting to the right a little 6 (garbled) down a half.

CAPCOM. 30 seconds.

EAGLE. (garbled). Forward. Drifting right. (garbled). Contact light *[meaning that the sensors under the landing pads had touched the moon's surface]*. Okay, engine stop. ACA out of detent. Modes control both auto. Descent engine command override, off. Engine arm, off. 413 is in.

CAPCOM. We copy you down Eagle.

EAGLE. (Armstrong). Houston, Tranquility Base here. The Eagle has landed.

CAPCOM. Roger. Tranquility. We copy you on the ground. You've got a bunch of guys about to turn blue. We're breathing again. Thanks a lot.

In the press center's auditorium the newspapermen were jigging wildly, waving their arms and yelling. The astronaut's wives were asked what they thought. Mrs. Joan Aldrin, an actress, said, "It's like a dramatic television show, but it seems unreal. There are just no words. Don't you agree?" She said her husband had taken a piece of the blessed bread from Webster Presbyterian Church but didn't know when he planned to eat it.

Mrs. Pat Collins said, "It was positively marvelous. From what I can tell everything is going like clockwork." Was she disappointed that her husband would not be walking on the moon? "Don't you think he's probably right there with them in spirit?" said Mrs. Collins brightly.

Mrs. Jan Armstrong, formidable short-haired sportswoman who lives with every heartbeat of her husband's flights into space, had followed Eagle's descent on a moon chart saying aloud, "Good . . . good . . . good . . . good . . ." Mrs. Armstrong said she planned to stay up until the two men were safely back on board the lunar module.

The reason why the overloaded computer almost caused a disaster did not emerge till later. Fifteen percent of its capacity was being taken up in processing signals from Eagle's rendezvous radar which was not actually needed at all during the descent. This was enough to use up the machine's margin of space capacity. With hindsight, the emergency could have been avoided entirely simply by throwing a switch to cut out the rendezvous radar; but this precaution had been omitted from the flight plan.

If the situation had continued, the computer would have fallen behind on its essential tasks of controlling Eagle's stability and the firing of the descent engine. As Christopher Kraft, Operations Director of the Manned Spacecraft Center, put it after the flight, "The computer would literally give up the ghost and you would have been forced to abort the mission." Armstrong would have been ordered to punch the abort button in the center of the control panel to blast Eagle's cabin free from the descent stage and back into orbit, abandoning any chance of a moon landing before the flight of Apollo 12. Overriding the alarm, on the other hand, meant taking the risk that the overloading would prove unmanageable and leave Armstrong and Aldrin falling toward the moon with a broken-down control system. Stephen Bales would have been remembered in a very different fashion if his decision had been a wrong one. For his cool decisive performance he was later awarded a medal, presented by President Nixon.

Decisive action by Armstrong and Aldrin had placed the human mind momentarily ahead of the robot. There had been nothing quite like it since 1520 when the explorer Magellan, on the first journey round the world, was confronted with mutiny among his captains who thought the journey too dangerous. Magellan shot the captains, buried them at sea and sailed on to vindication. Armstrong and Aldrin ignored the known limitations of their machine and by landing on the moon buried a myth that it was smarter than they.

"Be advised," Mission Control said, "there's lots of smiling faces in this room, and all over the world."

"There's two of them up here," said Eagle.

"And don't forget one in the command module," said Collins, almost forgotten as he orbited sixty miles above.

And to Eagle he said, "It sure sounded great from up here. You guys did a fantastic job."

"Thank you," said Armstrong. "Just keep that orbiting base ready for us up there now."

The problems after landing seemed minor—"little funnies," NASA called them—though they caused a certain amount of bother to Mission Control. No one knew, for example, exactly where Eagle had landed, and the crew could not help with visual sitings. Armstrong observed through his window that they were on a level plain "cratered with a fairly large number of craters and small ridges . . . and literally thousands of one- and two-foot craters around the area . . . There is a little hill ahead of us, difficult to estimate but might be half a mile or a mile."

Mission Control came on to say that touch-down occurred 102 hours

45 minutes and 40 seconds into the flight after a powered descent lasting 12½ minutes. But it was three hours after the landing before NASA began to display its thoughts less prosaically. "Reverting, if we could, to the terminology of an earlier form of transport, the railroad," Mission Control announced. "What we're witnessing now is man's very first trip into space with a station stop along the route. At 105 hours 43 minutes, continuing to monitor the loop, this is Apollo Control, Houston."

But outside Apollo Control, life was not so smooth. A small contingent of Negroes and whites from the Welfare Rights Organization invaded the Manned Spacecraft Center, settled down by a dummy lunar module outside the press center, and unfolded placards denouncing the treatment of America's poor.

> He's got a lunar module in His hands;
> He's got the astronauts in His hands;
> He's got the welfare children in His hands;
> He's got the whole world in His hands.

As demonstrations go it was pathetically small, but it made one low-rank NASA employee furious enough to wave thirty dollars of mock dole over the group's heads and demand an alligator-stocked moat to keep such people out. "You've no feelings, no feelings at all," he shouted, "sitting down here at a time like this. *Anyone* can tell you've no feelings."

Back on the moon, Armstrong, understandably enough, was anxious to move out to explore the countryside and asked for permission to start EVA ("Extra Vee-hicular Activity," Astronymish for getting out for a walk) earlier than planned, without having a rest first.

Control agreed, but first it had a small confession to make. As a NASA spokesman put it, "Our best information at this time on the orientation of the Eagle is that the plus Z axis, that's the leg with the ladder on it, is yaw 13 degrees south of the ground track. The sun behind Eagle with the leg of the ladder on it in a generally westerly direction along the ground track, but yaw at 13 degrees south from that ground track."

What the spokesman meant to say was that the ladder-leg was in shadow and shouldn't have been. It was just possible that the TV

camera recording Armstrong's descent to plant the first human boot
on to the surface would run into problems.

Inside the module the astronauts helped each other dress, sounding like two elderly knights squashing each other into their armor.

ARMSTRONG. Let me do that for you.

ALDRIN. (Garbled)

ARMSTRONG. Mark I

ALDRIN. (garbled) valves.

ARMSTRONG. All of the (garbled)

ALDRIN. (garbled) locked and lock-lock.

ARMSTRONG. Did you put it . . .

ALDRIN. Oh, wait a minute.

ARMSTRONG. Should be (garbled)

ALDRIN. (garbled)

ARMSTRONG. Roger (garbled)

ALDRIN. I'll try it on the middle.

ARMSTRONG. Miss marked.

ALDRIN. Sure wish I would of shaved last night.

It took them longer than they expected to get the cooling units in
their back packs operating and to depressurize the cabin. A quarter of
a million miles away Mission Control waited impatiently, trying to restrain itself, not too successfully, from telling the moon-walkers to get
a move on. Finally, six hours and thirteen minutes after touchdown,
the door opened and Armstrong wriggled feet first out onto Eagle's
porch, fat in his spacesuit, a Cyclops with a single eye bulging at the
front of his helmet.

Aldrin coaxed him into position. "Neil, you're lined up nicely. To-
ward me a little bit, OK down, OK make it clear . . . Here roll
to the left. OK now you're clear. You're lined up on the platform.
Put your left foot to the right a little bit. OK, that's good. Roll left."
"How am I doing?" Armstrong said, a little anxiously. "You're doing
fine," Aldrin said. "OK Houston," Armstrong said a moment later.
"I'm on the porch." "Roger, Neil," said control. "OK right now, Neil,"
Aldrin said, looking through the hatch door.

Sixty miles up, Mike Collins moved round the moon's corner and
would be one of the few men to miss the final descent. Armstrong
started down the ladder, pausing to open the door of the compartment containing the TV camera. On earth a strange black and white

pattern filled tens of millions of TV screens. It sorted itself into the ladder on the leg of the lunar module, upside down, a boot clumsily groping for the next rung. The picture righted itself. The boot grew into a leg, the leg into a man, weird but familiar in his spacesuit.

"I'm at the foot of the ladder," said Armstrong. "The LM foot pads are only depressed in the surface about one or two inches, although the surface appears to be very, very fine-grained as you get close to it. It's almost like a powder. Now and then it's very fine. I'm going to step off the LM now. That's one small step for a man. One giant leap for mankind."

Armstrong's foot had touched the moon 109 hours 24 minutes and 20 seconds after lift-off from Cape Kennedy, but the controlled high voice betrayed no elation. "The surface is fine and powdery," Armstrong said, in mild puzzled tones. "I can . . . I can pick it up loosely with my toe . . . I only go in a small fraction of an inch. Maybe an eighth of an inch, but I can see the footprints of my boots and the treads in the fine sandy particles."

The sun was low on the horizon, smaller and sharper than on earth and blazing with an unearthly intensity on the airless surface. "It's quite dark here in the shadow," said Armstrong, "and a little hard for me to see if I have a good footing. I'll work my way over into the sunlight here without looking directly into the sun."

He took the first pictures with a camera Aldrin had lowered down to him while Houston began to show some concern. In case he had to return to the lunar module in a hurry, his first job should have been to collect the contingency samples of moon dust.

"We see you getting some pictures and the contingency sample," said Mission Control tactfully but untruthfully.

"He's getting some pictures and the contingency sample," echoed Aldrin. But Armstrong failed to take the hint. "Neil, this is Houston," said Mission Control. "Did you copy about the contingency sample, over." "Rog," replied Armstrong, with a trace of irritation in his voice. "I'm going to get to that just as soon as I finish these picture series."

Eventually he fished the sample collector, a kind of butterfly net with a collapsible handle, out of a pocket just below his left knee.

"This is very interesting," said Armstrong as he scraped away at the surface. "It's a very soft surface but here and there where I plug with the contingency sample collector, I run into a very hard surface but it appears to be very cohesive material of the same sort. I'll try to get a rock in here. Here's a couple." He sealed up the bag and stowed it in his pocket, guided by Aldrin since in his clumsy suit he was unable to see what he was doing.

Aldrin joined his commander jauntily on the surface, making a great show of an effortless leap back up the last rung of the ladder. "Beautiful. Beautiful," he said.

"Isn't it something," said Armstrong. "Isn't it fun?"

Armstrong peeled away some silver plastic covering the commemorative plaque on the leg of the lunar module. Then he trudged over the gray sand pulling the TV camera on its long cable, and panned it round the lunar horizon before setting it up to face the lunar module for the first time.

The scene was surprisingly crude, like something knocked up in a garage for a low-budget science fiction film in 1927—an impression that was much heightened when the crew returned to earth and showed a speeded-up film of themselves scuttling around the lunar set.

With some difficulty, the two men hoisted the American flag before Aldrin began to practice moon-walking and running, first trying long, loping strides, then kangaroo-like hops with both feet together. He decided that the more normal method of locomotion was best.

Fears that men would find it extremely difficult to move and work in gravity only one-sixth that on earth were evaporating fast. Because the men weighed so much less than on earth the frictional grip between the soles of the astronauts' boots and the ground was reduced, but their momentum was the same. This made it difficult to turn suddenly or stop, but Aldrin found that he could do so in two or three paces; if he planned his moves four of five steps ahead he could stay out of trouble.

Both astronauts were out of shot when Houston came on the air to ask them to get in front of the camera. President Nixon, with Frank Borman at his elbow, came on the phone and the astronauts stood awkwardly near the flag while he put in a long-distance call: "This certainly has to be the most historic telephone call ever made," he said, ". . . For every American this has to be the proudest day of their lives. And for people all over the world . . . For one priceless moment, in the whole history of man, all the people on this earth are truly one."

"Thank you Mr. President," said Armstrong. "It's been a great honor and privilege for us to be here representing not only the United States but men of peace of all nations."

The crew saluted the little camera on the desolate moonscape and went off to work, taking photographs, laying out a few simple experiments, a seismometer to measure moonquakes, a reflector to pick up laser beams from earth and a sheet of aluminum foil to catch particles thrown out by the sun.

Both men photographed rocks, peered into small craters and collected samples with a kind of shovel and a pair of tongs. Aldrin hammered in a tube to collect material from below the surface. When the time came for him to re-enter the Eagle he seemed almost reluctant to do so, aware that the work outside the module had got behindhand. The boxes of rock samples were hauled on board by pulley, and finally Armstrong left the moon's surface after his two-hour walk, boarded the LM and closed the hatch. In Mission Control an official hoisted a replica of a flag blowing in a non-existent wind on the moon, and Mike Collins, still orbiting in Columbia, said, "Hallelujah."

The Eagle astronauts were as busy on board as they had been on the moon, clearing the module's decks for lift-off, jettisoning the backpacks that had kept them alive during the EVA. Mission Control watched them on its instruments, more aware than the astronauts themselves if something was not shipshape. "Tranquility Base, this is Houston. We showed a suit release valve still in the auto position. It should be closed. Over." And on board the Eagle one of the astronauts adjusted his dress.

At the end of their day, Mission Control told them to sleep. Aldrin curled up on the floor; Armstrong rigged himself a hammock and lay on the hatch and engine cover. In Columbia, Mike Collins slept like a baby. "Not since Adam," said the Mission Control press officer lyrically, "has any human known such solitude as Mike Collins is experiencing during this forty-seven minutes of each lunar revolution when he's behind the moon with no one to talk to except his tape recorder aboard Columbia.

"While he waits for his comrades to soar with Eagle from Tranquility Base and rejoin him for the trip back to earth, Collins, with the help of flight controllers here in Mission Control has kept the command module's system going 'pocketa-pocketa-pocketa.' "

No one could judge Aldrin's condition during the rest period on the moon because he was not plugged in to Mission Control. But Armstrong, who was being monitored by the duty flight surgeon, had a bad night sleeping over an engine that might or might not start for the ascent. Mission Control said, "Dr. Kenneth Biers says his data continues to indicate that Neil Armstrong may be dozing but he's sure that he is not sleeping soundly or well. He believes he may be sleeping fitfully and dozing, but stirring around quite a bit."

Collins was wakened an hour before the two astronauts on the moon and agreed with control that the attempts to spot Eagle from orbit were hopeless and should be abandoned. Eagle came alive and preened its morning feathers in a reassuring stream of figures from Houston. "Roger," the module said. "Leave those two circuit breakers open and have the updated link to voice backup; and we'll make the appropriate changes on the following circuit breaker status cards."

"Roger," said Houston. "And you might add a little note down there at the bottom of the page, page 61: Note, do not use tapemeter in PGNCS, i.e. do not place mode select switch to ping. Over."

Before his restless night's sleep, Armstrong had said he was too tired to transmit a geological account of the landing site. Now he awoke and made sure that the geologists back on earth would have a full report even if Eagle's launch failed and eliminated the post-flight briefings back on earth. "We are landed," he said, "in a relatively clear crater field of elongated and circular secondary craters most of which have rims irrespective of their rays and of their size. That's not universally true. There are a few of the smaller craters around which do not have a discernible rim. The ground mass throughout the area is a very fine sand to a silt.

"I say the thing that would be most like it on earth is the powdered graphite. Immersed in this ground mass are a wide variety of rock shapes, sizes, textures, rounded and angular, many with varying inconsistencies with what looked to be plain basalt and particular basalt . . .

"We are in a boulder field where the boulders range generally up to two feet with a few larger than that . . . I suspect this boulder field may have some of its origin with this large sharp-edge rocky rim crater that we passed over in the final descent. Now yesterday I said that was about the size of a football field and I have to admit it was a little hard to measure coming in; but I thought it might just fit the Astro-dome [Houston's roofed-in sports stadium] as we came in."

But NASA's luck held, along with its engineering. Some twenty-two hours after touch-down, Eagle left the moon with a roar, sending shudders through the lunar seismometer (which had been sensitive enough to record the astronauts' last steps up the module's ladder) and in all probability flattening the wire-stiffened flag held precariously in the lunar sand.

"That was beautiful," Eagle reported. "Twenty-six, 36 feet per second up . . . Very smooth . . . Very quiet ride . . . There's that one crater down there."

When the engine fired, Armstrong's troubled heart settled down at once, beating 90 times a minute during the ascent compared with Aldrin's 120. At 32,000 feet Armstrong repeated a phrase he had used when Eagle first broke away from Columbia and plunged down to the Sea of Tranquility. "We're going right down U.S. 1," he announced.

Five thousand pounds of fuel burned through the module's engine as the truncated ship soared vertically for 200 feet before canting over to pick up horizontal speed and going into lunar orbit at 60,000 feet. "Man," said Armstrong, looking back. "That's impressive looking, isn't it?"

"Eagle," said Houston, mopping its brow as the module slipped into orbit. "The whole world is proud of you."

To reach Columbia, the legless bug climbed three mathematical humps, each of them immortalized in the mind-bending terminology of Astronymish. Concentric Sequence Initiation put Eagle in orbit behind and below Columbia; an hour and eighteen minutes later it shifted into closer line with the Terminal Phase Initiation, and one hour after that—Terminal Phase Finalization, no less—the two ugly tourists posed close together for photographs.

Their coupling was not a happy one; Eagle and Columbia shook frighteningly as they came together, giving all three astronauts a nasty shock; it was a chilling reminder that there is precious little room in space for overconfidence. One explanation offered later in Houston was that Collins pulled back with his docking probe before it was properly connected to Eagle; at that moment a thruster aboard the lunar module fired briefly, making both craft wobble.

A minor consequence of the incident was NASA's anxiety to get the record not only straight but cleaned up. Collins, alarmed by the shaky docking, had said, "That was a funny one. You know, I didn't feel it strike and then I thought things were pretty steady. I went to retract there and that's when all hell broke loose." But the official transcript, released half an hour later, put it another way. "I went to retract there," it said, "and then it went all NO/GO."

Apollo 11's splashdown in the Pacific on July 24th was ten seconds late after a voyage lasting 195 hours and 18 minutes, and within a mile of the target point after a round trip of half a million miles. For a time the spacecraft was in stable mode 2—Astronymish for upside down— the crew hanging from their straps inside. Then the flotation bags righted it and a swimmer passed in plastic suits to protect earthmen from moon germs. One by one the astronauts were hoisted up into a helicopter and flown back to U.S.S. *Hornet,* where they disappeared into a sealed container.

Soon they reappeared at the window, normally dressed now, but looking uncomfortably like monkeys imprisoned in a cage. There was President Nixon, his friend Frank standing next to him, waving and grinning at them through the glass. The high drama of Aldrin's terse reports as Eagle plunged toward the moon and of Armstrong's boot fumbling for the ladder dissolved in a welter of bonhomie and coy jokes.

"Neil, Buzz and Mike," said the President, "I want you to know that I think I'm the luckiest man in the world. And I say this not only because I have the honor to be President of the United States, but particularly because I have the privilege of speaking for so many in welcoming you back to earth . . . I had a telephone call yesterday. The toll wasn't, incidentally, as great as the one I made to you fellows on the moon. [Laughter.] I made that collect, just in case you didn't know. But I called the three of, in my view, three of the greatest ladies and most courageous ladies in the whole world today, your wives. And from Jan and Joan and Pat I bring their love and congratulations. And also I've got to let you in on a little secret—I made a date with them. [Laughter.] I invited them to dinner on the 13th of August, right after you come out of quarantine. It will be a state dinner held in Los Angeles. The governors of all the fifty states will be there, the ambassadors, others from around the world and in America.

And they told me you could come too. And all I want to know—will you come? . . . We want to honor you then."

"We'll do anything you say, Mr. President," replied Armstrong huskily. "Just anything."

Back at Houston, the jubilant mission controllers were packing up for the Saturnalian splashdown parties which would rend the air of Clear Lake City that night. In the auditorium of the Manned Spacecraft Center, some of the leading men behind Apollo appeared for one final press conference. George Low was there and Sam Phillips, George Mueller and Charles Berry, Deke Slayton, Robert Gilruth and Christopher Kraft. In the end, they had done it. They had put a man on the moon and returned him safely to earth within the decade, as Kennedy had told them to. It had been a close-run thing, with only five months to spare, but the national goal had been achieved.

The mood was mainly of gratitude and quiet pride. There was even a disbelieving quality to some of the statements, as if these men had to pinch themselves to prove that they were not dreaming. One speech, however, sounded significantly different, rehearsing once again some of the grandiose oratory on which Apollo had been launched and reminding the world, with obvious calculation, that space had a future as well as a past.

It was made by George Mueller, director of Manned Spaceflight and a man who more than once during the decade of Apollo had shown that his engineer's trait of apparent mildness was thoroughly deceptive.

"We now stand at what is undoubtedly the greatest decision point in the history of this planet," Mueller began. "Four billion years ago the earth was formed. Four hundred million years ago life moved to the land. Four million years ago man appeared on earth. One hundred years ago the technological revolution that led to this day began. All of these events were important, yet in none of them did man make a conscious decision that would change the future of all mankind. We have that opportunity and that challenge today.

"There remains for mankind the task of deciding the next step. Will we press forward to explore the other planets or will we deny the opportunity of the future? To me the choice is clear. We must take the next step. Should we hesitate to exploit the first step? Should we withdraw in fear from the next step? Or should we substitute temporary material welfare for spiritual adventure and long term accomplishment? Then will man fall back from his destiny. The mighty surge of his achievement will be lost and the confines of this planet will destroy it.

"This is the time for a decision. This is the time for rededication to the spirit of our forefathers. A time for all men to move forward and together. The organization that brought men to the moon stands ready for the next step. The knowledge possessed by men is sufficient, the resources are adequate for the task of carrying out this next step. The will of the people of this nation and of the world will determine whether mankind will make the great leap to the planets.

"In this moment of man's greatest achievement it is timely to dedicate ourselves to the unfinished work so nobly begotten (sic) by three of us. To resolve that this nation, under God, will join with all men in the pursuit of the destiny of mankind will lead to the way of the planets."

To Mueller's listeners, on this triumphant day of completion for the greatest feat of engineering in history, his message was unmistakable. The managers of the American space program indeed believed they had taken only one small step. Now they were bidding for a truly giant leap—to Mars.

14.

Meager
Harvest

One can search history in vain for parallels with Project Apollo. The Manhattan Project for the development of the atomic bomb immediately suggests itself. It, too, involved the urgent, single-minded pursuit of a technical goal. But besides the difference in sheer scale ($2000 million for the Manhattan Project compared with Apollo's $24,000 million) there is a crucial difference in the circumstances in which the two projects were undertaken. The drive to develop the atomic bomb was spurred by perfectly rational, if ultimately groundless, fears of the hideous possibilities of such a weapon in Hitler's hands. No such compelling urgency attached to the reasons advanced for proceeding with Apollo.

Other societies offer remote instances of massive resources spent on goods of vague utility: Egypt with its pyramids; medieval Europe with its cathedrals towering over the surrounding squalor; seventeenth century France and its supreme monument to prestige, the palace of Versailles. But in truth, it is unique in history for a nation to invent and accept a challenge like Apollo, costing so much and promising few material rewards, and then to commit itself publicly to completing it in a time which made no allowance for failure. The moon landing demanded from America, her people and her institutions a combination of qualities never previously seen in the history of any nation.

Sheer engineering skill was certainly one of them, but it was far from being the most important. The Saturn V, the Apollo spacecraft, the lunar module, the world-wide tracking network and the control center are all among the most complex and sophisticated products of technology. But if some individual component—a radio, a rocket motor, a cabin window—is examined coldly, without any thought of its glamorous use, it is seen not to be unique. Hundreds of thousands of people have been involved in the Apollo program and they were not all geniuses, nor was their skill specifically American. Virtually every component for the Apollo program could have been designed, developed and manufactured in any advanced industrial country.

What, then, were the peculiar demands that the program made on America? The answer lies in the organization needed to control it; in short, the management. There are many firms in many parts of the world which could have produced adequate components for Apollo. There are rather fewer which could have done so as rapidly as their American counterparts. But there is no organization outside the United States which could have supervised the whole operation well enough to specify what was required, control the design, manufacture and testing of components, the assembly of components into systems, systems into complete rockets and spacecraft, all in the eight years between Kennedy's speech of May 25, 1961, and Eagle's landing in the Sea of Tranquility on July 20, 1969.

Much has been said and written about NASA's management expertise, notably by its manager-in-chief from 1961–68, James Webb. Claims that it developed wholly new techniques are of doubtful validity. Managing the space program is not different in kind from managing any other major technological project, such as the development of the Polaris submarine and missiles. But in one comparatively unglamorous area, reliability, NASA has broken entirely new ground. The Apollo spacecraft contains more than a thousand times the number of functioning components in a motor car. It follows that if the components were built to the same standards of reliability the spacecraft would go wrong a thousand times more often. But of course a spacecraft cannot be allowed to fail as often as a car does, let alone a thousand times more often. The need for reliability in Apollo hardware was therefore quite literally unprecedented; and the fact that it was met was as much a triumph for management as for engineering. Research can father products capable of meeting particular specifications; only the most elaborate system of inspections and tests, most rigorously enforced, can guarantee that they will actually be met.

Apollo also demanded extraordinary national endurance. It is hard to recall any comparable instance of a nation sustaining such an effort over eight undeviating years. The cost of the effort, in both money and other resources, was known before the project began. And as the years passed, bringing countless unforeseen claims from other quarters, the cost continued to be met. The landing on the moon was that rarest of phenomena in public life, the open and complete fulfillment of a policy openly set forth.

These qualities—engineering skill, endurance and, above all, management—were the most obvious contributions to the final achievement, and they will never cease to be regarded with awe. They were also achievements in themselves. Apollo has proved that America could deploy these estimable virtues on any undertaking, should she choose to do so, in greater measure than anyone had previously known to be possible.

But there was more to Apollo than the facts of its accomplishment. It is not enough to describe how it was done, charting the troubles it surmounted and recording the brilliant work which brought it to completion. With an endeavor so immense and at the same time so weird as the moon landing, it is tempting to do this: to accept it as a giant fact scored across the history of the millennium: to insist, now that it is done, that any examination of its relevance beyond itself is the cavilling of a mean mind. Yet somehow we cannot leave Apollo there. The project was the work of rational men. Therefore it was presumably not an artifact of supernatural powers pushing their helpless creatures toward some inexorable Homeric destiny. The fact that its objective was another celestial body, rather than the atomic bomb or the conquest of the world, cannot be allowed to disqualify it from some evaluation in a human and earthly context.

It was a successful enterprise, yes. But was it also justifiable? Given the resources it consumed, has it proved in any sense a good way to have spent them? Apollo was begun with certain objectives. It was designed to have a specific impact. Was this objective a reasonable result to expect in the first place? Was it achieved in the end? If it was not achieved, what was? And this achievement, whatever it is: is it something of which we must indeed stand in mute and resigned admiration?

First, then, it is necessary to return to the beginning of Apollo and recall why it was launched. The project was born of calamity. It was begun as a hasty response to an immediate crisis: the crisis thought to have been brought about by Soviet space triumphs. The nature of the crisis was somewhat confused at the time. Some people believed the threat to be directly to national security, envisaging orbital bombs and other crude disturbances in the military balance of power. Others saw in it the menace of the unknown. They could not see any definable danger to security, but they were frightened of possible developments which were beyond the power of their fevered imaginations to articulate.

The decisive aspect of the threat, however, was its bearing on American prestige. This was the fear which impelled President Kennedy. This was the threat which Apollo was meant to answer. Prestige is not an easy concept to define. It was cited time and again in the arguments composed by James Webb and Robert McNamara to persuade Kennedy that the moon journey was imperative for American security. But the term was never very carefully examined. In the confusion of the times, when hysteria and recrimination were louder than reason, it seemed to subsume a large number of factors which added up to a belief that America could not afford to be beaten by the Russians.

Prestige, in other words, was equated with power in the world, and the moon was seen as a medium through which worldly power might be increased. Theoretically, this notion has a quite respectable pedigree. Hans Morgenthau, in his magisterial study of international relations, *Power Among Nations*, suggests that the purpose of prestige is "to impress other nations with the power one's own nation actually possesses, or wants other nations to believe it possesses." For America, manifestly, the importance of high prestige in this sense is twofold. It relates to her power vis-à-vis the Soviet Union on the one hand, and the lesser nations on the other.

Whether the moon could ever reasonably have been expected to add to the reputation for power of a nation already possessing a complete nuclear armory is seriously questionable. It was not universally believed, even in Washington. Although the Pentagon and the White House, not to mention NASA itself, were committed to the idea, the professional practitioners of diplomacy were more sceptical. Dean Rusk, the Secretary of State, was distinctly cool. "When you are talking about questions like Berlin or disarmament," he told a BBC interviewer in 1962, "or these great issues that affect war and peace and the security of nations, I don't think demonstrations of this sort enter into the relationships very much. The underlying issues are too fundamental and far-reaching."

There were, of course, those who believed that the moon had actual military uses beyond its supposed contribution to America's powerful reputation. These are no longer very widely accepted; but it is worth noting, as evidence of the extreme reluctance of the great Powers to acknowledge their invalidity, how meaningless a document is the 1966 United Nations Treaty on Outer Space, which allegedly preserves the moon and the planets for peaceful purposes. The treaty does not establish whether "peaceful" means "nonmilitary" or merely "nonaggressive." It does not, therefore, demilitarize the moon, which could still legally be used for satellite-inspection, for an early warning system, or perhaps as a base from which to knock out enemy satellites which are in breach of the Treaty. In Article IV, moreover, the Treaty omits to specify that the moon as well as other "celestial bodies" shall be immune from the installation of weapons of mass destruction: not an accidental omission but one made after the Americans had pressed for it.

In fact, however, a conspicuous feature of the decade of Apollo has been the steady decline of any belief in the military uses of man in space. Doubt, mounting to complete scepticism, has been registered not merely about the military value of a man on the moon but about the value to national security of putting him anywhere in space. The disillusionment of the services, who had fought for so long for the right to put their men up there, culminated only weeks before Apollo 11 flew, with President Nixon's decision to cancel the so-called Manned Orbiting Laboratory, the Pentagon's prize space exhibit. The end of the MOL underlined the larger point: that if the capture of the moon was seen as a necessary symbol of American military power, it will surely seem to future historians to have been grotesquely redundant.

There are still people, nevertheless, who see in Apollo a guarantee of America's reputation, if not for military power then at least for something almost as formidable: technological power. The purpose here is much the same as with military power. It is to inspire in the world an essentially fearful respect.

Some of the prophets of this view are to be found in NASA itself. Christopher Columbus Kraft, for example, who is one of the senior directors of manned spaceflight, recently expressed amazement at the inability of every American to see the moon program the way he did, "as the salvation of our way of life, of everyone's way of life, which the Russians are trying to take away from us." Much the same spirit animated Congress's insistence on seeing Old Glory planted on the moon.

Here too, however, we find an optimistically narrow view of prestige, as if it depended solely on some species of power. In fact a nation's reputation derives from other sources as well. A wise policy of prestige seeks the voluntary support as well as the fearful obedience of the world. Quite clearly the journey to the moon included this among its purposes: to strike the world not merely with awe but with admiration for the American way of life. This is a constantly recurring theme of space rhetoric, from both Moscow and Washington. At the beginning of the sixties, Russia regularly asserted that "Soviet successes in space provided concrete evidence that the Soviet communist system was superior to Western capitalism."

Kennedy himself said, and Webb never stopped repeating, that space triumphs played a decisive part in persuading nations that "they could meet their economic problems without engaging in a Marxist form of government."

Two developments during the decade of the moon have rendered this simple conviction obsolete. Both America and the world have changed. Together these developments strongly suggest that, in the short-term impact which was sought from it, Project Apollo will be counted among the more palpable miscalculations of the twentieth century. Although the immediate task was performed perfectly, its ultimate objective was in ruins. Men took their step on the moon, but there was no giant leap in the drawing-power of the American way of life.

As America moved to the moon, the world did not stand still. Relations between nations, and the condition of Americans themselves, were both being transformed as swiftly as space technology. The hope that by landing on the moon the nation would greatly advance its position in the world was born of a static view of history. Apollo will stand as perhaps the classic illustration of Morgenthau's dictum when he cautions against the misuse of a policy of prestige. A nation expects too much, he writes, if "insecure in the awareness of its power, it invests a particular move with a measure of prestige out of all proportion to its actual importance."

Kennedy did invest Apollo with that kind of importance. And while his decision was being enacted, much else was happening to deface the American image. If space has produced an image of strength, Vietnam, assassination, ghetto violence and economic injustice have created one of uncertainty and social incompetence. In the terms which men can understand as relating to their own lives, American capitalism of the sixties does not have an enviable record. It has created great wealth, and it has sent Americans to the moon. But around the world, the United States is despised as much as she is feared, its citizens pitied at least as much as they are envied.

This is far from being the result of Apollo. The moon landing in fact temporarily did a good deal to erase the memory of streets in flames and innocent citizens slaughtered at random. Nevertheless Apollo is the product of a society prepared to devote greater national effort to reaching the stars than to rebuilding its decaying cities. This choice of values is noted by the world, and makes its mark on the American reputation. All along it is what has concerned Americans who claim that the prestige of a nation rests on broader qualities than a single, stunning achievement. Senator Fulbright put the point aptly six years ago when he said, "What about the prestige that Sputnik gave the U.S.S.R.? It does not feed their people. It was a trick, a kind of gambit. It does not convert anyone to communism. So far as real prestige goes, it is nothing unless it is followed through."

Thus, it would be a singularly optimistic patriot who believed that American prestige stood higher after the completion of Apollo than it did before Apollo was launched. But there is another reason, besides the condition of America, why this hope has proved to be a delusion. The quest for prestige through the moon was based on a premise which has been betrayed by events.

When Kennedy began Apollo, it was widely believed that no part of the world stood far from "the fluid front of the cold war." The globe was divisible, so the argument went, into the spheres of influence of the two super Powers, Russia and America. Every advance by one was a loss to the other in the battle for the minds of men. Space generally, and above all the moon, was a uniquely powerful medium through which to impress people with the supremacy of the system which conquered it.

But now, at the end of the decade, the world does not look quite the same. It is no longer possible to speak of a bipolar system, in which every part of the world leans gratefully or helplessly to one side or the other. The Soviet empire has begun to crack. The belief in nationalism and independence has emerged as a competitor to both Marxism and capitalism, to create a third world of uncommitted nations. In the capitals of Asia and Africa, an ambitious politician proves his credentials not by subservience to the power of older nations, but by forging a separate path. Developing nations have looked East and West and determined that they have little to learn from either.

It is improbable that Apollo, springing from a society so obviously defective in other respects, will persuade them to change their minds. It is very difficult indeed to imagine an Asian or African statesman viewing the moon conquest as a manifestation of technological competence with any relevance to his own problems. Still less can one suppose that it will sway his position in a world contest from which it is his most intense ambition to escape altogether.

There is, in fact, only one part of the world where American prestige has incontrovertibly been lifted by Apollo, and that is in America itself. The moon landing was a source of fully justifiable pride to many Americans. It persuaded them, if not many other people, to believe more passionately in American capitalism and the American social system. Moreover, when it was begun, it was economically, politically and psychologically a convenient exercise for them to undertake.

Apollo may not have impinged greatly on American power in the world. Arguably, it is a rebuke to the immaturity of a nation which does not yet have the political will to remove the cancers which afflict it. But it has provided jobs for men and an outlet for ambitions which might otherwise have found far more harmful tasks to occupy them. In its own terms, it has been one unmistakable triumph to set beside the failures and miasmic confusions of the daily national grind at home and abroad. It may not have persuaded the world that America was a

greater country than she was known to be already, but it has done
something which should certainly not be discounted: in response to
Sputnik and Gagarin, it stilled the demon of Americans' own belief in
their inferiority.

That is a limited and inevitably transient achievement, very much
smaller than Kennedy hoped for. America went to the moon to score
a political triumph. She occupied Tranquility, but the triumph she
sought eluded her. For this expensive blunder, therefore, some com-
pensation must be discovered. Apollo did undeniably have results,
even though they were not the results Americans were looking for in
1961. What exactly are these fortuitous by-products of Gagarin and
the Bay of Pigs? Men did not go to the moon in search of knowledge,
but what knowledge have they come by?

The samples of the moon's crust which Armstrong and Aldrin
brought back enabled geologists and astronomers to come closer to
answering a problem on which speculation had fed for decades, if not
centuries. Some of the samples showed unmistakable signs of having
once been molten, a feature which virtually closed the debate about
whether the moon was a hot or a cold body. Almost all schools of
thought now agree that the moon was shaped both by volcanic activity
and by meteoric impacts. Thus the argument has ended in stalemate:
neither side was wholly right. Further samples retrieved by later
Apollo missions will embellish this discovery. They may also help
to resolve another pressing question, the question of the origin of the
moon. Eventually there can be little doubt that the uncorrupted
moon, "the Rosetta Stone of the solar system," will disclose infinitely
more information about the history of the solar system than is ob-
tainable on earth itself, even though the broader question of the nature of the universe is likely to remain little less murky than before.

The rocks, of course, did not need man to bring them back. The
cornucopia of knowledge which reposes in lifeless moon grit could
quite feasibly, and much less expensively, have been opened by unmanned machines landing on the moon and being brought back by
remote control. Now that men have done the job, that is a hypothetical
point. But the distinction is profoundly relevant to the other scientific
benefits of space.

Scientifically and practically the profits from the space program have been immense. The invention of the space satellite has produced advances many of which have barely begun to be exploited. In weather-forecasting, communications and navigation the bounty of space has already proved very lush. In charting the earth's resources— the location and movement of raw materials on and below the surface—the potential of space has still to be put to its full practical use. In education, likewise, the uses of the satellite over large, unreachable populations in countries such as India offer measureless possibilities.

These, however, have nothing to do with Apollo. They are often cited as evidence of the value obtained from Apollo's billions. But it is false and ironic that they should be; for far from contributing to the new dimensions implicit in earth satellites, Apollo has if anything shrunk them. Owing to the supreme urgency of Apollo, scientific and economic space projects were cut to the financial bone. It is significant that in the catalogues of "spin-off" which apologists for the space program grew accustomed to producing in order to persuade the American taxpayer that he was gaining some benefit from it, Apollo's fruits in the consumer economy were hard to find. They rarely went beyond such esoteric items as more protective fire-fighting suits and "filament-wound brassiere supports."

Clearly those are not the only technological by-products of the moon journey. Electronics, metallurgy, data processing, quality control procedures, instrumentation, medicine: these are all disciplines on which Apollo has made greater demands than ever before. Many parts of the economy were touched by space. Advances in a fantastically diverse area may be attributed to it. It is often hard to be sure how many of these sprang directly from Apollo, and not from other developments in space hardware. But the space program has indubitably been a "cutting edge" for American technology, and Apollo has been the cutting edge of the space program.

As justifications of Apollo, however, these are trivial offerings. They were strictly secondary consequences of the project. They do not explain why Apollo should have been undertaken in preference to some great project of earth-bound engineering, something with similar by-products but a more conspicuously beneficial focus. They are rationalizations after the event, and to many judges of mundane scientific priorities they sound sadly inadequate.

In the end, therefore, it would seem that Apollo is not to be judged by reason at all. It was done by reasoning men for thoroughly pragmatic motives, toward what they took to be a quick and visible result. But between what they sought and what they achieved there stands a very wide chasm. What they are left with is an exercise not in logic but in something close to mysticism: a ritual, supposedly lying deep among man's primitive aspirations, has been completed.

Had that proposition been spelled out before Apollo began, it might have been possible to discover whether the aspiration to reach the moon is widespread among men and high among their unsatisfied desires, or whether it is the property of only a handful of dreamers. In fact this was not the proposition put to the world. Instead, it was obscured by argument that the journey to Tranquility would be *useful* —indeed, that it was imperative for the security of the nation which made it. Yet now that the journey is complete, the mysticism alone is left.

We are therefore invited to judge the completion of the ritual without serious reference to logic. Its value, the argument runs, is incapable of measurement against any rational criterion. Of course, attempts are made to rationalize it. The need to put man on the moon has been expounded in many intricate treatises on his special intelligence, his powers of observation, his ability to select the information he wishes to retrieve, the contributions he can make to science. But these are disguises for a romantic and irrational leap. We are told that man must go. But no impressive body of questions which the exploit is intended to answer has ever been formulated. As one sceptical scientist, Dr. Philip Abelson, has said, "Nowhere in the program for manned exploration of the moon and planets is there a hint of major future development of a puzzling body of facts or even speculations that could fall into place as a major new enlightenment."

As the pragmatic case for the moon visibly dwindled, the mystical argument grew more pervasive. And, despite its unscientific quality, scientists themselves have been found among its most compassionate exponents. Harold Urey, one of America's foremost physicists, epitomized it when he compared Apollo with the building of great monuments. "The real reason for undertaking the space program," he once said, "is an innate characteristic of human beings, namely, some curious drive to try to do what might be thought to be impossible—to try to excel in one way or another . . . These drives of people are akin to other activities such as building the Parthenon and the temples of the ancient world, the building of St. Peter's with its marvelous decorations at a time when it represented real sacrifice on the part of people . . . The space program in a way is our cathedral which we are building."

The great question which this analogy begs is how enduring the cathedral of the moon will be. St. Peter's and the Parthenon still stand. They can be appreciated as intensely today as they were when they were erected. The sacrifice left a life-enhancing residue. Will the landing on the moon leave a similar mark? Will the intense excitement of the journey to Tranquility in July 1969 be more than a transient, empty, virtuoso performance?

Very large claims have been made for its significance. Hugh Dryden, when he was second in command at NASA, claimed, "The impact can only be compared with those great developments of past history, like the Copernican theory which placed the sun, rather than the earth, at the center of our solar system; the work of Sir Isaac Newton in relating the fall of an apple to the notion of the moon round the earth through the universal law of gravitation; to the industrial revolution." A comparison more insistently made is between men landing on the moon and the first fish which flopped on to land and struggled to become an amphibian.

All that can be said of this is that it will take decades, very possibly centuries, to substantiate. The omens, so far as they can now be perceived, are not very encouraging. The moon is totally hostile to man. It offers no possibility of easy habitation or economic exploitation. Nor is there yet any compelling reason why men should seek to convert it into a retreat and an escape from earth, as an alternative to solving the problems of the world. Conceivably, such a reason may one day emerge. Conceivably, the capacity to populate the moon will one day be relevant to man. Conceivably, the scientific residue of Apollo will be found in problems which no one has even asked. But we should not be cowed by the immensity of Apollo's triumph into ignoring the rational probability that no such product will soon be seen.

This is the truth which must be faced in any consideration of man's future role on the moon or other planets. A decision to go further cannot be convincingly represented as a bid for immediate world prestige or identifiable scientific discovery. Apollo has shown that those

objectives, although they may be made to attract the support of the
mass of men for the enterprise, are in fact chimerical. In sending men
to Mars, it will be the act itself which counts, the great instinctual leap.

When he wound up the proceedings of Apollo 11, George Mueller
pleaded for man to continue and expand his adventures in space or
else "fall back from his destiny." "The mighty surge of his achievement
will be lost," Mueller went on, as if recalling the grand promises of
Dryden, "and the confines of this planet will destroy it." This, although it comes from a scientist, is not a statement of fact or even of
reasonable speculation.

It is a godlike prophecy, from a man with no greater claim to an
accurate vision of the future than other men. It is, however, with its
intimations of problems unknown and uncontemplated, the only impulse which will propel men further than the moon. Unadorned by
reason or logic, it is the proposition which men must examine as they
attempt to determine whether journeys beyond Tranquility are a necessary gratification of their primitive instincts, or an insane distraction from the real work of the world.

Index

298

Carpenter, Malcolm Scott, 138, 141, 148–49, 153, 160
Central Intelligence Agency (CIA), 84, 85
Centaur rocket, 10–11, 101
Cernan, Eugene, 238
Chaffee, Roger, 135, 184–88, 206
Clark, Senator Joseph, 167
Clear Lake City, 134, 154, 282
Collins, Michael, 260–61, 263–64, 266–68, 273, 275, 278–81
Collins, Mrs. Pat, 272
Columbia module, see Apollo 11
Columbus, Christopher, 3, 72, 180
Combined Intelligence Objectives Sub-Committee, 22
command module, 107, see Apollo, Saturn
Congress, 1, 2, 6, 9, 32, 44, 55, 58, 62, 65, 71, 84, 91–92, 100, 119, 155, 161, 163, 175–76, 192, 200, 205–6, 210–13, 289
Conrad, Charles, 178
Convair, 77, 98
Cook, Donald, 88
Cook, Sir William, 23, 25
Cooper, Gordon, 97, 138, 140, 158, 160, 177–78
Copernicus, 239, 242, 257, 295
Crisp, Amos, 6
Cronkite, Walter, 220
Crow, Sir Alwyn, 21, 29
Cuban crisis, 8, 85
Cunningham, Walter, 234

Daddario, Emilio, 204
Darwin, George, 248
Defense Department, U.S., 37–39, 41, 76, 82, 101, 119, 215
De Fontenelle, 243
De Orsey, Leo, 145–46
Donlan, Charles, 138, 147
Doolittle, General James, 51
Dornberger, General Walter, 11, 14–19, 23, 25, 27–29
Douglas, 119, 132
Douglas, James H., 76
Downey, 186, 200, 202, 205, 207, 208, 214, 234; see also North American Aviation
Dryden, Hugh, 64, 84–85, 119–21, 125, 173, 175, 295–96

Eagle Module, see Apollo 11
Edmundson, Governor, 126
Eisele, Donn, 234
Eisenhower, President Dwight D., 38, 40–42, 44, 48–51, 54–57, 61, 62, 64, 66–69, 71–79, 80–82, 87, 91, 93, 98,

122, 137, 159, 166; Administration and policy, 44, 51, 61
El Paso, Texas, 30–31
Elverum, Glenn, 223
Eniwetok, 33
Explorer I, 40–41, 42, 44, 54, 67, 71

F-1 Engine, 215–16, 224
Faget, Maxime, 97, 108
Fallaci, Oriana, If the Sun Dies, 8
Federal Bureau of Investigation, 127
Fleming, William, 98
Fulbright, Senator William, 90, 167, 290
Fulton, James, 84
Furnas, Dr. Clifford C., 43–45

Gagarin, Yuri, 83–85, 90, 93, 151, 159, 170–72, 251, 292
Galileo, 239, 243–44
Gardner, Trevor, 38
Garmisch-Partenkirchen, 19
Gavin, General James, 52
Gehrig, James, 205
Gemini, 149, 155, 172, 177–80, 182–83, 185, 195, 237, 264
General Dynamics, 119, 121
General Electric Co., 21, 77, 98, 119, 121
German Army Board of Ordnance, 11, 14, 16–17, 19
German Society for Space Travel, 12, 25
Gilbert, G. K., 245
Gilruth, Robert, 151, 268, 282
Glenn, John, 97, 138–39, 140–41, 144–46, 148, 151, 159–60, 237, 268
Glennan, T. Keith, 64–65, 67, 69, 73, 77, 80
Goddard, Robert, 13–14, 94
Goett, Harry J., 65; Committee, 65–66
Gold, Professor Thomas, 251, 253
Goldwater, Senator Barry, 168
Golovin, Dr. Nicholas, 101–2, 109, 113–14; committee, 102–3, 110
Goodwin, Francis, Bishop of Hereford ("Domingo Gonsales"), 243
Greenwich Observatory, Royal, 251
Grissom, Gus, 135, 138, 140–41, 160, 184–88, 202, 206, 211
Gruithausen, Franz von Paula, 245
Grumman Aircraft Engineering Corporation, 115, 119, 132, 222–24
Guggenheim Foundation, 14

Haney, Paul, 152
Healey, John, 234
Hello, Bastian "Buzz", 213
Hendel, Dr. F. J., 197
Heyland, Dr., 10, 15
Hickenlooper, Senator Bourke, 163